David Gordon Mitten · Suzannah F. Doeringer

MASTER BRONZES
FROM THE
CLASSICAL WORLD

The Fogg Art Museum
City Art Museum of Saint Louis
The Los Angeles County Museum of Art

EXHIBITION DATES   The Fogg Art Museum
December 4, 1967 — January 23, 1968

City Art Museum of Saint Louis
March 1 — April 13, 1968

The Los Angeles County Museum of Art
May 8 — June 30, 1968

Plate I, No. 77   Oinochoe with anthropomorphic handle
(page following)

TABLE OF CONTENTS

Lenders to the Exhibition 5

Foreword 7

Techniques of Working Bronze,
   by Arthur Steinberg 9

Contributors to the Catalogue 16

Greek Bronzes,
   by David Gordon Mitten 17
Catalogue of the Greek Bronzes 26

Etruscan Bronzes,
   by George M. A. Hanfmann 147
Catalogue of the Etruscan Bronzes 155

Roman Bronzes,
   by Heinz Menzel 225
Catalogue of the Roman Bronzes 234

Bibliographical and
Museum Abbreviations 315

Photographic Credits 320

Lenders
to the
Exhibition

Dr. and Mrs. Renato Almansi	*New York*
Ashmolean Museum	*Oxford, England*
Römisches Museum	*Augsburg, West Germany*
Römerhaus und Museum	*Augst, Switzerland*
Musée Romain	*Avenches, Switzerland*
Badisches Landesmuseum Karlsruhe	*Baden-Württemberg, West Germany*
Staatliche Museen Berlin, Antikenabteilung	*Berlin, West Germany*
Museum of Fine Arts	*Boston, Mass.*
Bowdoin College Museum of Art	*Brunswick, Me.*
The Brooklyn Museum	*Brooklyn, N. Y.*
Musées royaux d'Art et d'Histoire	*Brussels, Belgium*
The Ella Riegel Memorial Museum, Bryn Mawr College	*Bryn Mawr, Penna.*
Collection of Dr. and Mrs. Irving F. Burton	*Huntington Woods, Mich.*
R. H. Lowie Museum of Anthropology, University of California	*Berkeley, Calif.*
California Palace of the Legion of Honor	*San Francisco, Calif.*
M. and Mme. Victor Carton	*Blicquy, Belgium*
The Cleveland Museum of Art	*Cleveland, Ohio*
The Estates of Audrey B. and Stephen R. Currier	*New York*
The Eric de Kolb Collection	*New York*
Denver Art Museum	*Denver, Colo.*
The Detroit Institute of Arts	*Detroit, Mich.*
M. and Mme. Niklaus Dürr	*Carouge, Switzerland*
Mr. and Mrs. John Dusenbery	*Montclair, N. J.*
Collection of Mr. John B. Elliott	*New York*
Mr. N.A.C. Embiricos	*London, England*
The Fogg Art Museum, Harvard University	*Cambridge, Mass.*
Prof. and Mrs. George H. Forsyth, University of Michigan	*Ann Arbor, Mich.*
Musée d'art et d'histoire	*Geneva, Switzerland*
J. Paul Getty Museum	*Malibu, Calif.*
Collection of Mrs. Charles Goldman	*New York*
Prof. and Mrs. Nelson Goodman	*Newton, Mass.*
Mr. and Mrs. Edwin Grossman	*Saint Louis, Mo.*
Museum für Kunst und Gewerbe	*Hamburg, West Germany*
John and Ariel Herrmann	*New York*
Collection of Mr. and Mrs. Benjamin Hertzberg	*New York*
The Johns Hopkins University	*Baltimore, Md.*
Fries Museum	*Leeuwarden, The Netherlands*
The Los Angeles County Museum of Art	*Los Angeles, Calif.*
Musée du Louvre	*Paris, France*
Collection of Dr. Lawrence J. Majewski	*New York*
The Kelsey Museum of Archaeology, The University of Michigan	*Ann Arbor, Mich.*

The Milwaukee Art Center	*Milwaukee, Wisc.*
The Minneapolis Institute of Arts	*Minneapolis, Minn.*
Museum of Art and Archaeology, University of Missouri	*Columbia, Mo.*
Mount Holyoke College	*South Hadley, Mass.*
Antikensammlung (Glyptothek und Museum Antiker Kleinkunst)	*Munich, West Germany*
Nelson Gallery - Atkins Museum	*Kansas City, Mo.*
The Newark Museum	*Newark, N. J.*
Norfolk Museum of Arts and Sciences	*Norfolk, Va.*
Allen Memorial Art Museum, Oberlin College	*Oberlin, Ohio*
Olivet College	*Olivet, Mich.*
Collection of Mr. George Ortiz	*Geneva, Switzerland*
Roger Peyrefitte Collection	*Paris, France*
The Pomerance Collection	*Great Neck, N. Y.*
Portland Art Museum	*Portland, Ore.*
The Art Museum, Princeton University	*Princeton, N. J.*
Rheinisches Landesmuseum	*Trier, West Germany*
Museum of Art, Rhode Island School of Design	*Providence, R. I.*
The Memorial Art Gallery of the University of Rochester	*Rochester, N. Y.*
Royal Ontario Museum, University of Toronto	*Toronto, Canada*
City Art Museum of Saint Louis	*Saint Louis, Mo.*
The Schimmel Collection	*New York*
Seattle Art Museum	*Seattle, Wash.*
Mr. Thomas T. Solley	*Bloomington, Ind.*
Mr. and Mrs. Frederick Stafford	*Neuilly-sur-Seine France*
Nationalmuseum	*Stockholm, Sweden*
Mr. and Mrs. Joseph Ternbach	*Forest Hills, N. Y.*
University Museum, University of Pennsylvania	*Philadelphia, Pa.*
Provinciaal Oudheidkundig Museum	*Utrecht, The Netherlands*
Vassar College Classical Museum	*Poughkeepsie, N. Y.*
Virginia Museum of Fine Arts	*Richmond, Va.*
The Wadsworth Atheneum	*Hartford, Conn.*
Dr. and Mrs. Robert Waelder	*Broomall, Pa.*
The Walters Art Gallery	*Baltimore, Md.*
Prof. Frederick M. Watkins	*New Haven, Conn.*
Collection of Hon. and Mrs. Edwin L. Weisl, Jr.	*Washington, D. C.*
Worcester Art Museum	*Worcester, Mass.*
A Private Collection	
A Swiss Private Collection	

FOREWORD

Should the highest art serve for public admiration or for private delight? To this age-old problem different epochs have found answers as different as Mayan sculpture and Gothic miniatures, as Sung landscapes and Versailles. Few cultures decided the issue more clearly and held to one solution more consistently than did ancient Greece and Rome. No private person commissioned either the Parthenon or the column of Trajan, and hardly any collectors have ever owned the greatest masterpieces of Greek and Roman art. Yet just because their highest achievements addressed the public so affirmatively, the ancients carried to unsurpassed levels of refinement such private arts as vase painting, jewelry, and small scale sculpture in bronze.

During the years since World War II when many American artists were rediscovering the challenge of monumentality, many American connoisseurs were becoming aware of the rewards of intimacy. Where private collectors led, curators have followed. The discriminating assemblage of choice works of ancient art by such men as Albert Gallatin, Walter Baker, Norbert Schimmel and Leon Pomerance has inspired our museums to arrange comprehensive loan exhibitions. Had the vessels been strong enough to travel, we would have long since seen an important exhibition of vase painting. In 1965—66 there was a major loan exhibition of Greek gold, and now this assemblage of ancient bronzes.

The preparation of this exhibition revealed an astonishing fact. Both in antiquity and since the Renaissance many famous collectors have pursued ancient bronzes. But apparently this is the first time they have been brought together in an ambitious loan exhibition. A "first" should be comprehensive. Chronologically this show represents the art of twenty three hundred years. Geographically it includes objects made in every part of the Mediterranean world, objects assembled from seventy-nine collections in nine countries. Typologically it illustrates every phase of the bronze worker's activity, from armor to safety-pins, from statuettes to cooking pots. But a "first" should also have focus. We emphasize the representation of the human figure in the art of Greece, Etruria and Rome, between 800 B.C. and 400 A.D. and the collections of the United States.

Centuries of consistent private appreciation and comparative public neglect have scattered ancient bronzes over a wide area. No small group of museums is dominant in this field as the Uffizi, the Victoria and Albert, and the Louvre are dominant in Renaissance bronzes. Precisely because it is still possible to acquire outstanding ancient bronzes, the organizers of the exhibition elected to minimize such dominance as does exist. The great majority of pieces come from lesser-known American collections. Sixty percent are virtually unpublished. To establish that the quality of these little known examples really does reach an international standard, as well as to extend the range of material, a number of the most famous ancient bronzes were borrowed from major European collections.

But these are a minority. Most of the works shown here were acquired by their present owners during the last fifteen years.

How were these bronzes made? Who made them and where? For whom and for what purpose? To those simple and basic questions the catalogue addresses itself, for as yet they have not been satisfactorily answered. It is only after more is known about the technique, the workshops, the patronage and the functions that one can reconsider problems such as the religious or secular significance of the objects or their meaning as symbols.

Our greatest debt is to George M. A. Hanfmann, the guiding spirit of the exhibition, to David Gordon Mitten, who was principally responsible for the selection of the objects, to Mrs. Suzannah Doeringer, who as executive secretary assembled the material, to Mrs. Jane Scott for help with every phase of the exhibition, to Herbert Hoffmann and Heinz Menzel, whose efforts made possible the European loans, to the editors, authors, and other scholars who contributed to the catalogue. Their names are listed on p. 16.

We are also grateful to the many others who have assisted the authors in its preparation, notably Miss Alexandra Dane, Mrs. George Hanfmann, Mrs. Paul Giese, Mrs. Marjorie B. Cohn, John H. Kroll, James K. Lyon, Arthur Steinberg, Cyril Smith, C. C. Vermeule; to the conservation department of the Fogg Museum, especially Arthur Beale and Elizabeth Jones, to that museum's photography department and to the staff of the Harvard libraries; to Dr. Leo Mildenberg and Dr. Herbert Cahn for assistance in procuring photographs. We would also like to express our appreciation to all those who installed the exhibition in each of the three museums where it was shown.

Finally we wish to acknowledge the obligation that the three museums owe to all the private collectors and the museum trustees without whose generosity in lending their treasures this exhibition could not have taken place.

Charles Buckley
Director, City Art Museum of St. Louis

John Coolidge
Director, Fogg Art Museum

Kenneth Donahue
Director, Los Angeles County Museum

TECHNIQUES OF WORKING BRONZE

This brief introduction is to serve two basic purposes[*]. First, it seems desirable to explain how the bronzes in this exhibition were manufactured, since this should add considerably to the reader's appreciation of the technological aesthetic of the individual objects. In so doing, it will be necessary to define many terms that are often used loosely and even inaccurately. Second, this introduction represents an aspect of the study of antiquities that is all too frequently ignored. By closer observation and study of the methods of manufacture of these bronzes more can be learned about the history of technology. The working of metals is one of the great revolutions in man's development; only through a close scientific study of these various techniques can we come to a fuller understanding of this crucial stage in our evolution.

Such a study can only be pursued properly by carefully examining objects with microscope, x-ray, and various analytic methods. Much more scientific work must be done before we can really understand and appreciate how these magnificent bronzes were made. Most of the observations about technique in this catalogue have been made on the basis of photographs and an occasional brief look at some of the objects, so that all the conclusions are tentative at best until proper metallographic studies can be made.

Bronze is basically an alloy of approximately 90% copper and 10% tin. But ancient bronzes vary greatly in composition and contain a great many impurities. Furthermore, bronzes (or brasses, consisting of copper and zinc) of different compositions were occasionally used on the same object when different colors, strengths, or other characteristics were desired (No. 87, Pl. III). Although tin was frequently hard to obtain in antiquity, the copper-tin alloy, bronze, was generally preferred to pure copper for its lower melting point and greater castability and hardness.

The two basic methods of working bronze are by *casting* the molten metal, and by *cold-working* it proceeding from a cast ingot.

CASTING

Casting is essentially a process whereby a model or pattern is reproduced by pouring a molten metal into a mold having the nega-

[*] This introduction could not have been written without the many helpful suggestions of my colleagues at M.I.T.: Prof. Cyril S. Smith, Miss Heather Lechtman, and Mrs. Katherine Ruhl. The drawings were adapted from H. Hodges, *Artifacts* (London, 1964), through the courtesy of Praeger, New York, and John Baker, London, joint publishers. I am grateful to Marjorie B. Cohn for making the adaptations.

tive shape of the model. The mold is made by carving the form of the model in the mold material (stone, metal, or hard clay) or, more commonly, by impressing the model in an easily shaped refractory material (often a sandy clay which does not shrink unduly on drying). The greatest problem in casting is withdrawing the model (or the finished product) from the mold: if the model is undercut in more than one place, withdrawing it from the type of mold described above will be impossible.

Two different methods were developed to solve this problem: *piece-mold* and *lost-wax* (or *cire perdue*) casting. In the former, the mold was made removable from the model by partitioning it; in the latter, the model was made removable by making it of a material that could be melted out of the mold. The various methods developed in antiquity for meeting the problem of model withdrawal were then as follows.

Open molds were used to cast pieces with a single finished surface (No. 314 A and B). Two such molds fastened together, with a place for the introduction of the molten metal, constitute a *bivalve* mold. The mold division marks a surface (usually a plane) intersecting the object at its widest dimension (Fig. 1). Axes, spears, and swords were often cast thus; a *core* might be placed in the mold to form a cavity for later inserting the weapon handle. Open and bivalve molds of metal or stone could be used repeatedly.

In *piece-mold* casting (Fig. 2) the model or pattern was fashioned out of clay or wood, and the mold, usually of clay, was built over it and cut into sections so that it could be dismantled and the model could be removed. After removal of the model the mold pieces were reassembled; the mold was then heated to drive out volatile matter and prevent premature *freezing* (hardening) of the molten metal. The metal was poured into the mold, and the whole was allowed to cool slowly. The mold was finally disassembled, revealing a *solid* piece-mold casting.

Before the mold was reassembled for casting, however, a *core* (of some refractory material) could be introduced, over which the pieces were then reassembled. In order to prevent displacement of the core it was set off from the mold by *chaplets,* pins passing from the mold into the core to hold it in place; these would be trimmed off when the casting was finished. Alternatively, small spacers of metal might be introduced, which would simply be enveloped by the molten metal and included in the cast object. Such coring results in a *hollow* casting, particularly desirable in a large object both to conserve metal and to compensate for the shrinkage and possible cracking of thick and variable sections of bronze.

The *lost-wax* method (Fig. 3) seems to have been employed for most of the objects in this exhibition. Here the model was made of wax and then covered with clay to make the mold. The first coat was of very fine clay which would take up all the details of

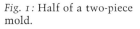
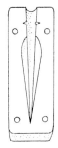

Fig. 1: Half of a two-piece mold.

Fig. 2: PIECE MOLD CASTING. 1) model, 2) clay mold built in sections over model, 3) model removed, core inserted, mold reassembled and fastened together, bronze poured in.

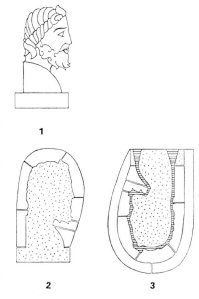

1

2   3

Fig. 3: LOST WAX CAST-ING. 1) core with protruding chaplets, 2) wax model over core, 3) clay mold built over model, 4) wax melted out, bronze poured in.

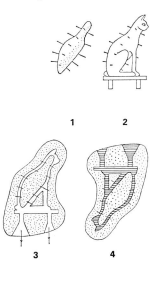

Fig. 4: 1) cross-section of chaplet, 2) core, 3) casting.

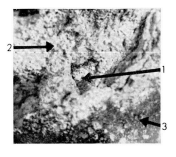

Fig. 5: Patch

the wax model; the outer coats were of coarser clay. After drying, the mold was heated to melt and burn out the wax and prepare it to receive the molten bronze, which was then poured into the cavity left by removal of the wax. Either a solid or hollow casting could be thus produced, since the wax model could be made of solid wax or could be built over a core (again using chaplets; see Fig. 4). When a core was employed it might either be partial, in which case it was removed from the finished product, or it might be completely enveloped by bronze so that it was either left inside the finished object or removed through small openings (Nos. 279, 313). When cores were employed, they generally did not extend into the thinnest parts of the casting, so that statuettes frequently have solid extremities (Nos. 171, 250). Where there is much open work on a bronze while other parts are solid, a partial core was used, over which the wax model was fashioned, resulting in a combination solid and hollow casting (Nos. 17, 21).

Because of the relatively high temperature at which casting takes place (varying with the alloy, the metal is poured at about 1000–1200° C.), many problems can arise. The mold, when struck by the molten bronze, produces much gas which, if not allowed to transpire through the mold or through vents, could produce bubbles in the casting. Furthermore, the mold may crack if it is baked out too rapidly before casting, or when the hot metal strikes it. Other defects arise from the mold sections or core becoming displaced, and from inadequate allowance for the shrinkage of the metal as it passes from liquid to solid. We have many examples of such casting faults; some of these were repaired in antiquity (e. g. patches, Fig. 5; Nos. 131, 255), others were left exposed (Nos. 22, 234). If the casting came out too badly, the bronze was melted down again and reused.

JOINING

If a bronze was made in several pieces the sections had to be joined after the metal had cooled. Joins could be made mechanically or metallurgically, but it is difficult to distinguish between the various methods used without close examination and even analyses of different parts of the joint. Pieces could be joined *mechanically* by *riveting,* by *peening* over a dowel inserted through a hole, or by *force-fitting* a dowel or tenon into a socket which is slightly smaller in diameter (Nos. 219, 221).

Metallurgical joints, using molten metals, are also possible but more difficult to accomplish because of the tendency of hot bronze surfaces to oxidize rapidly, thus preventing other metals from fusing with the bronze. In *soft-soldered* or *leaded* joints (No. 127) a different metal of lower melting-point was used to join two pieces (this method was frequently used with a mortise and tenon joint in which a projection is fitted into a socket). In a *hard-soldered* or *brazed* joint a metal with a melting-point near that of the bronze was used, and actually fused with the two surfaces to be joined. In both kinds of soldering a *flux* was necessary to keep the bronze surfaces free from oxide, enabling the molten metal to "wet" the solid surface. In a *cast-on* joint a precast portion of the object (e. g. a leg or handle) was inserted into the mold for the larger part, and molten bronze was then poured into the mold. *Running-on* is a closely related process in which the two parts to be joined were placed in a mold with space between them; very hot metal was then run in, preferably until the surfaces to be joined were fused; upon solidification, a single mass of metal resulted. *Welding,* heating the two pieces to near their melting-point and then hammering them together, was common with iron but virtually impossible with bronze, both because of oxidation (see above) and because bronze is extremely fragile when hot.

Though insufficient research has been done in this area, it would appear that organic *adhesives* (water soluble glues, heat-melting rosin and other materials like bitumen) might also have been used for joining parts of bronzes. These, however, would not have the great strength of mechanical or metallurgical joints.

After removing the casting from the mold and finishing all the accessory joining, the bronze was cleaned and polished in a number of different ways. It appears that files, scrapers and hammers were used to remove the major blemishes; then various grades of abrasives (probably both stones and powders) were employed to achieve the extremely fine finish and polish characteristic of most ancient bronzes.

SURFACE DECORATION

Finally, surface decoration was added to the finished casting. This is often erroneously called *chasing,* which refers rather to the work done on the front of cold-worked sheet metal (see below). The principal methods of adding linear decoration were *tracing* (with related *punching*) and *engraving.* (The descriptions of these methods apply to their use on cold-worked sheet bronze as well.)

Tracing (Figs. 6:1–2 and 7) was done with a chisel-like tool with a slightly blunt edge which leaves a linear impression when hammered against the metal surface; by successive overlapping strokes designs were built up. In this operation the metal is displaced and compressed (on a thin sheet it appears on the back as a bulge), but not removed from the object. *Engraving* (Fig. 6:3–4), on the other hand, was done with a sharp, hard cutting-tool (usually with a V-section) which was pushed along the bronze so as actually to cut and remove a long thin curl of metal. In engraving the tool had to

Fig. 6: 1) tracing, 2) section through traced line, 3) engraving, 4) section through engraved line.

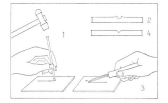

be harder than the metal it was cutting, but presumably a 20⁰/o tin bronze would cut a 10⁰/o tin bronze, or stone tools might have been used before steel came into use for this purpose. It is difficult to distinguish between tracing and engraving unless the line can be examined under a microscope in order to detect parallel longitudinal scratches and the piling up of metal at the end of the line (in engraving) or parallel vertical scratches and distortions and the piling up of metal alongside the line (in tracing). *Punching* is closely related to tracing in that a pointed or patterned tool is hammered, displacing the metal and reproducing its pattern on the object (Nos. 26, 171).

As another sort of decoration metals of different colors could be applied to the surface of the bronze. *Inlaying* was done by cutting grooves into the metal, which were then filled with another metal such as copper or silver, held in place simply by the tightness of the fit (Nos. 140, 255). Also, a metal like *niello* (a composition of sulphur, silver and copper with a relatively low melting point) could be forced into a cavity and heated until it fused with the bronze (No. 251?). Colored pastes and glass-like substances were also used as inlays on bronzes, especially to accentuate eyes (Nos. 189, 190). *Revetting* or *overlaying* involved pressing or gluing a thin sheet of metal to the surface of the bronze. If the bronze surface was roughened slightly, the overlay adhered better. Silver was occasionally used (No. 290), but gilding (No. 110) was the most common type of revetment; it was done in a number of different ways. Gold sheet could be applied like silver, pressing or gluing it to the prepared bronze surface, which could take the gold better if it had been heated. Gold leaf could be applied in the same way; it adhered merely by being pressed onto the roughened and heated bronze surface. Still more effective was gilding with an amalgam of mercury: mercury and gold were formed into a paste, which was applied to the areas to be gilded and then heated; the mercury vaporized at a very low heat, leaving only the gold adhering to the surface of the bronze.

COLD-WORKING

Cold-working is the other major method of working bronze. Bronze is reasonably malleable, though it hardens and becomes brittle when hammered too much. This tendency becomes more pronounced with higher tin contents. Such brittleness and hardness can be overcome by heating the bronze to a red heat *(annealing)*, which rearranges the crystal structure of the metal, softening it and thus allowing it to be hammered again. Thus, beginning with a cast ingot, bronze could be formed into vessels and similar objects through repeated hammering and annealing, which greatly improves the strength and ductility of the metal.

Forming something like a vessel from a bronze sheet could be done either by *raising* (No. 108) (hammering it over an elongated anvil, or *stake,* the hammer striking the outside of the object), or by *sinking* (hammering the bronze down into a depression, the hammer striking the inside of the object). Bars and similar objects could be produced by skillful hammering of bronze against an anvil (No. 315), sometimes finishing them by hammering them into *dies* or *swages.* These dies, with patterns cut in them, might also be used to produce a rim or border with a repeating design. Wire was made by cutting strips from sheet metal and rounding them by filing, abrasion, and hammering.

Cold-worked bronzes were joined in much the same way as castings, though mechanical joins occur more often than metallurgical ones (there is evidence for some soldering of wire to backgrounds, but little else). *Riveting* was the most common method, used both for attaching pieces to larger objects (No. 198) and for forming entire vessels by joining sheets of bronze (No. 157). Bronze sheets could also be joined by turning the edges over each other and then hammering them flat *(crimping).* Hinges (Nos. 203, 227) were produced by turning over the edges of sheet metal to form tubes or loops, cutting them to interpenetrate, and passing a bar through the tubes.

Fig. 7: Arrows indicate traced lines.

DECORATION

The methods of decorating cold-worked bronzes, like most other sheet metals, were similar to those used on castings, but here too, as in joining methods, there are preferences and specialized techniques demanded by the nature of the material. Hammering a design up from the back of sheet metal is called *repoussé* or *embossing* (convex areas in Figs. 7–8; Nos. 113, 158). This was done with a blunt tool, hammering the sheet against a bed of pitch or some similar soft material. Hammering the metal down from the front to produce a raised relief (done by hammering down around the relief area) is called *chasing* (Fig. 8, depressed areas outlining the relief). The relief surfaces were further enhanced by tracing (Fig. 7) or engraving (described above), used for outlining. Tracing and engraving could also be used without repoussé. Punching (described above) and *stamping* (using a patterned tool from the back of the sheet metal) were also employed.

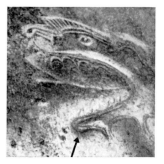

Fig. 8: Arrow indicates chasing.

PATINA

One of the striking characteristics of the bronzes in this exhibition is the great variety of their colors. The smooth greenish-blue or black surface of the bronze is called the *patina.* It consists of naturally formed corrosion products. Depending upon the composition of the metal and its environmental history, such as the conditions of its burial, the degree of corrosion and composition of the surface will vary, resulting in a variety of colors and surface textures. It should be remembered, however, that the patina is a result of time, and that the bronzes as enjoyed by their original owners looked very different from the way they do today.

Arthur Steinberg
Department of Humanities
Massachusetts Institute of Technology

FURTHER READING

L. Aitchison, *A History of Metals* (London, 1960).

N. Barnard, *Bronze Castings and Bronze Alloys in Ancient China* (Tokyo, 1961).

H. H. Coghlan, *Notes on the Prehistoric Metallurgy of Copper and Bronze in the Old World* (Oxford, 1951).

P. F. Davidson, "Technical Introduction," in P. F. Davidson — H. Hoffmann, *Greek Gold*, (Mainz, 1966).

H. Hodges, *Artifacts* (London, 1964).

H. Maryon, "Metal Working in the Ancient World," *AJA*, 53 (1949), 93—125.

R. F. Tylecote, *Metallurgy in Archaeology* (London, 1962).

R. J. Gettens, Technical section in forthcoming catalogue of bronzes in the Freer Gallery, Washington, D. C., vol. II.

Contributors to the Catalogue

Suzannah Doeringer	SD	Fogg Art Museum
George M. A. Hanfmann	GMAH	Fogg Art Museum
Herbert Hoffmann	HH	Museum für Kunst und Gewerbe, Hamburg
Heinz Menzel	HM	Römisch-Germanisches Zentralmuseum, Mainz
David Gordon Mitten	DGM	Fogg Art Museum
Andrew Ramage	AR	Fogg Art Museum
Jane Ayer Scott	JAS	Fogg Art Museum

Use of the Catalogue

All dimensions are given in meters and are assumed to represent the maximum dimension unless otherwise stated:

H = height; W = width; D = depth; L = length; Th = thickness; diam. = diameter.

In most cases we have relied upon the lenders' information regarding dimensions, casting, and surface color. L. and r. indicate the figure's, or proper, left and right. Bibliographical abbreviations follow the *American Journal of Archaeology*, 62 (1958), 3–8, or the list on pp. 315 ff. An asterisk (*) is used to designate an exhibition with or without catalogue. Roman numerals indicate book volume numbers only, except in cases where confusion would otherwise result. The abbreviation, "No. ——," refers to the entry number in this catalogue.

Greek Bronzes

Plate II, No. 31   Cretan mitra

Greek bronzes comprise a miniature gallery of Greek art, helping us recreate the monumental sculpture in stone and bronze which has largely perished. Small objects, exquisitely worked and often highly original in conception and manufacture, they invite us to examine them closely, to appreciate their grace, harmony, and humor. Mostly cast by the "lost wax" method, which precludes exact duplication, the bronzes vividly illustrate the inexhaustible creative imagination of Greek artisans in portraying human and animal forms as well as that array of legendary beings which populated their religion and myth.

The term "bronzes" can be misleading. Unlike its use in reference to the Renaissance, where it is limited mostly to statuettes, the term can be applied to almost any bronze object produced in Classical times: utensils, vessels, armors and their attachments, as well as sculptures, large and small. From this vast and heterogeneous body of objects we can gain valuable insights into many different aspects of Greek culture: art, economics, religion, language, and history.

The casting of small human and animal statuettes intended as votive offerings was already important in Minoan metallurgy in the first quarter of the second millennium B.C. Among the hundreds of these recovered from the palaces, residences and sacred caves of Crete are figures of men and women, usually with their right fists clenched over their foreheads, a gesture evocative both of prayer and of religious awe (Nos. 2—4). Surprisingly summary in casting and finishing, they nonetheless convey a lively stereotype of a religious experience whose nature and import is hidden from us. Their chronological development, principal centers of manufacture, and method of fabrication are only imperfectly known.

The Mycenaean Greeks seem to have been puzzlingly inactive in producing bronze statuettes, although they fashioned vessels and weapons of the metal, especially rapier-like swords, found in noble burials. With the destruction and movements of populations that signalled the end of the late Bronze Age civilization in the Aegean there occurs a precipitous decline in the technique and employment of bronze. Iron weapons and tools, introduced from around 1150 through 950 B.C., did not entirely displace bronze, however; it was still used for long pins, fibulae, and other adornments.

About 800 B.C., under the influence of indigenous and foreign stimuli (from both the Near East and central Europe), a resurgence in the artistic use of bronze took place, resulting in the small human and animal figures whose great variety of style and expression is masked under the inclusive term, "Geometric." The conceptualization of these figures, disclosing a strong sense of structural and decorative stylization, foreshadows many of the foremost qualities of Archaic and Classical sculpture: harmony, a sense of proportion, individual abstraction, and a basic insistence upon design. Whether a toy-like horse (No. 17), waddling water bird (No. 23), or mysterious seated man (No. 10), these statuettes furnish fundamental clues to the birth of that drive to embody, to recreate living forms, that more than any other quality dominates the subsequent course of Greek art. Almost exclusively used as votive offerings, they have been found in profusion in most great sanctuary sites, reminders of the vivid direct relationship between worshipper and divinity which is evidenced in the Homeric epics and may to some extent be an inheritance from the Bronze Age.

The study of these statuettes, however, is still in its infancy. Thousands, most of which are still inadequately published, are scattered throughout the museums of Greece and the collections, public and private, of Europe and America. H.-V. Herrmann has made an auspicious beginning in discussing the possible regional styles and workshops among Peloponnesian Geometric bronzes, but until the material from both old and new excavations at Olympia is fully treated, any such analysis must remain tentative. We also do not know how or whence the prototypes of these figures came to Greece, or whether there was any survival of theme or technique from the Bronze Age.

Though the style of Geometric animal votive figures lingered long in provincial backwaters, the Geometric tradition and approach to sculpture was soon displaced by a new, organic way of representing the human figure. Most familiar perhaps in the monumental stone *kouroi*, or nude male statues, which first appeared as dedications in Attic, Peloponnesian and Cycladic sanctuaries around the end of the seventh century B.C., the severely proportioned, stiff, almost Egyptian-looking male figures also existed in miniature. Nos. 33 and 34 are examples of the variant interpretation of the ideal male nude on the Ionian coast in the first half of the sixth century B.C. Large round heads, oval eyes and enigmatic smiles furnish expression to bodies in which anatomical structure is submerged beneath fluid, rounded surfaces.

The great contribution of Ionia to this developmental phase of Greek sculpture, however, was the invention of a type of draped female figure that, by the end of the sixth century B.C., was to exclude all other conceptions. This was the *kore*, "maiden" in Greek, used to depict Artemis or Aphrodite, as well as aristocratic mortals, priestesses or worshippers. As did their life-sized counterparts, kore statuettes could stand free as votive offerings or ornaments, or could serve as caryatids, effortlessly balancing on their heads the discs of elaborate mirrors.

The major sanctuaries, focal points for the Greeks' relation to their gods and to each other, became scenes for display and propaganda for the various, often opposing, city-states. Important here was the exhibition of prized battle trophies, armor stripped from slain foes and inscribed by the victors with proud dedications. From Crete comes a unique find of such trophies of Dedalic armor (Nos. 29—32) that would have done justice to Achilles himself, and indeed may have been fashioned with some such emulation in mind.

The new maturity of late Archaic Greek culture is embodied in some startling bronzes, which transform standard types into wholly new creations. The Arcadian shepherd (No. 47) is metamorphosed by gesture and costume into a figure of transcendant dignity, a herald, bard or king (No. 48). The heavy-armed foot-soldier (*hoplite* in Greek), whose forward stride and poised spear tell more about the invincible performance in battle of the Spartan ranks than whole chapters of written history, is portrayed in a sequence of powerfully expressive statuettes (Nos. 37, 39). No. 37 pulses with Peloponnesian vigor and is probably the earliest in the Lakonian series. An unknown master, perhaps also Lakonian, just before the turn of the century protrayed a hoplite swathed in a cloak (No. 49), creating a figure that is more an apparition than a human image. This warrior seems immersed in thought, his body unconsciously mirroring his meditation. Seldom has the innate Greek sense of design been so skillfully embodied.

At this time the Greeks began to cast hollow life-sized and larger statues in bronze, over clay cores built around armatures of iron rods. A casting pit for a small kouros has been found near the temple of Apollo Patroos in the Athenian Agora; we can now visualize the finished product from a superb example unearthed in the Piraeus in 1959, and datable c. 525 B.C. Fashioning such statues in so structurally stable a medium permitted a freedom for experimenting with daring active poses that was undreamed of before. The running youth (No. 51) probably made on Samos c. 515 B.C. displays movement in a manner not seen in monumental sculpture until the 460's, when such works as Myron's *Discobolus* were created. It is well-known that such new poses began to appear on the earliest Attic red-figured vases; not so often realized is that this freedom likewise appears in many contemporary bronze statuettes.

We still do not know the reason for the profound transformation of Greek sculpture during the decades before the Persian Wars. It may be helpful to think of Archaic art, which had nearly exhausted itself, turning into something wholly new under the mingled threat and stimulus of danger from abroad and political turmoil within the Greek city-states. The resulting sculpture turns its back completely on the frills and whims of late Archaic convention, striding forward with a sober confidence and modesty which emanate from within, a capacity for introspection now implied along with organic bodily action. The family likeness visible in these figures, with their large, simplified forms, deep, rounded heads with large eyes, full chins and unsmiling mouths, has helped to give rise to the name, "Severe Style," commonly applied to this art which serves as a transition between the late Archaic and the fully developed Classical style of the mid-fifth century B. C. A fascinating mixture and juxtaposition of Archaic and advanced characteristics is often visible in these works. The dynamic pose of a nude seated god (No. 78) who seems ready to rise from his seat to assert his power, contrasts with the square, almost block-like modelling of his hips and thighs and his sharply delineated beard, holdovers from a previous artistic generation. The youth (No. 83) pouring an offering of wine could be a mortal victor as easily as a youthful Apollo or Dionysos. This ambiguity of subject tells us much about the nature of the Greek gods and the Greeks' own character in relation to them.

Dignity and grace also permeate the female figures of the Severe Style, with their architectonically arranged peplos folds (Nos. 87, 88, 90). Dignity remains, modified by heightened naturalness, in statuettes of three almost

Classical goddesses: the elegant Aphrodite (No. 93) pensively regarding a dove, the stocky Arcadian Artemis (No. 89) in the garb of a peasant or housewife, a fitting regional manifestation of the protectress of wild game and flocks in the remote mountains, and Athena (No. 92), seen before as a primitive armed image or striding into battle, but now studying the owl perched on her hand; in conception she evokes an echo of the Athena Lemnia and other early creations of Phidias, from which she may be derived.

Decorative relief work and attachments for large bronze vessels also underwent a thoroughgoing change during the first half of the fifth century B.C. The siren became the decorative attachment *par excellence,* amenable to varied decorative compositions in a thicket of acanthus, palmettes, and volutes. She occurs on hydriai and their handles (Nos. 106—108), as well as on hand-held mirrors as a transitional member between handle and disc (No. 105). A new type of mirror, however, became fashionable during the latter decades of the fifth century B.C. Constructed like a modern compact, with round disc and lidded circular box, this form often displayed a tondo scene in repoussé on its lid — sometimes a female head (No. 111), sometimes a mythological scene (No. 112) — complementing its use both in structure and subject. The ties of repoussé bronze work of this sort with contemporary coins and gems are close and striking. In these miniature media the subjects revolve and float before us, fully foreshortened, now shown with a freedom and control of technique which occasionally, however, dwindles into a facile mannerism.

The Classical characterization of animals attained a balance of sympathetic interpretation and naturalistic representation never surpassed. Illustrations of this synthesis range from the comic, frightened lion at bay (No. 99), probably produced in South Italy early in the fifth century B.C., to the regal standing goat (No. 101). The leaping deer (No. 100), one of the few bronzes in the exhibition to have been found in a controlled archaeological excavation, seems to be springing onto the handle of a large dish. In delicacy of rendition and sensitivity of character it has few equals among Classical animal sculpture. Greek interest in rendering natural forms extended to flora as well (Nos. 104, 152).

A rare and novel container for oil or perfume is the exquisite vase in the form of a lady's head (No. 114), allegedly from Thessaly, and perhaps of Corinthian workmanship. Such plastic flasks in pottery were made throughout Greece during the sixth through fourth centuries B.C., but few metal examples have survived. Asymmetries of form and a slight tilt of the head only accentuate its sensitive, momentary quality; we almost perceive the intake of breath.

Bronzes from the Hellenistic world reflect the tumult and variety of Greek culture, which now embraced and absorbed the entire eastern Mediterranean area. Alexander the Great employed great sculptors to portray him and the company of heroes and gods to which he claimed membership; portraits and images thus created left their mark to the end of Classical antiquity and beyond. Probably reflecting a monumental statue of Poseidon by Lysippos is No. 129; his stance and wiry physique are human. Equally Lysippan is the concept of Herakles as weary hero. Although No. 238 is probably Roman in date, it is faithful rendition of the "Farnese Herakles" of Lysippos, who showed in his "Herakles Epitrapezios" that he could create small bronzes as well as towering colossoi.

Hellenistic humor was raucous, bawdy, and uninhibited, often relying upon an almost clinical interest in human oddities and deformities that seems savage to us. Many of its subjects were connected, in one way or another, with the theater, whose slapstick plots have left us many mute witnesses in figures of actors from Old and New Comedy. The actors may be cooks (Nos. 118–119) bearing stews or pies; a standing actor (No. 120) seems to declaim a peroration that may be invective or apology, both the special resource of the cunning slave. The silenus (No. 125), theatrical in pose if not identity, may be a throw-back to satyr plays or comic choruses of the fifth century. We do not know whether the cheerful dwarf with amphora (No. 117) is a vignette of Alexandrian street life or a mythological creature bearing refreshment to his beleaguered comrades locked in battle with the cranes. The remorseless, almost repulsive realism with which the hunchback (No. 116) is endowed identifies him as a crippled beggar or fisherman who eked out bare subsistence on the street-corners and waterfronts of Hellenistic ports like Alexandria, the city which played a leading role in creating and maintaining genre subjects like these as a principal current in Hellenistic art. The realistic portrayal of the aged was also popular — for example, the old man clad in a ragged himation (No. 123) — as was the depiction of exotic types, such as bald priests of Isis (No. 126), and of children (Nos. 127, 128).

Dionysiac themes were often chosen; the merry troupe of satyrs in Hellenistic times have become playful adolescent boys (No. 130) instead of lustful horse- and goat-men.

The kingdoms which inherited the territories conquered by Alexander, whose balance of power was precariously maintained, produced state art glorifying the divine might of the ruler and his legitimizing claims to govern. Such a figure, reminiscent of the famous "Hellenistic Ruler" in the Terme Museum and faintly recalling Alexander the Great, is No. 132; the debt of such figures to the ideal nude forms of Polykleitos, Skopas, and Praxiteles is amply demonstrated in the torso of Nr. 131, which displays features borrowed from each and combined into a new eclectic whole. The barbarian opponents of the Philhellene kings were represented as heroically defiant, as in the "Dying Gaul," or slavishly suppliant, as in No. 134. Athletics, formerly the competition of aristocratic contestants for a god-given prize in the Olympic Games, became the brutal mayhem of professional toughs (No. 133).

With the *dénouement* of the Classical Style it becomes less easy to establish the date of a bronze on the basis of stylistic affinities. Consequently, objects datable from the contexts of their discovery are particularly important. The complexity of stylistic currents and countercurrents within the Hellenistic world and continuing into Roman art which often carries on Hellenistic themes, makes it difficult in many cases to decide whether a statuette was cast in the second century B. C. or A. D.

Recent finds of Greek bronzes have added immensely to our understanding of the field. A royal chariot grave in eastern France contained the most splendid archaic bronze vase surviving to us, the Krater of Vix, probably made in South Italy. Equally amazing and even more ornate is a late Classical bronze krater from northern Greece, discovered in a masonry tomb of the late fourth century B.C. at Derveni, just north of Salonika. An underground shrine at Paestum produced six Archaic bronze hydriai that have enabled scholars to reassess the achievement of South Italian schools of bronze working. New excavations at the Isthmian Sanctuary of Poseidon and continued explorations at Olympia, the Samian Heraion, and Dodona have greatly augmented the store of bronzes from these sites; the Piraeus hoard has at one stroke doubled the number of monumental classical bronze statues from Greece.

Also important have been recent scholarly studies and catalogues such as the 1960 show in Basel and recent exhibitions of the Pomerance and Schimmel collections. The publication of the Stathatos collection included masterly studies of the important bronzes by E. Kunze and C. Rolley. Kunze's fundamental studies in the seventh and eighth *Olympiaberichte* place the astonishing new finds from Olympia in the context of current scholarly opinion. D. K. Hill, R. Blatter, and others have forged ahead in the systematic study of handles and decorative ornament of Archaic and Classical bronze vessels. The entire ambient of major compositions on large bronze vessels in the sixth century, with their workshop connections and influence on provincial schools, has undergone a thorough re-examination by H. Jucker. H. Biesantz has outlined the rich Thessalian achievement in figurative bronzes from the eighth through fifth centuries, and N. Himmelmann-Wildschütz has critically re-evaluated the Corinthian and Argive schools in the sixth century B.C.

Republication of the magnificent series of kouroi and striding Athenas from the Acropolis in Athens compels a complete re-evaluation of Athenian bronzes of the late Archaic and Severe styles. Comprehensive publication of the bronzes from the Mahdia shipwreck by W. Fuchs, and the first volumes of the corpus of Roman bronzes from Germany, by H. Menzel, are fundamental contributions to the study of Hellenistic and later bronzes in the Classical tradition. In addition, a growing series of technological and metallurgical studies promises to revolutionize much of our present approach to the problems of workshop identification, procedures of manufacture, and interrelations between shops.

Such studies, accompanied by good photographs, will lay the broad basis of knowledge from which more accurate synthetic studies, including a history of Greek bronzes, will eventually emerge. Of first importance is the thorough publication of major museum collections, an important example of which is the forthcoming catalogue of the bronzes in the Museum of Fine Arts, Boston. Equally vital is the re-study and re-publication of the vast assemblages of bronzes recovered during the first excavations of the major Greek sanctuaries and neglected ever since. This will materially assist the long-overdue revision of workshop attribution. Bronze ateliers may come to be understood as a spectrum of minor variations within broad regional patterns, supplementing the orthodox view of clearly defined workshops and styles at major urban centers.

The place of Greek bronzes in the development of Greek art, their contribution to this development, and their varying relation to other forms and media at crucial points of stylistic transition are further important questions for consideration. The attention to these crucial periods has not proceeded uniformly. Geometric, late Classical, and many types of Hellenistic bronzes have received only superficial consideration, while Archaic and early Classical works have undergone comparatively searching study. The term "Graeco-Roman" still occurs far too often, a chronological latitude which, while not completely invalid, can be considerably constricted under systematic and persistent study. A critical re-examination of this concept may produce a more accurate understanding of the occurrence of and interaction between such stylistic phenomena as classicism, eclecticism, mannerism, and archaism.

Because small bronzes have survived in large numbers, they will play an increasingly vital role in the reconstruction and synthesis of the development of Greek art. Their direct visual appeal and intrinsic charm, however, certainly match their scholarly importance. Among these miniature sculptures are some of the most sublime creations of Greek civilization, and indeed of all western art. As tangible evocations of the attitudes and ideals which suffused and motivated Greek society and culture, they help us recapture something of the essence of the Greeks' intensely exhilarating exploration of human life and destiny, a quest that haunts and compels our imagination even today.

David Gordon Mitten

1. Spouted Bucket

Middle Minoan II–III, c. 1700 B.C.; H. with handle: 0.249, without handle: 0.187; max. diam.: 0.255, of outer rim: 0.203, of base: 0.090; W. of handle: 0.028; Th. at rim: 0.035. Copper with traces of arsenic (0.8%) and silver (0.04%); splotchy reddish and gray-green surface; marine deposits left intact in interior. Allegedly found in sea near Euboea.

The graceful stamnoid shape is familiar from later MM II (Kamares) pottery. The body was hammered from a circular sheet of copper with a round cutout in the center; the bottom, now almost entirely corroded, was hammered from a much thinner sheet and probably riveted over the turned-in rim of the base. The triangular beak-shaped spout was probably cast, and attached at the rim with eleven evenly-spaced rivets. The strap handle, aligned with the spout and attached with two pairs of rivets, was made of a wide metal strip folded longitudinally over a core consisting of two parallel rods.

Metal prototypes have been postulated for the delicate shapes and strap handles of Middle Minoan pottery (cf. J. D. S. Pendlebury, *The Archaeology of Crete* [London, 1939], 136), but no actual examples have come to light. Metal vessels of the immediately succeeding period, which A. Evans called Middle Minoan IIIb – Late Minoan Ia, have been found in some numbers and variety (A. Evans, *Palace of Minos*, II:2 [London, 1928], 623–654). Close parallels for the shape can be found in Kamares pottery (Pendlebury, pl. 22:3f; S. Marinatos–M. Hirmer, *Crete and Mycenae* [New York, 1960], pl. 20, VII) but these lack the strap handle. The only stamnoid spouted bucket with strap handle known to me is a Melian (Phylacopi) imitation of the Minoan type, of Late Cycladic date (C. Zervos, *L'Art des Cyclades* [Paris, 1957], figs. 306–307).

E. Sangmeister (Arbeitsgemeinschaft für Metallurgie des Altertums, Römisch-Germanisches Zentralmuseum, Mainz), who conducted a metallurgical analysis of the vessel, states that the trace components conform precisely to those documented for Cretan copper objects of the Middle Minoan period. I am beholden to W. Lampert, the restorer of the Hamburg museum, for much of the technical information on the vessel. (HH)

Unpublished.

Lent by the Museum für Kunst und Gewerbe, Hamburg (1966, 109).

2. Standing Man (Votary)

Late Minoan I, c. 1600–1500 B.C.; H: 0.077 without tenon, W: 0.032; solid cast. From the Diktaean Cave.

The substantial proportions and backward bend of this male figure are strongly reminiscent of a large votive statuette of burly physique from Tylissos, in Heraklion, which may be contemporary. A short tang projects downward, joining the two separate rectangular plates on which the feet are placed. The figure wears a long apron. (DGM)

Boardman, 6–7, 10, no. 6, pl. 1, with bibl. and comparanda. For Tylissos figure, P. Demargne, *Naissance de l'art grec* (Paris, 1964), fig. 220.

Lent by the Ashmolean Museum, Oxford (AE. 23); gift of A. J. Evans, 1894.

3. Standing Man (Votary)

Middle Minoan III–Late Minoan I, c. 1600–1500 B.C.; H. 0.043; solid cast; both feet missing.

His upper body bent backwards in a characteristically elastic posture, this small votive figure touches r. fist to forehead in the standard Minoan gesture of adoration. He wears a girdle with codpiece. Summary modelling, indistinct features, and rubbery arms betray a provincial version of the principal type of male votive statuette dedicated in considerable numbers in cave sanctuaries of eastern and central Crete, such as No. 2. (DGM)

Odyssey of an Art Collector, Isaac Delgado Museum of Art, New Orleans (Nov. 11, 1966–Jan. 8, 1967), 140, no. 6, ill. For general discussion cf. Boardman, 6–7; S. Alexiou, *Du,* 27 (Jan. 1967), 38–39.

Lent by Mr. and Mrs. Frederick Stafford.

4. Standing Woman (Votary)

Middle Minoan III–Late Minoan I, c. 1600–1500 B.C.;
H: 0.072, W: 0.047, min. D. at base of skirt: 0.029;
top solid cast, skirt hollow cast, filled with modern
plaster. From the Diktaean Cave.

This buxom votive lady, vigorous despite her
haphazard workmanship, is reminiscent of the
masterly praying woman in Berlin. Anatomy,
pose, and costume have here been fused into one
flowing form, animated despite its sketchiness
(DGM)

Boardman, 8, 12, no. 23, pl. 4, with bibl. and comparanda. For the Berlin woman, Neugebauer, *Kat.*, I,
1–2, no. 1, pl. 1; for a tiny counterpart in the MFA
C. C. Vermeule, *CJ*, 62 (Dec. 1966), 100, fig. 5.

Lent by the Ashmolean Museum, Oxford (AE. 596);
gift of A. J. Evans, 1905.

5. A and B A Pair of Female Votaries

Late Minoan 1a–1b, 1600—1450 B. C. (Evans), Neo-
palatial, phase II (N. Platon); H: A. 0.113, B. 0.115,
W. of skirt: A. 0.06, B. 0.063, D. of skirt: A. 0.042,
B. 0.034; solid cast tops, skirts hollow cast, whitish
green patina with crystalization, surface heavily
corroded; r. arm of A has deep fissure. Allegedly
from a cave at Tsoutsouros, southeastern Crete.

These two ladies, although possibly from the
same workshop, exhibit marked differences in
pose and characterization. A, her r. hand placed
upon her breast, is closely related to such figures
as No. 4. The sturdy dignity of her powerful body
with jutting bosom and head thrown back, is
worthy of a Victorian dowager. Three plastic
locks of hair, twining down neck and shoulders,
lend serpentine rhythms to her body's swelling
life. Diagonal lines, incised toward a central vertical groove, decorate her skirt. B, slightly larger
and cruder, holds both hands above her breasts,

A Pair of Female Votaries

a gesture reminiscent of Near Eastern fertility figurines. Though generally dated c. 1600 B.C., such statuettes could have been cast at least as late as the destruction of the major Minoan palaces, c. 1450 B.C., or perhaps later in outlying districts (e.g. No. 7). (DGM)

Unpublished. For a Middle Minoan prototype for A cf. terracotta statuette from Piskokephalo, near Siteia, eastern Crete (S. Marinatos—M. Hirmer, *Crete and Mycenae* [New York, 1960], pl. 17). For Tsoutsouros, cf. P. Faure, *Fonctions des cavernes crétoises* (Paris, 1964), 90–94.

Lent by the Collection of George Ortiz.

6. Crawling Baby

Late Minoan I, c. 1600 B. C.; H: 0.028, L: 0.048; solid cast, surface worn. From the Diktaean Cave.

One of the most startlingly realistic examples of Minoan naturalism known, this plump child crawls tentatively yet eagerly toward his goal. Presumably votive, its specific relevance to the cults practiced in the cave where it was found is uncertain. The two closest parallels, ivory children from Palaikastro, may reflect Egyptian or Near Eastern prototypes. Whatever its antecedents and function, it furnishes the most sympathetic and knowing interpretation of babyhood until the Hellenistic period. J. Boardman concedes as a remote possibility that the piece might be Roman. (DGM)

Boardman, 8, 11, no. 22, pl. 3, with bibl. and comparanda. For the Palaikastro children, S. Marinatos—M. Hirmer, *Crete and Mycenae* (New York, 1960), 148, with bibl., pl. 109, bottom.

Lent by the Ashmolean Museum, Oxford (1938. 1162); gift of A. J. Evans.

7. Female Figure with Upraised Arms

End of Late Minoan III or Sub-Minoan, c. 1200–1100 B. C.; H: 0.044; solid cast, greenish patina. Allegedly from a Cretan cave.

This small, stylized votive figure, with one palm facing forward, the other toward her head, is closely related to large terracotta figures, perhaps goddesses, found at Karphi and Gazi in Crete, products of Minoan religion in the twilight of the Bronze Age. She thus provides a rare example of the continuity of votive statuettes to the end of the Minoan artistic tradition. (DGM)

Unpublished. For the Karphi and Gazi figures, S. Marinatos—M. Hirmer, *Crete and Mycenae* (New York, 1960), 153, pls. 128, 131 (Gazi); 153–154, pls. 135–137 (Karphi, somewhat later). For life-sized and nearly life-sized figures from Agia Irini, Keos (c. 1400–1200 B. C.), J. L. Caskey, *Hesperia*, 33 (1964), 328–331, pls. 57–61; ——, *Hesperia*, 35 (1966), 369–371, pls. 87–89.

Lent by Mr. and Mrs. Edwin Grossman.

8. Warrior

Peloponnesian, perhaps 800–750 B. C.; H: 0.11; W: 0.039; solid cast, both eyes inlaid with lead, green patina; r. hand missing. Allegedly found on the Greek mainland.

The warrior wears a cowl-like helmet enclosing his face in an oval frame, topped by a short crest. His upraised r. arm probably brandished a spear. His rubbery arms contrast with the tautly bulging muscles of his legs. The figure may be from the top of a ring handle of a large bronze tripod (cf. No. 27). E. Kunze (by letter to the owner) called it Peloponnesian, first half of the 8th century B. C. If his date is correct, this warrior may be the earliest developed Geometric human figure yet recognized. (DGM)

Unpublished. Cf. Himmelmann-Wildschütz, figs. 28–30 (female statuette from Ithaka). In later warriors the cowl becomes part of the flattened mask of the face, cf. *Ibid.*, figs. 18–19; H.-V. Herrmann, *JdI*, 79 (1964), figs. 42–44.

Lent by the Eric de Kolb Collection.

9. Seated Man

Lakonian or Elian, 750–725 B.C.; H: 0.072; combination solid-hollow cast, dull brownish green, pitted surface. Allegedly found in the Alpheios Valley.

The rounded bends in the limbs, the meeting of knees and elbows, give a tectonic yet fluid quality to this self-contained masterpiece. His scooped-out eyes and small ears help establish his Peloponnesian pedigree. The object he holds to his mouth has been considered a flute, bud, or piece of food. He sits on a staple-like stool, mounted on one end of a T-shaped base. This appears to have been cast on or otherwise attached to the figure. (DGM)

Hill, 77, no. 167, pl. 36, with earlier bibl.; U. Jantzen, *AA* (1953), col. 63; L. Alscher, *Griechische Plastik*, I (Berlin, 1954), 21–22, fig. 16; *4,000 Years of Modern Art*, Baltimore Museum of Art (1956–57), 38, no. 42; WAG *Bulletin*, 10 (Feb. 1958); Himmelmann-Wildschütz, 11, figs. 51–53. For the closest parallel, from the sanctuary of Artemis Orthia, Sparta, cf. Himmelmann-Wildschütz, figs. 54–56. Also related are de Ridder, I, 19, no. 84, pl. 10 and *Pomerance, 79, no. 89, with bibl.

Lent by The Walters Art Gallery, Baltimore (54.789); purchased 1925.

10. Seated Man on Openwork Sphere

Thessalian or Macedonian, late 8th cent. B.C.; H: 0.095, W: 0.035; combination solid-hollow cast, dark green patina; sphere filled with incrustation.

A Geometric harbinger of Rodin's "Thinker," the little man sits atop a flat bench with perforations on either end, supported by a peg rising out of the sphere. His eyes are small compass-drawn or stamped circles flanking a beak-like nose; incised crossed "bandoliers" run over the shoulders on his back; other circles include one on rump, two on back of seat. Hands on knees, feet slanting on the shoulder of the sphere, he is closely related to free-standing seated figures from southern Greece (No. 9) and to squatting ape-like figures surmounting knobbed rods, commonly found in northern Greece and thought to be bottle stoppers (U. Jantzen, *AA* [1953], cols. 56–67) or pendants (P. Amandry, *Collection Hélène Stathatos*, III [Strasbourg, 1963], 242), to which class he probably belongs. Similar figures are known, both humans (MMA, Richter, *Greek*, 22, pl. 13c; Fitzwilliam, unpublished; Kozani, G. Daux, *BCH*, 85 [1961], 777–781, figs. 8, 9) and quadrupeds (Pherai, Biesantz, 109, no. L69, pl. 52), but their significance is unclear. (DGM)

Ars Antiqua Auktion II (14 May, 1960), 36, no. 80, pl. 80, with bibl.

Lent by the Eric de Kolb Collection.

11. Seated Figure

Late 8th cent.–650 B.C.; H: 0.04, W: 0.027, D: 0.022; solid cast, green patina; r. foot missing.

The seated figure leans forward to examine the bottom of his l. foot, bent upward across his r. knee. His blurred, oval face is framed by heavy, upswept hair. The diagonal of his neck repeats that of his leg. This early "Spinario" is a unique variant on the theme of the sitting man (Nos. 9 and 10), closely related to the "helmet-maker" in the Metropolitan Museum (Richter, *Greek*, 22, pl. 13d, Peloponnesian), though he appears to be merely examining his foot, not engaged in an exacting task. (DGM)

Sale, Sotheby (6 July, 1964), 45, no. 147, ill.

Lent by the Eric de Kolb Collection.

12. Warrior from Italy

Early 7th cent. B.C., H: 0.177; solid cast, riveted attachments, light emerald green patina. Allegedly found northeast of Rome.

The warrior was probably fastened to a large vessel or tripod through a hole in the middle of his parallelogram-shaped base. His upraised r. fist is perforated for a lance, now missing; a shield was riveted to his l. palm. His helmet, merging with his large head, sports a high crest with see-saw patterns. The back of his wig-like hairdo has irregular parallel horizontal incisions. His lower torso, terminating in loincloth-like briefs, is bordered by punched circles, which also indicate nipples and navel; the owner suggests the garment may be a tunic covering the entire torso.

The statuette stands in transition between the Geometric and early Archaic aesthetic viewpoints, combining severe stylization and symmetry with an awakening drive toward organic structure and action. In this it is analogous to the statuette dedicated by Mantiklos in Boston (Vermeule, 58, fig. 41). The angular body and rough-hewn features support the owner's comparison with late Geometric bronzes from Thessaly (cf. Biesantz, nos. L61, L79, pls. 51, 53). A northeastern Peloponnesian or Lakonian workshop cannot, however, be ruled out. (DGM)

Ars Antiqua Auktion II (14 May, 1960), 36, no. 81, pl. 37, "Italic".

Lent by the Collection of George Ortiz.

13. Flute Player

Anatolian (?), 8th–7th cent. B.C.; H: 0.105, W: 0.041; solid cast, light and dark green corrosion. Allegedly from Attica.

The squat musician, feet braced apart, bends to his tune played perhaps upon a straight pipe-like flute. In proportions, form and action, he suggests Greek Geometric seated musicians (No. 9). Standing musicians, however, are unknown among Geometric bronzes; the curving cap is also atypical. Similarities to a trumpeter said to be from Mylasa (H. S. Cowper, *JHS*, 29 [1909], 197, fig. 1) and a priest (?) with large jar from Ephesus (G. M. A. Hanfmann, *AJA*, 66:1 [1962], fig. 7) make it at least as likely that this bronze comes from western Asia Minor as from the Greek world. It might be the product of an Ionian workshop or of some non-Greek center (Lycian, Carian, Phrygian?). A figure belonging to R. Blanchet, Boulogne-sur-Seine, France, is similar. (DGM)

Mentioned Worcester Art Museum, *Annual Report* (1958), vii.
Lent by the Worcester Art Museum (1957. 138).

14. Horse and Rider

Peloponnesian, c. 775–725 B.C.; H: 0.057, L: 0.06, D: 0.025; solid cast, black to brown patina.

Showing the contours of its wax model, this equestrian group represents the birth of a favorite theme in Greek sculpture. Common in terracotta during the 7th century B.C., it is rare among Geometric bronzes. The stumpy legs and long neck of the horse and the rider's pinched nose and long torso resemble features in the horse and rider from Olympia (Furtwängler, no. 255, pl. 15). Possible Near Eastern prototypes come from northwestern Iran (E. Terrace, *Syria*, 39 [1962], 212–224) and Syria (G. M. A. Hanfmann, *Syria*, 38 [1961], 243–255). Women riding sidesaddle, in Vienna, Karlsruhe (both from Lousoi), and Tegea, may come from the same workshop. (DGM)

Unpublished. For rider in Berlin from Olympia, Neugebauer, *Kat.*, I, 18–19, no. 27, pl. 5; Vienna, E. Kunze, *OlBer*, IV (Berlin, 1944), 107, fig. 89; Karlsruhe, unpublished; Tegea, C. Dugas, *BCH*, 45 [1921], 354, no. 49, fig. 17.
Lent by the Eric de Kolb Collection.

15. Mare and Foal

Peloponnesian, c. 750–725 B.C.; H: 0.095, L: 0.115, W: 0.055; combination solid-hollow cast, openwork base. Allegedly from Olympia.

Small groups of female animals nursing their young, a beloved subject in Geometric bronze sculpture, required great technical competence in casting. This group, compact in structure, also demonstrates sophisticated awareness of space as an integral component of design. Horses and deer are the only animals so depicted (cf. Furtwängler, nos. 217, 219, pl. 14; de Ridder, *Acropole*, 174–175, nos. 480–481, figs. 139–140; Vermeule, 33, fig. 26; de Ridder, I, 19, no. 85, pl. 10). (DGM)

Odyssey of an Art Collector, Isaac Delgado Museum of Art, New Orleans (Nov. 11, 1966–Jan. 8, 1967), 12, 141, no. 13.

Lent by Mr. and Mrs. Frederick Stafford.

16. Bull with Bird on Back

Italic (?), 8th–7th cent. B.C.; H: 0.07, L: 0.07, H. of bird: 0.025; solid cast, dark gray-green, dull patina.

The rotund, sturdy proportions of the bull, quizzically turning his head to survey the bird perched on his rump, are non-Greek, although the theme is favored in Greek Geometric bronze animals; Greek animals, too, rarely look back. A mate to this group is in the Allard Pierson Museum (Van Gulik, 59–60, no. 84, pl. 20); a second is in Brussels (A. Roes, *Greek Geometric Art* [London, 1933], 101 f., fig. 84). (DGM)

Unpublished. For the motif cf. U. Gehrig, *Die geometrischen Bronzen von dem Heraion von Samos* (diss. Hamburg, 1964), 38, and C. C. Vermeule, *CJ,* 61 (April 1966), 290.

Lent by The Johns Hopkins University (1178, 2518).

17. Horse on Openwork Stand

Peloponnesian, 750–700 B.C.; H: 0.078, base: 0.060 by 0.028; combination solid-hollow cast, dark brown-green patina. Ex-coll. V. Simkhovitch.

This small horse has unusually long, forward-curved ears and a trumpet-shaped snout. The leg joints are indicated by tiny spurs; the legs slant inward to a narrow rump. The rectangular base is pierced by four oval perforations which radiate out from the center. Treatment of form, while still solid, tends in this individualistic statuette toward the abstraction and emphasized silhouette which characterize many "manneristic" horses of the late 8th century B.C. (DGM)

Handbook of the Rochester Memorial Art Gallery of the University of Rochester (Rochester, 1961), 11, ill. Cf. Furtwängler, no. 200a, pl. 13.

Lent by The Memorial Art Gallery of The University of Rochester (53.43).

18. Horse on Openwork Stand

Lakonian or western Peloponnesian, c. 750–700 B.C.; H: 0.087, L: 0.08; combination solid-hollow cast, shiny, uneven patina.

This fine horse appears to be steadied by his long tail as he leans backward; the tail rests on a square projection at the rear of the openwork base. The neck is short, the ears upright, the muzzle conical with a knob at the end. There are two rows of four wide perforations each in the flat base. This horse is closely related to No. 17, but is perhaps earlier; both have similar spurs at the knee joints. (DGM)

D. Amyx, *AJA*, 53 (1949), 147 f.; *Selection 1966* (Berkeley, 1966), 14–15, no. 18, ill. p. 13. For Lakonian Geometric bronzes, H.-V. Herrmann, *JdI*, 79 (1964), 21–24.

Lent by the R. H. Lowie Museum of Anthropology, University of California, Berkeley (8–74); gift of Mrs. P. A. Hearst, 1901.

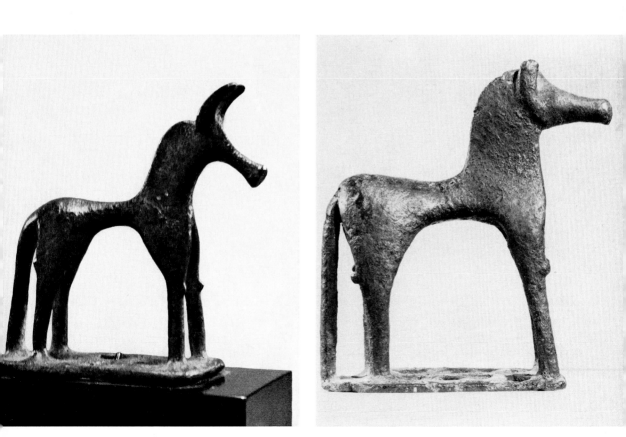

19. Horse on Openwork Stand

Thessalian, c. 725–700 B.C.; H: 0.083, L: 0.08;
combination solid-hollow cast, shiny dark
brown patina. Ex-coll. Ambassador Brecken-
ridge Long.

Incised lines run across legs at joints;
circle and dot stamped or punched designs
dapple the flanks. Short incised strokes lie
on the tail and edge of mane, alternating
diagonal strokes on sides of base. The hollow stand has a single row of triangular
perforations. The underside of front and
back legs is hollowed out, while the body
and muzzle are cylindrical. Derived from
Peloponnesian models, this horse is one
of the finest late Geometric examples from
northern Greece. Such horses, in which
flat, sheet-like forms are connected by
rods, are often termed "manneristic,"
from the exaggeration and abstraction of
the silhouette, resembling horses on late
Attic and Peloponnesian Geometric vases.
H.-V. Herrmann (*JdI*, 79 [1964], 28–32) has
proposed that large horses of this style
may be Corinthian. Closer to this horse:
one from Pherai, Thessaly (Biesantz, no.
L65, pl. 51 [Volos Museum]). (DGM)

Unpublished.
Lent by the Eric de Kolb Collection.

20. A and B   Horse and Man

750–700 B.C.; horse (A), H: 0.099, L: 0.067, D. of spheres: 0.023; man (B), H: 0.053, W: 0.028. A, combination
solid-hollow cast; B, solid cast; blackish brown surface. From Thessaly, allegedly found together.

The horse, fashioned into the same fanciful object as No. 21, again represents the "silhouette" type of
late Geometric sculpture. Curving, plate-like flanks, joints indicated by projecting spurs, and tiny
horizontal muzzle, as well as form and placement of the openwork spheres, each with eight triangular
perforations, confirm attribution to Thessaly. Pellet eye and crescent-shaped ears interrupt the flat
head and neck. Dots, each surrounded by two concentric circles, decorate the mane.
The tiny man, faithfully reflecting his origin, a handmade wax model, is more likely a groom than
rider; compare the horse and groom group atop a cast tripod handle from Olympia (E. Kunze, *OlBer*,
VII [Berlin, 1961], 150–151, figs. 92–93) or single rudimentary figures (Furtwängler, nos. 235, 236, 238,
260, pl. 15). He may, of course, be totally unrelated to the horse. (DGM)

Unpublished.

Lent by the Collection of George Ortiz.

21. Doe on Openwork Spheres

Thessalian, late 8th–early 7th cent. B.C.; H: 0.075, L: 0.05, D: 0.025; combination solid-hollow cast, green patina. Allegedly found at Pherai, Thessaly.

Front and hind legs balance upon biconical openwork spheres with eight triangular perforations, linked at their mid-sections by a bead. Flat upright ears and short pointed tail identify it as a deer. The flanks are marked by dot-in-circle, lower legs by horizontal incised lines. Ridged tangs project from the bottom, perhaps for insertion into a larger object. Possibly a pendant, the doe corresponds to birds, animals, and seated men atop single hollow spheres (No. 10), common in late Geometric Thessaly. (DGM)

Unpublished. For Pherai finds, Y. Béquignon, *Recherches archéologiques à Phères de Thessalie* (Paris, 1937), pls. 19–20; Biesantz, pls. 51–54.

Lent by the Eric de Kolb Collection.

22. Fawn or Doe

Northern Greek (?), 750–700 B.C.; H: 0.082, L: 0.085, D: 0.02; combination solid-hollow cast, light green patina; damage to l. front may be casting defect.

Slender solid horizontal members contrast with flute-like legs and flat tail in this highly individual animal. The shy grace of the deer speaks through spindly limbs, upturned tail and short, vertical ears. It stands on a hollow rectangular frame. The base suggests a northern Greek origin. A Thessalian horse with similar base is on the New York art market. (DGM)

Unpublished. For Geometric deer in general cf. D. K. Hill, *AJA*, 59 (1955), 40, no. 2, pl. 29, figs. 4–5.

Lent by the Eric de Kolb Collection.

23. Water Bird

Thessalian or Macedonian, late 8th cent. B.C.; H: 0.068, L: 0.083; body hollow cast, dark green patina with light spots. Ex-coll. G. Spencer-Churchill.

The rounded, boat-shaped body of this bird resembles Italic fibulae of the *navicella* type. It stands firmly on stumpy legs, spurs indicating joints; two horizontal incised lines occur at this point. A vertical zone of two rows of incised squares adorns the chest and is repeated, horizontally, at the tops of the legs. A loop for suspension, transverse to the body, lies at the neck. Incised lines also adorn the tail. Probably a votive offering, this bird could be stood on a flat surface or suspended from a tree. Probably Thessalian, its cousins are: WAG 54.2401; D. K.

Hill, *AJA*, 60 (1956), 36–37, pl. 28, figs. 2, 3; and Biesantz, no. L72, pl. 54, from Pherai. The Baltimore bird is hollow cast; the de Kolb example may be likewise. A plump bird in the MFA has an openwork body, but is otherwise very similar (C. C. Vermeule, *CJ*, 61 [April 1966], 290–292, fig. 3). (DGM)

Sale, Christie's (June 21, 1965), no. 441, pl. 49; sale, Sotheby (Nov. 14, 1966), no. 160.

Lent by the Eric de Kolb Collection.

24. Deer

Argive or Corinthian, c. 725 B. C.; H: 0.054, base: 0.035 by 0.025; solid cast, dark brown-green patina; transverse perforation (casting failure?) through neck, intaglio design (chevrons and meander) on underside of base.

This small deer, perhaps a stag, shows, in its compact yet delicate proportions and solid base with design beneath, characteristics that ally it with a group of bronzes which H.-V. Herrmann plausibly attributes to the Argolid (*Jdl*, 79 [1964], 24–28). Geometric stags have been found at Olympia, Tegea, and the Argive Heraion; cf. also the superb Peloponnesian example, probably Lakonian, in Munich (no. 3695; H. Marwitz, *Pantheon* [Nov.–Dec. 1965], 365, figs. 13–15). (DGM)

Mentioned *Record of the Art Museum, Princeton University*, 6 (1947), 8. Cf. also H. F. de Cou, in *The Argive Heraeum*, II (Boston, 1905), 200–201, nos. 19–21, pls. 73–74; Furtwängler, nos. 205–207a, pl. 13; Tegea, C. Dugas, *BCH*, 45 (1921), 347, nos. 13–17, figs. 2, 6, 19; Herrmann, *op. cit.*, 29, n. 52, considers many of these deer to be Corinthian.   Lent by The Art Museum, Princeton University (46–93).

25. Fanciful Bird

Northern Greek (?), c. 750–700 B. C.; H: 0.145, L: 0.185, W: 0.032; hollow cast, dark green patina; pitting on body, light green spots on head and neck, r. leg bent inward slightly.

This comic bird forms an almost symmetrical U. Its giraffe-like head has slight swellings at eyes below an axe-shaped crest. Diagonal lines, in alternating groups of three, adorn its sickle-shaped tail. A triple-ridged collar marks the connection of body with tail and neck. One of the largest such birds known, it belongs to a group nicknamed "peacocks", although they probably represent poultry or large-crested birds such as the hoopoe. Their stylization is analogous to anatomical flattening in late Geometric horses (Nos. 19, 20 A). Most common in northern Greece, they also occur in central Greece and the Peloponnesus. Removal of extensive restorations on r. of body has revealed that head, tail, and body were three separate fragments, and bared the fired core in the body with one of the chaplets that held it in place. The piece is the earliest known Greek hollow cast bronze with core, and analysis of the core promises to yield new information about early techniques of hollow casting.

Unpublished. Cf. H. F. de Cou, *The Argive Heraeum*, II (Boston, 1905), 205–206, nos. 46, 47, pl. 77; C. Dugas, *BCH*, 45 (1921), 350, nos. 24–26, fig. 10; P. de la Coste-Messelière, *Delphes* (Paris, 1943), 15, fig. 7; Richter, *Greek*, pl. 13f.; Ars Antiqua Auktion III (29 April, 1961), 29, no. 66, and bibl.; H. Payne, *Perachora* I (Oxford, 1940) pl. 37:3. Detailed publication forthcoming.

Lent by The Schimmel Collection.

26. Fibula

Late 8th cent. B.C.; H: 0.06, L. including pin: 0.09, solid cast.

The fibula, ancestor of the safety pin, enjoyed wide popularity throughout Geometric Greece. The enlarged catchplates of many elaborate fibulae bear incised scenes, as does this fine example with bird and grazing horse. The reverse depicts a grazing stag in a small panel enclosed by a meander border. The deeply-cut semicircles surrounding one panel appear to have been cut with a compass, a technique related to the rotation of multiple brushes to paint concentric circles on Protogeometric and early Geometric vases. The shape and exquisite miniature drawing style find closest parallels in Thessalian fibulae. (DGM)

Unpublished. Cf. C. Blinkenberg, *Fibules grecs et orientales* (Copenhagen, 1926); R. Hampe, *Frühe griechische Sagenbilder in Böotien* (Athens, 1936); H. Müller-Karpe, *JdI*, 77 (1962), 59–129. For similar fibulae cf. *Early Art in Greece*, Andre Emmerich Gallery (New York, May 7–June 11, 1965), 34–35, nos. 97–101; a very similar piece from Philia, A. H. S. Megaw, *Archaeological Reports* (1963–64), 15, fig. 15; —, *Archaeological Reports* (1965–66), 14–15, fig. 24, upper r. Cf. also Fogg Art Museum 1965.27, probably Thessalian.

Lent by The Estates of Audrey B. and Stephen R. Currier.

27. Ring Handle from a Tripod

C. 750–725 B. C.; H: 0.284, diam.: 0.232; solid cast in pieces. From the Idaean Cave.

Such cast openwork handles were attached in pairs or trios to man-sized Geometric tripods, the most elaborate dedications in early Greek sanctuaries. Devised for cooking sacrificial meat, tripods, mentioned as athletic prizes in Homeric poems, were also coveted in the first decade of the Olympic games. Large quantities of their cast legs and ring handles have been excavated at Olympia. The handles, both cast and hammered, are usually surmounted by a small animal, most commonly a horse. This fine example, one of a few known from Crete, could be either a native product or a Peloponnesian import. (DGM)

Boardman, 79 ff., no. 377, pl. 27, and bibl.; F. Willemsen, *OlFor*, III (Berlin, 1957), 57.
Lent by the Ashmolean Museum, Oxford (G. 391); gift of A. J. Evans, 1898.

28. Kouros

Early Archaic, late 7th–early 6th cent. B.C.; H: 0.12, W: 0.04, D: 0.03; green patina; l. hand and both feet missing. Allegedly from Sparta.

This early "proto-kouros", a miniature bronze parallel to the colossal nude figures of Richter's "Sounion Group," retains vestiges of the late Geometric aesthetic in the disproportionately large head and rubbery arms. The slanting brow and prominent chin resemble terracotta figurines of the second half of the 7th century B.C. The hair is defined by a deep groove running over the forehead to the ears, then horizontally around the back of the head; an undercurl falls straight to below the shoulders. The figure apparently rests his weight upon his slightly advanced l. foot. His eyes are large, convex ovals. The smooth surfaces and curving outlines suggest considerable Ionian influence upon this ostensibly early Lakonian work. (DGM)

Unpublished. For Ionian parallels cf. Nos. 33, 34; cf. man wearing tunic from Bayrakli, end of the 7th cent. B.C., now lost, E. Akurgal, *Die Kunst Anatoliens* (Berlin, 1961), figs. 137–139.

Lent by the Eric de Kolb Collection.

29.-32. A Find of Bronze Armor

These four items, part of a larger find representing the spoils of a battle, are introduced in this preliminary publication by Herbert Hoffmann and Antony Raubitschek. Said to have been found in Halbherr's excavations at Afrati, this armor somewhat supercedes the evidence of the decorated armor excavated in 1899 by Halbherr at Axos, until now the most important published document for the development of bronze sculpture in Crete during the early Archaic period. The battle trophies published here were inscribed when they were captured; the inscriptions date from c. 600 B.C. A good summary of the previously known material, with bibliography, is given in Boardman, 46 ff. and 141 ff.

The Helmets Both helmets are of Cretan shape, a modification of the standard Corinthian type, having a profiled cheek piece and no nose guard (cf. A. Snodgrass, *Early Greek Armour and Weapons* [Edinburgh, 1964], 28 ff., fig. 16). They consist of longitudinal halves joined by a riveted overlapping seam, along which the crest was fastened. They were worked in repoussé, with additional outlines and details chased and traced. The helmet edges are turned over a bronze wire. Both helmets originally had separately attached visors, but only that of No. 30 remains.

29. HELMET
max. H: 0.21; recomposed from many fragments, some areas missing, visor missing, parts of crest holder preserved. Inscribed (above the missing visor):

The neck guard is decorated with traced ornament in two registers separated by three ridges in relief: above, dogtooth pattern; below, tongue pattern, each tongue doubly outlined and containing a dotted circle. At the ends, an Assyrianizing palmette on a dotted curving stem. A traced eight-petal rosette with double outlines fills the round projection of each cheek piece.
Shown in relief, supplemented by a double outline, on each side of the helmet are a pair of heraldic winged youths, holding two serpents entwined in a figure eight between them. A small double-bodied Corinthian panther is shown in the tympanum formed by the serpents' tails.
Each youth grasps one of the serpents behind the head with his r. hand and treads on its tail with his r. foot. The serpents face inwards; the youths, in the running position peculiar to Archaic art, face outwards. The r. youth raises his l. hand with the fingers extended as if in greeting; the l. youth has his free hand lowered. Each wears a rosette diadem and short belted kilt edged with a welt and decorated with a pattern of alternately plain and hatched lozenges. The wings curve downward and are apparently fastened to the back by a waist and shoulder harness; a puzzling detail is the double circle on each shoulder. Smaller, sickle-shaped wings, rendered by traced line only, are attached to the youths' feet.

The youths' physiognomies are of a type peculiar to early Archaic Crete: eye with large iris and flattened lower lid; jutting nose with flaring nostril; fleshy lips; double volute ear. Above the diadem the hair is rendered by broken lines, below it by banks of curved lines. It is gathered at the nape by a ring or cord and falls onto the shoulders in two long wavy tresses.

The figures have broad shoulders and narrow waists. Although some plasticity is achieved by the use of relief, there is little attempt at anatomical differentiation except in the legs, the thigh and calf muscles being suggested by long ridges, bordered by traced lines. The kneecaps are stylized ball and socket.

Similar anatomical conventions, including that for representing a clenched fist (see drawing), occur also on Cretan bronze cutouts (see most recently Boardman, 46 ff., n. 2).

Although the style of the reliefs is familiar, their subject remains unexplained. A winged figure on a fragmentary cutout relief from Afrati (Boardman, pl. 16, top r.) may belong to a similar group. A variety of interpretations has been offered for the Afrati relief, but there is no certainty that a mythological subject is intended; the composition seems almost too symmetrical, too heraldic.

Drawings by Suzanne Chapman

30. HELMET

max. H: 0.245; recomposed of many fragments, substantial areas missing. Inscribed (in the field between the horse's legs):

The neck guard is ornamented as on No. 29, but for the ends, where elongated tongues stacked horizontally replace the palmettes. A horse in relief decorates each side of the helmet. The animal is of the stiff, long-legged Cretan variety. The mane is indicated as a series of S-shaped locks in relief, ending in sharp points. Three locks project along the forehead; others topple on the brow. The eye is lentoid; anatomical details are indicated by tracing.

The helmet can be assigned to the same hand as No. 31; the inscriptions are also the same. Synenitos the son of Euglotas dedicated both the helmet and the mitra, which he probably took from the same enemy. The inscriptions should be the work of one man, presumably Synenitos.

The nearest parallels to the style of this relief are to be found among the Cretan terracotta pithoi (cf. J. Schäfer, *Studien zu den griechischen Reliefpithoi* [Kallmünz, 1957], esp. 43). It is not clear whether the pithoi inspired the toreutic artist or vice versa (as Schäfer suggests). See also the fragmentary helmet from Dreros, D. Levi, *ASAtene*, 13–14 (1930–1931), 80 f., n. 2, fig. 29, and one from Delphi, J. Marcadé, *BCH*, 73 (1949), 421 ff.

The Mitrai

These semicircular abdominal shields are designed to be suspended from a belt (cf. A. Hagemann, *Griechische Panzerung* [Leipzig, 1919], 99 ff.). They were hammered, with traced details added, and have an upturned rim at the top. The type appears to have been a Cretan specialty. See Snodgrass, *op. cit.*, 88 ff., n. 56; Boardman, 141 ff.; H. Brandenburg, *Studien zur Mitra* (1966), 19 ff.; H. Bartels, *OlBer*, VIII (1967), 196–207, pl. 100–105.

31. MITRA
(see Plate II, p. 20)

H. (without rings): 0.154, L: 0.242; preserved intact with all suspension rings. Inscribed (in two lines, l. sector of field):

A pair of facing horse protomes in relief is framed by a wide border of parallel ridges. The manes are indicated by pointed S-strands in relief. A forelock with traced S-strands extends along each horse's forehead. The eyes are lentoid, with traced iris and pupil, the ears spade-shaped. It was produced by the same hand as No. 30.

Horse protomes — single and double — are popular in early Archaic art (Levi, *op. cit.*, 103 ff.). The style of this relief, like that of No. 30, is related to that of the pithoi.

32. MITRA

H. (without rings): 0.174, L. (actual): 0.22, L. (reconstructed): 0.245; parts of
rim missing, with only l. suspension ring preserved.

Two confronting winged sphinxes in relief are bordered as in No. 31. Their
forequarters are stiff-legged, one leg advanced; their hindquarters rest against
the steep up-curve of the panel sides. The bodies are slender and elongated, the
wings long and sickle-shaped. The heads, with short "perukes" adorned with
horizontal chevron patterns, face the beholder. The sphinxes wear tall spreading poloi framed laterally by a hatched border. An engraved palmette "floats"
behind each polos, attached to its base by a curling stem.

A double-bodied panther in relief, half-standing, half-seated as are these sphinxes,
occurs on a bronze mitra in the Metaxas Collection and is probably by the
same hand as No. 32. For the characteristically Cretan head type of the sphinxes
see E. H. Dohan, *MMS*, 3 (1931), 209 ff., esp. 216; E. Kunze, *Kretische Bronze-
reliefs* (Stuttgart, 1931), 233 f. The subject is especially popular on pithoi
(Schäfer, *op. cit.*, 31 ff.). (HH)   Lent by The Schimmel Collection.

33. Kouros

Ionian, c. 580–575 B. C.; H: 0.165, W: 0.042; smooth surface; feet broken off above ankles.

This kouros has played a controversial role in the evaluation of early Ionian sculpture. It was probably cast in a major Ionian center, perhaps Ephesus (cf. E. Kjellberg, *Konsthistorisk Tidskrift*, 6 [1937], 33 f., ivory from Artemision deposit). The sleek, liquid modelling of compressed forms, almost an exaggeration of the Ionian norm, perhaps led Poulsen to call it Etruscan, with which Richter disagrees. Its large head, flowing surfaces, and soft, unarticulated anatomy illustrate fundamental contributions of Ionian sculpture to the portrayal of the nude male in Archaic Etruscan art. (DGM)

Nationalmusei Konstsamlingar (Stockholm, 1911), 35, no. 314; F. Poulsen, *Der Orient und die frühgriechische Kunst* (Leipzig, 1912), 160; V. Müller, *AA* (1921), 231; ——, *Archaische Plastik* (Bilderhefte zur Kunst- und Kulturgeschichte, iv, Bielefeld and Leipzig, 1927), fig. 5; ——, *Frühe Plastik in Griechenland und Vorderasien* (Augsburg, 1929), 191; *CAH*, IV, 584, vol. of plates I, 353; Lamb, 75, 102, pl. 21C; E. Kjellberg, *Grekisk och romersk konst* (Stockholm, 1932), 59; V. Poulsen, *From the Collections of the Ny Carlsberg Glyptothek*, 2 (Copenhagen, 1938), 102–103; O. Antonsson, *Antik Konst* (Stockholm, 1958), 31, ill. 33; Richter, *Kouroi*, 56–57, no. 26, figs. 123–125, and earlier bibl.; E. Akurgal, *Die Kunst Anatoliens* (Berlin, 1961), figs. 162–164; H. Hoffmann, *AJA*, 65 (1961), 320.

Lent by the Nationalmuseum, Stockholm (NM Sk 314); gift of Queen Josefina of Sweden, 1866.

34. Kouros

Ionian, c. 550 B. C.; H: 0.102, W: 0.033; green patina; feet missing. Allegedly found on Samos.

The youth's broad shoulders, concave sides with long pointed oval gaps between arms and sides, and triangular groin bespeak an individual interpretation of the early Archaic kouros canon. The broad egg-shaped head has wide-spaced, deep-set flat, oval eyes and lips of similar form; the ears, placed high, separate horizontal and vertical divisions of hair, which falls in a spreading mass of wide horizontal corrugations to just below the shoulders. Very close are two other miniature kouroi from Samos (Richter, *Kouroi*, nos. 23, 52, figs. 120–122, 187–189), probably from the same workshop; a third, excavated at the Heraion in 1965, is dated c. 550–540 B. C. (E. Homann-Wedeking, *AA* [1966], 160–161, fig. 6). Shared with No. 33 are the modelling of body, position of hands, and right-angle convention around the ear. (DGM)

Unpublished.
Lent by the Eric de Kolb Collection.

35. Nude Youth

Greek (?), late 6th cent. B. C.; H: 0.126, W: 0.042; solid cast, mottled light and dark green patina; l. foot missing, r. foot broken at ankle and repaired. Allegedly from the Peloponnesus.

This stocky kouros, both of whose fists are perforated to hold objects, perhaps javelins, may be an athlete. The non-organic structure of his upper body contrasts strongly with his muscular legs. His upraised r. arm is probably not in its original position. If Greek, this statuette may be from a provincial workshop, perhaps in Arcadia (K. Schefold suggested, orally, an Etruscan or Italic origin). (DGM)

Mentioned Worcester Art Museum *Annual Report* (1958), vii; *Worcester, 1967, no. 14.
Lent by the Worcester Art Museum (1957. 139).

36. Athena Palladion

C. 550–500 B. C.; H: 0.169; solid cast, base cast with figure, surface black with red spots, gray-green deposit on back; front scraped. Allegedly found at Sparta.

Athena was frequently represented in Archaic Greece as a semi-columnar image, armed with spear and shield. A number of Archaic Palladia are known: E. Kunze, *OlBer*, VII (Berlin, 1961), 160–163, pls. 70–71 (Peloponnesian, 700–650 B. C.; not certainly Athena); Gortyn, Heraklion, D. Levi, *ASAtene*, 33:4 (1955–56), 302, pl. 4 (650–600 B. C.); Bührle Coll., Zürich, R. Lullies, *Griechische Plastik, Vasen und Kleinkunst* (Cassel, 27 May–27 Sept., 1964), no. 15; and Thessaly, Biesantz, 33, no. L85, pls. 57, 78 (600–550 B. C.). The type was probably the forerunner of the striding Promachos Athena, which became very popular in the late 6th century B. C. This Palladion, with elongated yet massive body, clinging helmet with crest, and elaborate girdle, belongs near the end of the earlier tradition. (DGM)

Hill, 84–85, no. 183, pl. 38; H. G. Niemeyer, *Promachos* (Waldsassen, 1960), 23, n. 41.

Lent by The Walters Art Gallery, Baltimore (54.780); purchased 1929.

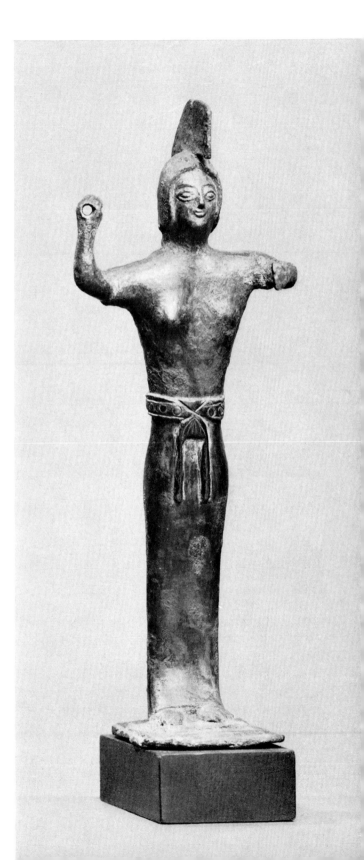

37. Striding Hoplite

Lakonian, mid 6th cent. B. C.; H: 0.083, W: 0.042, D: 0.025; solid cast with plinth, dark patina; l. ankle broken, front of crest broken off, l. hand missing.

Such heavily armed warriors made Sparta the bane of Greece during the Archaic period and her savior at Plataea. He wears a Corinthian helmet, tunic, two-piece "bell" cuirass, and greaves; he once held a spear and shield. Large triangular eyes, prominent nose, and incised mustache and beard characterize his face. Corrugated curls flank his chest and fall over his shoulders. E. Langlotz, by letter to owner, has called it the finest Spartan bronze he knows. The piece foreshadows hoplites on the Vix Krater. The two open spaces where the crest joins the edge of helmet and neck are unusual. Proportions and pose strongly resemble the Herakles from Mantineia (Richter, *Handbook*, 179 fig. 267); the powerful stride recalls a warrior from Dodona in Berlin (Neugebauer, *Kat.*, I, 56—58, no. 46, pl. 25), the lunging fighter from the east pediment of the Aphaia Temple, Aegina, both just before 500 B. C., and the so-called "Leonidas" marble hoplite torso of the early 5th century B. C. in Sparta. (DGM)

Unpublished. For other Lakonian bronze warriors, slightly later, *Deltion* (1916), 106, pl. Δ; H. Jucker, *Bronzehenkel*, 83—85, pls. 52—54. No. 37 may be the earliest. For warriors on Spartan relief vases, Jucker, *op. cit.*, 67—70, 105—107, 112, pls. 29—32.

Lent by the Eric de Kolb Collection.

38. Youth in Helmet and Boots

Northeast Peloponnesian (?), c. 520 B. C.; H: 0.196; green patina with red traces. Allegedly from Olympia.

The vibrant energy that courses through the tense, sensual forms of this nude youth and the radiance of his wide-eyed smile lend this masterpiece of late Archaic characterization great immediacy and force. The lofty crest atop its finger-like support lends added stature. Helmet and boots, not the usual garb of late Archaic hoplites, may be the mark of a hero or athlete, perhaps the young Theseus or Achilles. His perforated r. fist may have held a javelin or walking stick. The rectangular plinth has holes at diagonally opposite corners. Reminiscent of Lakonian work in face and physique, the youth may have been made there or, as the owner believes, somewhere in the northeast Peloponnesus (Argos, Sikyon, or Kleonai). (DGM)

Charbonneaux, 141, pl. 8:1; *Basel, 1960, 34, 181, no. 173, "perhaps Sikyonian?".

Lent by the Collection of George Ortiz.

39. Hoplite

Lakonian, late 6th cent. B. C.; H: 0.143, W: 0.064; solid cast with plinth, thin green patina; fingers of l. (shield) hand broken off, hole in top of helmet (for crest?). Allegedly found at Sparta, 1936.

A late Archaic Lakonian hoplite, he exhibits careful detailing on head and upper torso: ridges over the eyes, punctate dots around the cheek pieces, tongues below the neck of the cuirass, and spirals at the breasts. Such armor was often dedicated at Olympia. The hair hangs down the back; the r. fist is perforated for a spear. His square plinth was attached to its base through two holes, front and back. The figure, while less dynamic and organic than No. 37, is nevertheless impressive. (DGM)

Worcester Art Museum *Bulletin*, 2:3 (Dec. 1936), 1; *Annual Report* (1937), 9, 15; *Annual*, 2 (1936–1937), 7, 26, n. 5, figs. 5, 6; *Buffalo, 1937, no. 73, ill.; E. Hill, *JWalt*, 7–8 (1944–1945), 106, ill.

Lent by the Worcester Art Museum (1936.45).

40. Striding Bearded Figure

Peloponnesian, perhaps Arcadian, c. 525 B. C.; H: 0.11, W: 0.053; shiny dark green patina; l. hand and front of feet broken off. Allegedly found in Arcadia near Bassai.

This sturdy, older man, an ideal personification of a hero such as Herakles or Poseidon, reminds one in his massive limbs and square truncated torso of the Herakles from Mantineia, with which he is contemporary. His missing hands may have held weapons or a staff, on analogy with an old man from Olympia (E. Kunze, *OlBer*, I [Berlin, 1938], pl. 22). (DGM)

Unpublished.
Lent by the Eric de Kolb Collection.

42. Sphinx

C. 550–540 B. C.; H: 0.072; solid cast, surface dull brown without patina, chemically cleaned. Allegedly found at Locri. Ex-coll. Lambros.

Crouched on a rectangular plinth and similar to large sphinxes in limestone and marble from votive columns and grave stelae, she is probably an appliqué. The wing anatomy and openwork tail argue for a 550–540 B. C. date; the broad face and inorganic transition from profile body to frontal head bespeak South Italian reworking of mainland models. The type is based on polos-wearing sphinxes of 575–550 B. C. such as that from Spata, c. 570 B. C. (G. M. A. Richter, *The Archaic Gravestones of Attica* [London, 1961], 16, no. 12, figs. 40–41). Such bronze reliefs may have inspired the terracotta relief sphinxes which were popular votive offerings in Corinth in the late 6th-early 5th centuries B. C. (DGM)

Hill, 120–121, no. 279, pl. 54; *Flight, Fantasy, Faith, Fact*, Dayton Art Institute (1953–1954), no. 57, pl. 3. Cf. Jantzen, *Bronzewerkstätten*, pl. 33; L. von Matt–U. Zanotti-Bianco, *Magna Graecia* (New York, 1962), pl. 106.

Lent by The Walters Art Gallery, Baltimore (54.770).

41. Sphinx

Cretan, late 7th cent. B. C.; H: 0.078, W: 0.05; solid cast. Ex-coll. R. Zahn.

The sphinx appears to steady herself with outstretched wings. The l. wing projects horizontally; the r. is raised diagonally backward. Details (feathers in wings, strands of locks) are traced. A small disc lies over her forehead. The vase-like attachment atop her head may be the base of a columnar shaft. The fine three-dimensional modelling and wings, poised for flight, suggest a 7th century B. C. date for this worthy companion to such early Archaic Cretan master bronzes as the bronze calf-bearer in Berlin (Neugebauer, *Kat.*, I, 61–62, no. 158, pl. 19) and the youth from Delphi (P. de la Coste-Messelière, *Delphes* [Paris, 1943], 18–19, fig. 10). (DGM)

E. Langlotz, *Corolla Curtius*, I (Stuttgart, 1937), 60 ff., pl. 5; E. Kirsten, *Die Antike*, 14 (1938), 321, fig. 9; G. Lippold, *Die griechische Plastik* (Munich, 1950), 21, n. 11; P. Demargne, *Naissance de l'art grec* (Paris, 1964), 446, fig. 458.

Lent by the Staatliche Museen Berlin, Antikenabteilung (Inv. 31342).

43. Banqueter

Ionian (Samian?), c. 540–530 B. C.; H: 0.05, L: 0.07; combination solid-hollow cast, dark brown-green patina; l. hand missing. Ex-coll. E. P. Warren.

The banqueter supports himself on his l. forearm as he rises to a half-seated position, forming a lozenge-shaped composition. The articulation of anatomy is summary, definition of the upper edge of the skirt vague and unsure. His wide, rounded face, with ridge-lined horizontal oval eyes and compressed lips, suggests an origin in Ionia, if not specifically on Samos. The underside is hollow, and its edges are slightly concave. He was one of two to four such figures fastened to the rim of a tripod or lebes-cauldron. The l. hand probably held a cup or libation phiale. (DGM)

Casson, 14, no. 103; V. Müller, *Art in America*, 32 (1944), 19–25, figs. 1, 2; Herbert, 118, no. 418. The closest banqueters are in Samos, Buschor, 50, figs. 181, 182, 193, and Brussels, M. Gjødesen, *Meddelelser fra Ny Carlsberg Glyptotek*, 5 (1948), 14, fig. 5.

Lent by the Warren Collection, Bowdoin College Museum of Art (1923.17).

45. Banqueter

Probably South Italian (Tarentine?), c. 515–500 B. C.; H: 0.053, L: 0.10, W: 0.03; dark brownish patina, greenish in spots; l. hand missing, r. wrist appears bent.

In an unusual pose befitting inebriation or even inspiration, this slender symposiast leans backward, head upraised, perhaps joining in a favorite Anacreontic drinking song or a paean (cf. E. Vermeule, *Antike Kunst*, 8 [1965], 34–39, pl. 13:1–2). The body is enveloped by a series of wide garment folds which set up a rhythm of smaller diagonals within the broad triangle of the entire form. The banqueter wears a scalloped diadem or garland over his clipped hair, which is rendered in a row of short, incised locks. The upper edge of his pointed beard is also clipped. His beard and small nose show wear. The l. foot, with toes, faces front; the r., its tip bent downward, is in profile and has no toes. Resemblance to terracottas suggests a Tarentine origin. (DGM)

Unpublished. Cf. Jantzen, *Bronzewerkstätten*, 4, no. 26, pl. 2:8–9; Neugebauer, *Kat.*, I, 111–112, no. 217, pl. 36. It is likely that the de Kolb banqueter was a free-standing figure, perhaps a votive offering.

Lent by the Eric de Kolb Collection.

44. Banqueter

Corinthian or South Italian, c. 550–540 B. C.; H: 0.051, L: 0.079; combination solid-hollow cast, dark brown patina; face and head worn, l. hand missing, pin for mounting through hem of garment. Purchased in Greece by Kemper Simpson.

This alert symposiast tilts his head back slightly, as if in song; his l. hand may have held a phiale or rhyton. Three almost identical banqueters are known, for which a South Italian source has been suggested. Close parallels on the Eurytios Krater (Louvre) suggest a date around the middle of the 6th century B. C. or a decade later. The four banqueters may have been cast in the same workshop, perhaps attached to the same vessel. (DGM)

Unpublished. Three parallels: Louvre Br. 4300, Charbonneaux, pl. 21:5; Athens, NM inv. 16353, P. Amandry, *BCH*, 73 (1949), 517–518, pl. 29:1; private coll., Jantzen, 101, pl. 61:3–5; see P. Nölke in *Dionysos* (Ingelheim, 1965), nos. 86–87, pl. 17. For banqueters generally, D. E. L. Haynes, *BMQ*, 20 (1955), 36–37; Jantzen, 89–90, 100–101, n. 146; for the Corinthian problem, M. Gjødesen, *AJA*, 67 (1963), 333–351; for Eurytios Krater, P. Arias –M. Hirmer, *A History of One Thousand Years of Greek Vase Painting* (New York, 1962), 282, fig. 32, pl. 9; for banqueters on rim of a rod-tripod from Trebenischte, in Belgrade, N. Vulić, *AA* (1933), 465–468, figs. 2, 3.

Lent by The Johns Hopkins University (K. 23).

46. Kneeling Boy

Lakonian, c. 530–525 B. C.; H: 0.118, W: 0.079; solid cast, small amounts of green patina; feet missing.

This kneeling youth probably served as one of three supports for a low basin or tripod. Although no such complete tripod is known, a tripod base for a volute krater from Trebenischte has three kneeling gorgons as supports. A small Etruscan tripod with three kneeling youths is in the MMA (Richter, *Etruscan*, 30, fig. 88). The youth's pose is strikingly like an Attic plastic vase, perhaps a victor about to tie a fillet around his head, from the Athenian Agora. Other late 6th century B. C. parallels include a statuette from the Isthmian Sanctuary of Poseidon, one in Berlin, and a kneeling kouros from a vertical hydria handle in the Volos Museum (Biesantz, 142–143, no. L92, pl. 60). He is also akin to standing youths serving as vertical handles of hydriai and pateras, and to nude female mirror caryatids. Taut, squarish yet delicate body, slender oval face with prominent slanting eyes, and corrugated locks characterize this Lakonian masterpiece. (DGM)

Münzen und Medaillen Auktion 11 (1953), no. 294; A. Greifenhagen, *Apollo*, 79 (Aug. 1964), 117, fig. 7. For Trebenischte krater and stand, L. Popović, *Katalog nalaza iz nekropole kod Trebeništa* (Belgrade, 1956), no. 17, pl. 23c; Agora vase, E. Vanderpool, *Hesperia*, 6 (1937), 426 ff., figs. 1–9, pl. 10.; Isthmian statuette, D. G. Mitten, *Antike Kunst*, 9 (1966), 1–6; Berlin statuette, Neugebauer, *Kat.*, II, 53–54, no. 42, pl. 7. For kneeling youths head to head, side hydria handles, C. C. Vermeule, *CJ*, 57 (Jan. 1962), 147, fig. 2; de Ridder, *Acropole*, I, 56–57, no. 168, figs. 31–32.   Lent by the Staatliche Museen Berlin, Antikenabteilung (1961. 2).

47. Shepherd

Arcadian, end of 6th cent. B. C.; H: 0.109, W. at elbows:
0.035; intact, shiny dark olive green patina; l. foot bent
upward slightly.

The leonine mountaineer stands soberly, muffled in a
knee-length cloak of heavy fabric, probably his winter
costume. He wears a conical *pilos* or felt cap, and ankle-
length shoes. The strands of hair, mustache, and beard
are painstakingly, almost microscopically, incised. The
figure combines vivid portrayal of a type with an ele-
mental feeling for structural design. (DGM)

Langlotz, 55, 61, no. 29, pl. 28c, "Argos"; RISD *Bulletin*
(May 1965), 9, no. 4. Cf. Lamb, pl. 31c; *Schimmel, no. 14;
and No. 48. For the initial definition of the "Arcadian
School," W. Lamb, *BSA*, 27 (1925), 133 ff.

Lent by the Museum of Art, Rhode Island School of Design
(20.056), gift of Mrs. Gustav Radeke.

48. Bearded Man with Staff

Arcadian, 525–500 B. C.; H: 0.122; solid cast, dark green
patina. Allegedly from Argos.

Attached separately through plinth and perforated r.
fist, the staff could be that of a shepherd, herald, or
rhapsode. His long cloak is like that worn by Archaic
bronze figures of Zeus, suggesting a god, or, as K. Schefold believes, a heroized Arcadian king. Hair radiates
from the crown of his head; mustache, side locks, beard,
pupils, and r. nipple, as well as the cloak's fringe are
skillfully incised. The garland, with tiny punched dots,
reworked from what had originally been the brim of
a conical hat, along with the staff and cloak, set him
apart from well-known shepherd types (No. 47). (DGM)

*Buffalo, 1937, no. 74, ill.; *Fogg, 1954, no. 211, pl. 65; D. G.
Mitten, *Fogg Art Museum Newsletter*, 3:3 (Feb. 1966), ill.
For Archaic Zeus statuettes, Lamb, pls. 26c, 28c.

Lent by the Fogg Art Museum, Harvard University (1965.
533); gift of Frederick M. Watkins.

49. Cloaked Warrior

Lakonian, c. 520–500 B. C.; H: 0.15; solid cast, green patina; l. hand missing, hole in back of cloak at bottom, vertical rod (for mounting?) visible there; feet made separately (modern?). Ex-coll. J. P. Morgan.

The Peloponnesian concern in the late 6th century B. C. with exploring the active form made monumentally abstract when mantled in cloth is dramatically embodied in this warrior. Only his l. hand and bare feet project beneath his robe. His cloak, wound tightly in broad, diagonal folds, contrasts with the ornate crest and hair. The transverse crest, known on late Attic black-figure vases, forms an effective frame for his head, masked in the Corinthian helmet. The sculptor has created an apparition of uniquely compelling force, perhaps portraying a character from heroic epic. (DGM)

C. Smith, 14–15, no. 35, pl. 21; M. L. Nichols, Wadsworth Atheneum *Bulletin*, 2:1 (1924), 5, fig. 9; Jantzen, *Bronzewerkstätten*, 36, 43, 72, pl. 34 (front and back views; feet not shown); *Buffalo, 1937, no. 7; *Detroit, 1947, no. 61; C. T. Seltman, *Approach to Greek Art* (London, 1948), pl. 29; *The Pierpont Morgan Treasures* (Hartford, 1960), no. 3, pl. 1; H. Jucker, *Bronzehenkel*, 50, n. 162. For transverse crest, Jucker, *op. cit.*, 50–51, figs. 16–17 (said to be Italic); E. Kunze, *Deltion*, 17 (1961–1962), 119, pl. 136.

Lent by The Wadsworth Atheneum, Hartford, Conn.; J. Pierpont Morgan Collection (1917.815).

50. Warrior Dedicated to the River Pamisos

Southwestern Peloponnesian (Messenian or Arcadian), c. 550–525 B. C.; H: 0.114; solid cast, green and tan patina; rectangular base perforated by two holes. Allegedly from Arcadia.

A stocky warrior, clad in a short tunic, advances to hurl a spear, now missing. On his back, incised l. to r. in three lines beginning at r. shoulder, last line (three letters) retrograde, is a dedicatory inscription: ΤΟΙ ΠΑΜΙΣΟΙ/ΠΥΘΟΔΟ/ΡΟΣ "Pythodoros (dedicated it) to the (river) Pamisos." A small shrine to the river god Pamisos, spirit of Messenia's principal river, has been excavated (F. Versakes, *Deltion*, 2 [1916], 103 ff., figs. 53, 55) and may be the source of this provincial but spirited little bronze. The inscription, consistent with the alphabet of Lakonia and Messenia during the second half of the 6th century B. C., has been called the earliest Messenian inscription known. (DGM)

G. M. A. Richter, *Archaic Greek Art* (New York, 1949), 89 f., fig. 154 (mid 6th cent. B. C.); F. F. Jones, *Archaeology*, 7 (1954), 240; F. F. Jones – R. Goldberg, *Ancient Art in The Art Museum, Princeton University* (Princeton, 1960), 30–31; L. Jeffreys, *Local Scripts of Archaic Greece* (Oxford, 1960), 202, n. 1, 206 (Messenia, no. 1).

Lent by The Art Museum, Princeton University (47–325); gift of Mrs. T. Leslie Shear.

51. Running Youth

Samian, 520—510 B. C.; H: 0.078, W: 0.04; lustrous blue-green patina; feet and l. hand missing.

His animated body twisted in running, this figure, probably an athlete, foreshadows the end of Archaic rigid frontality. The forms of the torso are close to Richter's "Ptoon 20" group, particularly the Samian youths in Berlin (A. Greifenhagen, *Antike Kunstwerke* [Berlin, 1960] pl. 6—9) and the Baker Collection (*Metropolitan, 1959—1960, 34—35, no. 133, pl. 44, 48). Eyes and anatomical details are delicately rendered; the incised curling locks become three-dimensional at the bottom of the hair mass. These details and his bodily proportions strengthen an attribution to Samos. (DGM)

Unpublished. Cf. also Münzen und Medaillen Auktion 22 (13 May, 1961), 32—33, no. 57, pl. 16, "workshops in Magna Graecia under Ionian influence."

Lent by the Eric de Kolb Collection.

Drawing by
Marjorie B. Cohn

52. Cloaked Youth

Eastern Greek, end of the 6th cent. B. C.; H: 0.091; solid cast, green patina, slight brown incrustation. Ex-coll. Spencer-Churchill (bought in Paris, 1928) (sale, Christie's, June 21, 1965, no. 473, "Etruscan").

This sturdy youth, wearing shoes and a long chlamys, the standard Greek traveling cloak, fastened over one shoulder, appears to have held a bow in his r. hand, an arrow in his l. As C. C. Vermeule suggests, these attributes suit either Apollo or a mortal worshipper offering these objects to him. His costume recalls earlier clothed kouroi, an Ionian specialty. Such a figure would have been an appropriate votive offering at the Archaic sanctuary of Apollo at Didyma, in Milesian territory. Wherever made, it represents the final flowering of Ionian sculptural independence before the ill-fated revolt against Persian domination (499–494 B. C.). (DGM)

C. C. Vermeule, *CJ*, 62 (Dec. 1966), 102–103, fig. 10. For robed Ionian kouroi, E. Akurgal, *Die Kunst Anatoliens* (Berlin, 1961), 229–233, figs. 193–199.
Lent by the Museum of Fine Arts, Boston (66.251), Harriet Otis Cruft Fund.

53. Warrior from Lid of Lebes

Campanian, late 6th cent. B. C.; H: 0.095; solid cast, dark green patina. Ex-coll. H. Oppenheimer.

An unusual lebes lid finial is this little nude warrior, with sword belt and quiver. His upraised r. hand and clenched l. fist are summarily treated as blocks. His Phrygian helmet connects him with the Scythian and Amazon riders who chase each other around the rims of Campanian dinoi. The square straps passing diagonally over the r. shoulder and straight over the l. support a rectangular case, more like a quiver or bow case than a scabbard; he is probably a dismounted Scythian archer rather than a conventional Greek hoplite. (DGM)

*Burlington, 1904, no. 54, pl. 50; Reinach, IV, 102:4. Also exhibited Detroit, 1958; *University Museum, 1964, no. 16.
Lent by Dr. and Mrs. Robert Waelder.

54. Athena

Attic (?), late 6th–very early 5th cent. B. C.; H: 0.063; shiny green patina; l. (shield) arm bent inward.

In martial pose, Athena once brandished a spear in her r. fist. Her helmet crest has minute incisions and a secondary perforation of unknown function. Her hair, drawn aside to either side of a button-like rosette, falls to below the shoulders in back. Her steady gaze, compact chin and pursed lips foreshadow the serious spirit of the Severe Style. The clean cut at her waist suggests deliberate intent, not a break. L. Pomerance suggests she may have belonged to a representation of the birth of Athena, springing full-grown from the head of Zeus. For such scenes in bronze reliefs see E. Kunze, *OlFor*, II (1950), 78 f., pls. 31, 39; K. Schefold, *Myth and Legend in Early Greek Art* (New York, 1966), 66–67, figs. 20–21. Marked similarities in Attic Athenas from the Acropolis (H. Niemeyer, *Antike Plastik*, III [Berlin, 1964], 34, pls. 1–5), in pose and features as well as exquisite detailing, suggest an Attic workshop, perhaps just before 500 B. C. (DGM)

*Pomerance, 81, no. 92, ill.
Lent by The Pomerance Collection; acquired 1965.

55. Warrior (Hoplitodromos?)

500–475 B. C.; H: 0.104; solid cast, dark patina; feet broken and mended.

Running slowly, with drawn-up fists, he wears a chlamys patterned with clusters of three punched dots and an Attic helmet with upturned cheek pieces. Its large crest is finely striated, with deeply scored lines dividing it into five sections. His shoulder-length hair frames the face in two rolls. The subject is puzzling, as he carries no shield, and an armed foot-racer would probably not wear such a cape. (HH)

Unpublished.
Lent by a Swiss private collection.

56. Kore

South Italian (?), early 5th cent. B. C.; H: 0.10; tang under each foot.

The maiden holds a small round object (fruit?) daintily between thumb and forefinger of her r. hand, and with two fingers of the l. plucks up a fold of her garment. The object on the over-fold, on analogy with a statuette in the Louvre (Giglioli, 125:2), may be identified as a loop of cloth. Though, as Wescher suggests, the incising of folds and ornament is Etruscan, stylistically the piece is close to South Italian Greek works, such as Neugebauer, fig. 34, in Berlin. (GMAH)

P. Wescher, *Bulletin of the J. Paul Getty Museum*, 1:1 (1957), 16, fig. 7c; *Etruscan Art*, Otis Art Institute (March 21–April 14, 1963), 33; Stothart, 14; J. Paul Getty, *The Joys of Collecting* (New York, 1965), 52, ill.; *Santa Barbara, 1967, 40, no. 43, ill.
Lent by the J. Paul Getty Museum, Malibu, Calif. (A 57.S–5).

57. Woman Walking

Probably South Italian, c. 500–475 B. C.; H: 0.154; surface dull black; tiny casting bubbles, especially thick on front, feet restored.

This willowy lady, wearing a sleeved chiton and diaphanous lower garment, has frequently been called "Chalcidian," or attributed to Rhegion, Chalkis' colony in South Italy. Her slender, athletic physique, infused with movement, relates her as well to such Etruscan bronze ladies as the MFA dancer (Vermeule, 193, no. 190, ill. 205). The object in her r. hand may be a dove, egg, or olive. Broad chest and shoulders, slender upright neck, and wide eyes with barely smiling lips show the rich fusion of Archaic and advanced traits characterizing sculpture from Magna Graecia in the early 5th century B. C. (DGM)

*Detroit, 1947, no. 64, ill.; Hill, 106, no. 239, pl. 47, with bibl.; L. Lawler, *Dance Perspective*, 4 (1962), 45; ——, *Dance in Ancient Greece* (London, 1964), 107, fig. 40; D. K. Hill, *Fashions of the Past – Ancient Greek Dress* (Baltimore, 1964), 3, ill.
Lent by The Walters Art Gallery, Baltimore (54.87); purchased 1906.

58. Horse and Rider

Attic (?), c. 500–490 B. C.; H: 0.084; solid cast, dark brown patina; lower hind legs of horse, lower l. leg of rider missing, r. forehoof slightly bent. Originally attached to rim or shoulder of vessel, a piece of which adheres to the r. forehoof.

This equestrian group finds its closest parallel in a group from Mantineia in the MFA. Both riders sit far forward on their steeds with l. hands raised and r. lowered; both horses are bridled and have similar clipped manes and foretops. The group is reminiscent of marble horses and horsemen from the Acropolis, as well as small bronze horse-and-rider statuettes dedicated there. Treatment of the topknot is close to two examples from the Isthmian Sanctuary of Poseidon (late 6th century B. C.) and to the chariot teams on the neck frieze of the Krater of Vix. (DGM)

E. Kunze–H. Schleif, *OlBer*, III (Berlin, 1941), 147, fig. 108; F. F. Jones, *Record of the Art Museum, Princeton University*, 7:2 (1948), 11, and 13 (1954), 3; F. F. Jones–R. Goldberg, *Ancient Art in The Art Museum, Princeton University* (Princeton, 1960), 38–39. For marble horses, H. Payne – G. Mackworth-Young, *Archaic Marble Sculpture from the Acropolis* (London, 1950), 51–52, pls. 134–140. For statuettes from the Acropolis, de Ridder, *Acropole*, II, 277–278, figs. 259–260; from North Slope, O. Broneer, *Hesperia*, 7 (1938), 203–208, figs. 38–40; from Mantineia, Jantzen, *Bronzewerkstätten*, no. 152, pl. 37, cf. also 72–73. For horse heads from the Isthmian Sanctuary, O. Broneer, *Hesperia*, 28 (1959), 328–329, pl. 69a; on Vix Krater, R. Joffroy, *Le Trésor de Vix* (Paris, 1964), 61, 125.

Lent by The Art Museum, Princeton University (48–8).

59. Appliqué with Heraldic Lions

Corinthian (?), c. 550–500 B. C.; H: 0.139, W: 0.145; solid cast, incised decoration; abrasion on ribs of lion. Allegedly from Macedonia.

The lions' upraised inner paws end in a flattened perforated flange through which this relief appliqué was attached to a large vessel or the like. Their manes are rendered in three vertical divisions, the two inner ones with curving hairs, the outer with diagonal hatching. Teeth and claws of hind feet, as well as details of palmette and plinth, are also incised. Tension within symmetry in heraldic ornament groups originates in the Near East and occurs also in the Aegean Bronze Age. It reaches a formal climax in such Greek works as this, as well as in Near Eastern objects (such as an Achaemenid mirror, *Schimmel, no. 74, also perhaps late 6th century B. C.). (DGM)

Neugebauer, *Führer*, 69, pl. 6. An almost identical, slightly larger, attachment is in the MMA (Richter, *Br.*, 7–8, no. 13).

Lent by the Staatliche Museen Berlin, Antikenabteilung (Misc. Inv. 10557).

60. Reclining Lion

Eastern Greek, c. 525–500 B. C.; H: 0.058, L: 0.097; partly hollow cast, some lead filling, green patina, pitted; iron pin in back. Allegedly from Asia Minor.

This alert lion, with narrowed eyes and large mitten-shaped ears high on his flame-incised mane, may have been a votive statuette or an attachment for a large vessel or piece of furniture. His compact body with bony haunches and tail neatly curled over his rump recalls early Archaic prototypes such as a marble lion from Sardis (D. G. Mitten, *Biblical Archaeologist*, 29 [May 1966], fig. 10, c. 600–575 B. C.), and a lion from the Smyrna region, Izmir Museum (E. Akurgal, *Die Kunst Anatoliens* [Berlin, 1961], 179, figs. 246–247, c. 550–525 B. C.). This lion, more serene than these temple or tomb guardians, seems to purr rather than snarl. (DGM)

C. C. Vermeule, *CJ*, 62 (Dec. 1966), 103–104, fig. 11. Cf. H. Gabelmann, *Studien zum frühgriechischen Löwenbild* (Berlin, 1965); L. Brown, pl. 37 a–b (similar lions on corners of wheeled brazier).

Lent by the Museum of Fine Arts, Boston (66.9).

61. Handle with Lion Heads

Northern Greek, late 6th cent. B. C.; H: 0.106, L: 0.295, D: 0.157; hollow cast. From Thessaly.

The curving handle ends in two upright lion protomes glaring fiercely in the direction of the vessel they guard. The outer front paw of each is visible from the back but is obscured on the front by the deep cuttings for attachment. The flaring projection from the middle of the handle has precedents in the knobs atop lateral handles on large basins (cf. the perirrhanterion from Isthmia, O. Broneer, *Hesperia*, 27 [1958], 24–27, pls. 10, 11a, and Attic black-figure "merrythought" cups). The handle is one of a pair, probably from a large bronze basin suitable for use in a sanctuary. The appealing and highly individual lions, with their mustaches, plastically rendered wrinkles, stubby ears, and ruff-like manes, are Greek, though perhaps influenced by Achaemenid conventions. Inlaid pupils must have heightened their lively expressions. (DGM)

H. Luschey, *Berliner Museen*, 59 (1938), 76 ff., figs. 1–2; Biesantz, 34, no. L95, pl. 78.

Lent by the Staatliche Museen Berlin, Antikenabteilung (Inv. 30948).

62. Fish Vessel

C. 500 B. C.; H: 0.095, L: 0.145, H. of spout: 0.03; hollow cast, green patina with some red areas; top of spout broken.

Carefully incised scales cover the body of this unusual flask. The fish is identified by G. W. Mead, Museum of Comparative Zoology, Harvard, as a generalized carp. Its ventral fins create a supporting surface. A handle may have joined the dorsal fin to the moulding on the spout, as breaks indicate. From the rim of the spout might have come a chain connected to a cap. Archaic plastic vases of fish form are known. DGM cites M. I. Maximova, *Les vases plastiques dans l'antiquité*, II (Paris, 1927), no. 117, and J. Boehlau, *Aus ionischen und italischen Nekropolen* (Leipzig, 1898), 44, 160, pl. 13:2 (Naucratite rather than Phoenician). The careful workmanship of this bronze fish would fit an Archaic date. The "palmette capital" motif of the spout has Archaic parallels, but comes originally from Egypt (F. Matz, *Geschichte der griechischen Kunst* [Frankfurt, 1950], 377, pl. 244b; W. B. Dinsmoor, *The Architecture of Ancient Greece* [London, 1960], 140, pl. 33). The vessel itself may be inspired by Egypt, where fish vessels of glass are known from the New Kingdom on. (GMAH)

Unpublished.
Lent by Mr. and Mrs. Joseph Ternbach.

63. Reclining Goat

Corinthian (?), late 6th or early 5th cent. B. C.; H: 0.055, L: 0.084; hollow cast, gray-green patina, brown to black incrustation.

Reclining goats were commonly attached to the shoulders or rims of kraters, cauldrons, or tripods. This one has fine detailing of ribs, horns, and goatee. The head, twisted completely around, is unusual. Such goats commonly turn their heads to one side. Similar goats are Coll. G. Ortiz (*Basel, 1960, 146–147, no. 115); Berlin (Neugebauer, *Kat.*, I, no. 185, pl. 29); University of Mississippi (B11), allegedly from Aigion, Achaea; Belgrade, National Museum, and Sofia, National Museum, from Trebenischte (B. Filow, *Die archaische Nekropole von Trebenischte* [Berlin, 1927], 53–54, pls. 52–54). (DGM)

Unpublished. Lists of similar goats, D. M. Robinson, *AJA*, 59 (1955), 20, figs. 4–5, pl. 12; Münzen und Medaillen Auktion 26 (Oct. 5, 1963), 8, no. 11, pl. 4 (550–500 B. C.).

Lent by the Vassar College Classical Museum; acquired 1942.

64. Ram

Early 5th cent. B. C.; L: 0.073, H: 0.51, base: 0.04; solid cast on rectangular base, green patina. From Syria.

The simplified organic rendering, arrested motion, and compelling characterization of this ram point to a product of the Severe Style, c. 500–470 B. C., the period of such superb animal sculptures as Myron's heifer on the Acropolis and the chariot horses from Olympia in Athens and New York. A large ram's head in marble in Hamburg (Hoffmann, 6, pls. 18–19) is said to be from South Italy; a workshop in the same area may have produced this forceful miniature interpretation, probably a votive statuette. (DGM)

Unpublished. For rams in general, Richter, *Animals*, 27–28, figs. 136–140, pls. 44–46. Cf. lebes with four ram protomes, from Leontini, in Berlin, G. M. A. Richter, *Archaic Greek Art* (New York, 1949), 129, fig. 209, and protome from Olympia, E. Kunze, *Deltion*, 19 (1964), pl. 172d.

Lent by a private collection.

65. Griffin Protome

Samian (?), late 7th cent. B. C.; H: 0.13, diam. of neck at base: 0.025, diam. of ring: 0.048; hollow cast, smooth, dark grayish patina; l. ear, part of lower edge near one rivet hole missing.

One of a set of three, four, or six attached to a large bronze cauldron, this griffin protome is an early example of the smaller, serpentine-necked cast variety. Thick neck at base, plump proportions of head, *Wulst* (fleshy fold under the jaw), and folds under the eyes, suggest an early, plastic interpretation. The scales covering head and neck were probably done with a half-circular punch; two spiral locks hang down each side of the neck; the "browlock" behind the eye is atypical. The knob on stem projecting from the forehead is an unusual variant of this standard feature of griffin anatomy. (DGM)

Unpublished. Cf. Jantzen, no. 45, pl. 15 (first cast group, 650–600 B. C.).

Lent by John and Ariel Herrmann; acquired 1964.

66. Griffin Protome

Samian or Olympian, c. 600 B. C. or slightly later; H: 0.160, diam. at base: 0.060; hollow cast, light green patina; knob, ears broken off.

This protome is typical of the griffins mass-produced at Samos and presumably in the Peloponnesus, c. 600 B. C. The neck and head have become more slender and serpentine; the structure of ears, *Wulst*, and head has become blurred, and the eyes are in relief. Decoration is limited to scales produced with a semicircular punch. The attachment holes still contain bits of rivets or nails. (DGM)

Casson, 15, no. 122; Herbert, 117, no. 417, pl. 40. For the later, slender cast griffins, R. Joffroy, *Mon Piot*, 51 (1960), 1–23, and Jantzen, 77–79, pls. 51–54 (seventh cast group, 600–550 B. C.); for slightly earlier set of three protomes, Vermeule, 39, no. 32, ill. 41.

Lent by the Warren Collection, Bowdoin College Museum of Art (1923.16).

67. Griffin Protome

Late 7th cent.–c. 575 B.C., H: 0.184; diam. at base: 0.071; hollow cast, dark green patina; tips of ears broken off. Allegedly found at Olympia. Ex-coll. S. Morgenroth, F. M. Watkins.

This large protome, whose eyes were probably inlaid, exemplifies the cast griffin protome at the height of its development, before attenuation of forms set in. Its neck is covered with small curving marks for scales, probably made by a lunate punch. An incised curling lock hangs on either side of the neck. The ears are hollow channels, with fine incision on the edges. This example, one of a pair, may have been made in the Peloponnesus or in a Samian workshop around the end of the 7th century B.C. or slightly later. (DGM)

*Fogg, 1954, no. 99, pl. 60; J. L. Benson, *Antike Kunst*, 3 (1960), 70, appendix, not discussed; *Santa Barbara, 1963, 8, no. 2, ill.; D. G. Mitten, *Fogg Art Museum Acquisitions* (1964), 11–19, ill. The other of the pair has not been traced.

Lent by the Fogg Art Museum, Harvard University (1963.130).

68. Centaur

East Greek, perhaps late 6th cent. B. C., H: 0.077, L: 0.075; dark shiny brown patina. Ex-coll. T. L. Fraser, London; Sevadian, Paris; De Frey, Paris; S. Morgenroth, Santa Barbara.

In a time-honored Archaic convention, this centaur is a man with hindquarters of a horse added behind. The broad, vigorous modelling, with the head and face in facets, bespeaks bold work in clay or wax before casting. The eyes are incised circles, the mouth a horizontal gash. The centaur belongs to a famous group of small East Greek bronzes discussed by D. E. L. Haynes, *JHS*, 72 (1952), 74 ff. (DGM)

*"Art of the United Nations," De Young Memorial Museum, San Francisco, 1945; *Fogg, 1954, 30, no. 194, pl. 57; *Santa Barbara, 1963, 8, no. 6, ill. Cf. J. M. Cook, *The Greeks in Ionia and the East* (New York, 1965), pl. 34; U. Gehrig, *Berliner Museen*, 16 (1966), 2–4; P. Baur, *Centaurs in Ancient Art, the Archaic Period* (Berlin, 1912); H. G. Niemeyer, *Antike Plastik*, III (Berlin, 1964), pl. 27, 32a.

Lent by the Eric de Kolb Collection.

69. Forepart of Rearing Horse

Northern Greek, 525–early 5th cent. B. C. (510–500 B. C. – owner); solid cast, socket in bottom, light green patina; two holes at edge of socket. Allegedly from around Trikala, Thessaly.

The socket probably fitted a long staff, which, when held diagonally, would suggest a leaping horse. Two overlapping topknots lie between the horse's disproportionately tiny ears. The modelling and gently rounded head belong in the early Severe Style. Although exact parallels are lacking, cauldron and furniture attachments may employ the entire forepart of an animal (cf. Jantzen, pls. 47, 48:4–6, 59). Closest parallel is a ram finial (E. Kunze, *Neue Meisterwerke griechischer Kunst aus Olympia* [Munich, 1948], 14–15, no. 27). (DGM)

Unpublished. For the ornamental use of horse protomes in the decoration of bronze hydriai, rod-tripods, etc., H. Jucker, *Bronzehenkel*, 62–64, pls. 8, 23:3, 35 (No. 42), 38, 40:2, 41–42, 44–45.

Lent by the Collection of George Ortiz.

70. Vertical Hydria Handle

Corinthian (?), c. 550–525 B.C.; H: 0.188, W: 0.132; dark green patina; shaft much rubbed.

The curved shaft has projecting flanges, the two at the top in the form of recumbent lions, those at the bottom, of recumbent rams, all facing front. The rams' bodies and lions' forepaws are pierced for attachment to the hydria. Behind the lions were two flat projections (one now missing), pierced for attachment to the vessel's rim. The top of the shaft is decorated with a palmette, now almost obliterated; the lions' tails hang down on either side. At its lower end is a grimacing gorgon mask in relief, a descendant of No. 71. (GMAH)

Unpublished. Cf. L. Politis, *ArchEph* (1936), 147–174; A. Fairbanks, *Greek Gods and Heroes* (Boston, 1948), 49, fig. 47; Münzen und Medaillen Auktion 26 (Oct. 5, 1963), 8–10, no. 13, pl. 3; Diehl, 15 ff.
Lent by Mr. and Mrs. Joseph Ternbach.

71. Handle Fragment – Kore and Gorgon

Probably Lakonian, c. 565–550 B.C.; H: 0.114, W: 0.082; plate solid cast, stump of handle appears to be filled with a ferrous substance. Allegedly from Greece.

Originally the base plate of the vertical handle of a large hydria, this fragment superimposes a wide-eyed Archaic lady atop a horned gorgon. The closest gorgon is on a similar base plate from Trebenischte, in Sofia; female heads occur frequently in the same position, as in the Telesstas handle in Mainz. Juxtaposition of the two, however, is unparalleled. The outward-curving locks and high cheekbones of the lady echo early 6th century B. C. sculpture. (DGM)

D. G. Mitten, *Fogg Art Museum Acquisitions*, 1962–1963, 11–16; D. von Bothmer, *Gnomon*, 37 (1965), 600 (associates it with Diehl's "Gorgoneion Group"); H. Jucker, *Bronzehenkel*, 47, 111–112, pl. 37; detailed publication in preparation. For Trebenischte handle, B. Filow, *Die archaische Nekropole von Trebenischte* (Berlin, 1927), 54–55, no. 70, pl. 9; for Telesstas handle, G. Hafner, *Charites, Studien zur Altertumswissenschaft* (Bonn, 1957), 119–126.

Lent by the Fogg Art Museum, Harvard University (1962.178).

72. Hydria Handle with Lions

Tarentine (?), c. 560 B.C.; H: 0.216, max. W: 0.144; hollow cast shaft (remains of core at top and bottom), dull blue-green patina; bit of sheet bronze from the vessel on inside of base plate. Ex-private coll. in Capua.

This elaborate piece is typical of ornate handle assemblages for ritual hydriai made in South Italy in the first half of the 6th century B.C., with rich juxtapositions of ornamental and symbolic elements. Rivets for attachment to the lip of a vessel lie just below the lions; others were fastened through the palmette just below the horses' legs. The kore protome, with high polos and incised leaf-shaped pendant at the neck, is derived from Lakonian models such as the Telesstas Hydria; the reclining lions suggest lion fibulae from the northeast Peloponnesus (cf. H. Gabelmann, *Studien zum frühgriechischen Löwenbild* [Berlin, 1965], 70 ff., 116, nos. 67 a–p, pl. 10: 1–3). The kneeling horses call to mind No. 69. (DGM)

W. Helbig, *BdI* (1881), 146 (information thanks to N. Schimmel); *Schimmel, no. 9; H. Hoffmann, *AJA*, 68 (1964), 186–188, figs. 2–4, pl. 64. Cf. review by D. von Bothmer, *Gnomon*, 37 (1965), 600; H. Jucker, *Bronzehenkel*, 127, pl. 35, and 125, pl. 12 (Grächwyl Hydria).

Lent by The Schimmel Collection.

73. Vertical Hydria Handle with Kore Protome

Corinthian (?), c. 520–510 B.C.; H: 0.247; solid cast, surface dark, little patina.

This unusual handle, in which the female head has moved from the base of the handle to its top, facing forward, is the predecessor of early Classical hydriai in which the head becomes a bust with arms extended along the rim to the rotelles, which here are still separate (D. von Bothmer, *BMMA*, 13 [Feb. 1955], 193–200). Discs or spools, in pairs at the rear of the rim, occur on late 8th century B.C. Phrygian bronze vessels and on Protocorinthian olpai as early as the Chigi vase; they are common thereafter in Corinthian and East Greek wares. The bead moulding that edges the rotelles, forming a tiara for the kore and a spine down the shaft, is characteristic of late Archaic metalwork. The wide-eyed, smiling lady wears a composite hairdo; the forehead curls hark back to elaborate spiral locks such as those of the Kerameikos Sphinx (G. M. A. Richter, *The Archaic Gravestones of Attica* [London, 1961], nos. 11, 15–16, figs. 38–39). (DGM)

A. Sambon, *Le Musée*, 3 (1906), 264–266, pl. 39; D. M. Robinson, *AJA*, 46 (1942), 184, n. 54, 188, fig. 22 (front); Diehl, 216, no. B 75 (as from Corinth). For predecessors on oinochoai cf. D. K. Hill, *AJA*, 66 (1962), 57–63, pls. 15–16.
Lent by The Walters Art Gallery, Baltimore (54.776); acquired 1906.

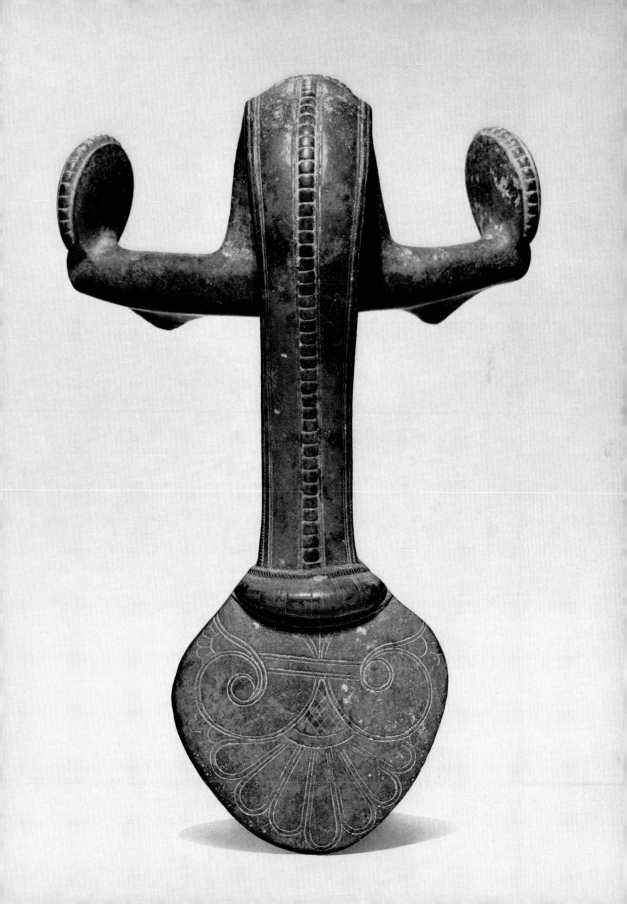

74. Mirror Handle

Corinthian or Argive, c. 600–560 B. C.; H. of figure: 0.162, Th: 0.005; cast, brown patina; recently cleaned and separated from mirror disc. Allegedly from Corinth.

This two-dimensional mirror caryatid, wearing a polos atop her horizontally waved hair and clad in a peplos, balances her mirror disc as easily as she would a water jar. The ring beneath her feet, for suspending the mirror, repeats the circle of the garland in her r. hand. Her buxom physique is closely related to a bronze statuette from Olympia (E. Kunze, *OlBer*, VII [Berlin, 1961], 166 f., fig. 98, pl. 69) and the "Mistress of Animals" on the Grächwyl Hydria (H. Jucker, *Bronzehenkel*, pl. 12). Her skirt displays a rooster and a flying eagle in metope-like panels. Her identity as Athena, as suggested by Lamb and Charbonneaux, must remain uncertain.

The handle is an early example of a type which is later made in one piece with its disc, the figure being incised on the handle. Examples are MFA 98.651 (G. Bruns, *Die Jägerin Artemis* [diss. Munich; Borna-Leipzig, 1929], pl. 1:3) and two from the Argive Heraeum (*The Argive Heraeum*, II [Boston, 1905], nos. 1566, 1581, pls. 95–96). They are generally thought to have been made in the northeast Peloponnesus. (DGM)

E. Michon, *BAntFr* (1892), 268; de Ridder, II, 42, no. 1684, pl. 76; Lamb, 127, n. 1, pl. 44a; M. Gjødesen, *ActaA*, 15 (1944), 165; Charbonneaux, 28.

Lent by the Musée du Louvre (Br. 1684). Shown only in Cambridge.

75. Winged Mirror Caryatid

South Italian, Tarentine (?), c. 550–525 B.C.; H: 0.20, max. W: 0.095; solid cast, green patina; large cavity, probably casting defect, on back of skirt above r. ankle, patch under upper r. arm. Allegedly from Greece.

This unusual winged figure, perhaps a goddess, stands with arms akimbo atop a small circular base. Her hands rest on a hem of two parallel lines on her short-sleeved, scale-decorated chiton. This garment covers a longer one mantling her legs to the ankles (the hem not shown in back). She originally supported a mirror disc on her head and wing tips. Her hair, which falls down her back in crinkly strands separated by vertical incisions emerging from beneath a cap, is reminiscent of "Dedalic" wig-like hairdos. The wings have semi-circles on their inner edges and feathers shown by diagonal lines. Protruding lidded oval eyes dominate the alert, unsmiling face. Punched circles joined by lines mark sleeve seams; a "collar" of diagonal strokes lies at the neck. Circles decorate the hems of outer and inner garments; the latter is marked by vertical lines. Although winged mirror caryatids are rare in Archaic and Classical Greece, the winged Artemis between animals, the *potnia theron*, Mistress of Animals, is common in 7th century art. She might also be a Victory. Perhaps foreshadowing this handle is a winged goddess on the vertical handle of the Grächwyl Hydria, now in Bern (H. Jucker, *Bronzehenkel*, 23–30, 117–119), thought to be Tarentine under strong Lakonian influence. The caryatid's features recall both Lakonian and Corinthian work, especially terracottas. (DGM)

Jantzen, *Bronzewerkstätten*, 7, no. 110, pl. 26.
Lent by Prof. Frederick M. Watkins.

76. Patera with Anthropomorphic Handle

South Italian (?), c. 500 B.C.; diam. of bowl: 0.30, L: of handle: 0.205; handle solid cast, fine brown patina with traces of green and red.

Pateras may have been used for sacrificial libations, as funeral gifts, and perhaps as serving dishes. The handle, as here, is usually a nude kouros supporting two reclining rams with his upraised hands, a wide Ionic capital emphasizing the point of attachment. His feet often rest on a ram's head. The type may have been inspired by Egyptian New Kingdom cosmetic spoons, where a nude swimming girl holds the bowl of the spoon. (DGM)

N. Leipen, ROM *Bulletin* (Dec. 1957), 18–21, with bibl. Cf. M. Gjødesen, *ActaA*, 15 (1944), 101–187; P. Amandry, *MonPiot*, 47 (1953), 47–70; Jantzen, *Griff.*, 5–29.

Lent by the Royal Ontario Museum, University of Toronto (957.161); purchased 1957.

77. Oinochoe with Anthropomorphic Handle

(see also Plate I, p. 2)
South Italian (Tarentine?), c. 530–520 B.C.; H: 0.175; dark green patina, patch of gray incrustation left on r. knee of youth after cleaning. Allegedly found in Sicily.

One of the finest known examples of a popular form of bronze pitcher, this superb oinochoe ("wine-pourer") with its lifelike, fanciful handle exemplifies the ornate treatment of sumptuous bronze vessels in the late Archaic period. The acrobatic youth, feet planted on double volutes above a seven-petalled palmette, grasps the tails of two miniature lions who crouch facing outward along the rim. This form of handle, employed on hydriai as well, has often been called Lakonian. It seems, however, to occur also in South Italy, where G. Vallet and F. Villard localize a large group of ornate bronze vessels, including a hydria and oinochoe from Sala Consilina, hydriai from Paestum, and the Vix Krater. The Pomerance oinochoe probably belongs to this group. (DGM)

Ill. *Apollo*, n. s. 84:56 (Oct. 1966), li. For this class of handle cf. D. K. Hill, *AJA*, 62 (1958), 193–201; intact oinochoai from Trebenischte, B. Filow, *Die archaische Nekropole von Trebenischte* (Berlin, 1927), 59–61, no. 72, fig. 63, pls. 10–11; from Sala Consilina, Charbonneaux, 44, pl. 3:1. Cf. G. Vallet-F. Villard, *BCH*, 79 (1955), 50–74.

Lent by The Pomerance Collection.

78. Seated Man

Corinthian, 505–490 B. C.; H: 0.074, max. W: 0.051; solid cast, dark green patina; l. foot and r. leg below knee missing. Ex-coll. Spencer-Churchill.

The bearded figure, who probably held a staff in his r. hand, may represent Zeus, though Zeus is rarely shown seated at this period. The sides of thighs and the buttocks are flat; the underside of legs and buttocks is unfinished and concave, joining the side planes at a sharp right angle. Fine tracing of hair and beard is barely visible. K. Schefold (orally) felt that the features indicate Corinthian origin. Subdivision of the abdomen as here is found in Attic vase paintings of 510–500 B. C. and in late Archaic Attic sculpture, such as the Herakles slaying the stag on a metope from the Athenian Treasury at Delphi. (SD)

Sale, Christie's (June 21, 1965) 110, no. 448, pl. 51.
Lent by Frederick M. Watkins; acquired 1966.

79. Athena

Peloponnesian, c. 480 B. C.; H: 0.171; solid cast, green patina; arms and feet missing, break on top of head. Allegedly from the Peloponnesus.

Athena in a fighting posture wears a headband, a helmet, and a short-sleeved, foldless tunic over her long chiton. The simple garment, proud posture, and alert young face present a very distinctive style. K. Schefold (orally) thought it Peloponnesian with Eastern Greek connections; the latter are evident in the facial type, which reappears in Sparta. A slightly earlier version of the stance is seen in the Athena of the Aegina pediment. (GMAH)

Unpublished. For face cf. Langlotz, figs. 48, 53, Sparta; 70, Samos; 73, garment; Charbonneaux, pl. 15, "Aegina." For stance cf. Picard, II:1, fig. 34; Walters, no. 190, pl. 39.
Lent by Mrs. Charles Goldman; acquired 1963–64.

80. Satyr

Greek (?), Campanian (?), c. 450–400 B. C.; H: 0.095; smooth light green surface with some red crystals; l. foot restored, r. foot, lower arm, phallus broken off. Ex-coll. Mrs. H. Walters (sale, Parke-Bernet, Dec. 1–4, 1943, 88, no. 503). Probably ex-coll. J. E. Taylor (sale, Christie's, July 1–4, 9–10, 1912, 91, no. 358).

The running satyr has an amphora slung over his shoulder, held in his l. hand and resting on his tail. His r. arm is thrust outward to help maintain his balance. Tail, pointed equine ears and one hoofed, one human foot betray his hybrid nature. (SD)

D. K. Hill, *Art in America*, 34 (1946), 9–13, ill., Greek, Etruscan, and S. Italian comparanda, with bibl.; Hill, 42–43, no. 86, pl. 20, with bibl., and rev. M. Pallottino, *StEtr*, 23:2 (1954), 459; *Worcester, 1967, no. 57. On unmatched feet, D. K. Hill, *AJA*, 50 (1946), 504. Cf. also Reinach, II, 48:3 and MFA 13.112 (*Worcester, 1967, no. 40) and comparanda in forthcoming catalogue. A similar head is Baker, no. 24. Terracottas: F. Winter, *Die Typen der figürlichen Terrakotten* I, (Berlin, 1903), 217:7, 8.

Lent by The Walters Art Gallery, Baltimore (54.2291); purchased 1943 from the Estate of Mrs. Henry Walters.

81. Dancing Satyr

Boeotian (?), c. 500–475 B. C.; H: 0.090, W: 0.055; green patina. Ex-coll. P. Arndt.

Of a charm equal to No. 80 and the terracotta satyr trio in the Schimmel Collection (*Schimmel, no. 20), this sprightly dancer may be a figure from a satyr play. His gesture is the characteristic *aposkopein* ("looking into the distance"). Similar in pose and type are a Silenus in Berlin (Neugebauer, *Kat.*, I, 105, no. 210, pl. 37) and a satyr pursuing a maenad in Naples (Giglioli, pl. 209:1). DGM compares Charbonneaux pl. 21 and C. Carapanos, *Dodone et ses ruines* (Paris, 1878), pl. 9. (SD)

I. Jucker, 45, figs. 15–17, and bibl. For the satyr drama in vase painting, F. Brommer, *Satyrspiele* (Berlin, 1959). See also E. Kunze, *OlBer*, VIII (1967), 245–250, figs. 92, 93, pl. 118—119.

Lent by a private collection.

82. Nude Youth with Pin on Head

C. 480–470 B. C.; H: 0.171; dark green patina with some brown incrustation, corrosion scraped down to original bronze in places; circular patch from casting failure on l. shoulder, feet and r. arm missing. From Thessaly.

The object must have served as a support — perhaps for a candelabrum or thymiaterion. The l. hand originally held a staff-shaped object; the r. would have been extended obliquely, perhaps holding a patera or in a gesture of prayer. The features are coarse and exaggerated, the torso thickset. Both the coiffure, in rope-like oblique strands with diagonal hatching, and the pubic hair, which ends in three points, are unusual. Neugebauer suggests Peloponnesian workmanship. (SD)

Neugebauer, *Kat.*, II, 27–29, no. 18, pl. 31, with earlier bibl.; Biesantz, 35, no. L109, pl. 62, "450–400 B. C." For maiden with pin on head, de Ridder, *Acropole*, II, 303–304, no. 785, fig. 291.

Lent by the Staatliche Museen Berlin, Antikenabteilung (Misc. Inv. 8093); gift of Kaiser Wilhelm II, 1888.

83. Athlete Pouring Libation

C. 470–450 B. C.; H: 0.225; solid cast, thin dark green patina, traces of gilding; r. leg has been bent inward, l. arm and fingers of r. hand missing; eyes and nipples originally inlaid. Allegedly from Piali (Tegea).

The pouring gesture is repeated in the Aderno and David-Weill athletes (Charbonneaux, pls. 13:2, 22:4) and an "Apollo" in the British Museum (Walters, 35, no. 270, pl. 2). His elaborate coiffure — two braids wrapped about the head, long front hair parted in the middle and looped under a fillet, the ends falling loose before the ears — leads K. Schefold to identify him as Apollo; the hairdo was apparently affected at initiation into manhood. Before damage both feet were flat on the ground, indicating, as does the musculature, pre-Phidian conception. Perhaps Sicyonian. (SD)

C. Galt, *AJA*, 33 (1929), 41–52, with technical analysis; *Buffalo, 1937, no. 86, ill. and bibl.; *Detroit, 1947, no. 67; *Basel, 1960, 67, 69, 230, no. 273, ill. 229, and bibl. For the hair style see W.-H. Schuchhardt, *Festschrift für C. Weickert* (Berlin, 1955), 71 f., figs. 5–6. A later manifestation of the type, *Cleveland Museum of Art Handbook* (1958), fig. 21.

Lent by Mount Holyoke College, South Hadley, Mass. (BOI. 1. 1926); purchased in Piraeus, 1926.

84. Athlete

South Italian (?), c. 460 B.C.; H: 0.085; dark green patina, some artificial patination of face; feet and hands missing.

The confident bearing and upward gaze suggest a victorious athlete, perhaps praying to celebrate his success. He may have held an athletic instrument. Related in stance and modelling is a mirror caryatid in London, attributed to Locri by Jantzen (*Bronzewerkstätten*, 4, no. 33, pl. 5:20). K. Schefold (orally) reinforced the attribution to South Italy. (SD)

*Fogg, 1954, supplement to catalogue no. A9; Münzen und Medaillen Auktion 14 (June 19, 1954) 10, no. 29, pl. 8. For the pose cf. A. Sambon, 19, no. 61, ill., "archer."

Lent by Dr. and Mrs. Robert Waelder; acquired 1954.

85. Zeus with Eagle

C. 460 B.C.; H: 0.126; solid cast, green patina, surface worn; l. foot and r. arm missing. Ex-coll. M. Cambanis, Athens.

The missing r. arm probably hung at his side, holding a thunderbolt (cf. de Ridder, I, 25, no. 128, pl. 14). The eagle is ready to fly from the l. The striding pose, often with r. arm upraised to hurl an object, is used for warriors from the 7th century B.C. (cf. Dutuit, II, 143, pl. 132), but becomes common for the bearded Zeus about 500 B.C. (Furtwängler, 18—19, pls. 7:43, 45; 8:44). Perhaps the finest examples are the colossal Poseidon (Zeus?) from Artemision and the Dodona Zeus in Berlin. Like coin representations, the Fogg piece has a narrow stride. (SD)

C. Hutton, *BSA*, 3 (1896–1897), 149–152, pl. 10; Reinach, III, 1:6. Louvre piece: Collection H. Hoffmann, sale Hôtel Drouot (May 26–27, 1886), 118–119, no. 451, ill. Development of type, S. Casson, *JHS*, 42 (1922), 211–212; G. Elderkin, *AJA*, 44 (1940), 225—233. For coins: B. Head, *Catalogue of the Greek Coins of Caria, Cos, Rhodes, etc.* (London, 1897), pls. 10, 25; C. Kraay–M. Hirmer, *Greek Coins* (New York, 1966), pl. 159, no. 511. Artemision god: G. Mylonas, *AJA*, 48 (1944) 143 ff.

Lent by the Fogg Art Museum, Harvard University (1952.127); gift of Edward W. Forbes.

86. Nude Girl (Aphrodite?)

South Italian (?), c. 490–480 B. C.; H: 0.225,
H. of figure: 0.200. Ex-coll. C. Loeser.

A mark on the head indicates that this
boyish nude probably served as a mirror
caryatid. Her hair, hanging loose before the
ears, is rolled under in back and bound
with a fillet. Both hands, held palm outward, are damaged, and objects they may
have held are lost; her r. leg is slightly
advanced. The moulded base and rectangular plinth are original. Female nudes are
rare at this period, though at least three
others from mirrors are known. The sculptor's feeling for swelling bodily forms suggests South Italian workmanship rather
than Etruscan, and is closely related to the
youth in Boston assigned to Kroton by
Jantzen (*Bronzewerkstätten*, 47, pl. 21). (SD)

*Burlington, 1904, 38–39, A9, pl. 44, "Greek";
refers to other early Classical nudes.

Lent by a Swiss private collection.

87. Caryatid Mirror

Argive or Corinthian, c. 470 B. C.; H: 0.28, H. of caryatid: 0.096, diam. of disc: 0.105; green patina on figure, brownish on disc.

Standing on a base with three lion feet, the maiden in Doric chiton (peplos) holds a duck or dove in her r. hand. The disc support has a central palmette flanked by volutes and half palmettes. Only a fragment and faint outline survive of the triangular member originally joining disc and support on the back. The slightly convex disc has a beaded rim, inside which is a guilloche design with punctate highlights. The frontal siren topping it has a wire hook on her back used for lifting the mirror or hanging it on a wall. The difference in patina color suggests that a different alloy (perhaps with a higher percentage of tin) was used to make the reflective surface of the disc. Very fine tooling delineates her hair and the bird's feathers. (SD)

N. Leipen, ROM *Bulletin* (June, 1957), 4–6, bibl.; J. Graham, *Archaeology*, 10:4 (1957) 286, ill.; L. O. K. Congdon, "Greek Caryatid Mirrors; technical, stylistic, and historical considerations of an archaic-early classical series," unpublished Ph. D. thesis, Harvard University (April, 1963), no. 36. For discussion of the identification of the lady as Athena or Helen, S. Karouzou, *Studies Presented to David Moore Robinson on his Seventieth Birthday*, I (St. Louis, 1951), 565–587. Particularly close parallels are Poulsen, fig. 16 (Berlin) and *Basel, 1960, no. 267 (Coll. G. Ortiz). On alloys, L. O. K. Congdon, *AJA*, 71 (1967), 149–153.

Lent by the Royal Ontario Museum, University of Toronto (956.156); acquired 1956.

Plate III, No. 87
Caryatid mirror

88. Caryatid Mirror

Northeast Peloponnesian, c. 460 B. C.; H: 0.43, H. of figure: c. 0.154; dark green patina with some red.

The caryatid stands upon a lightly-profiled tripod base. She holds a dove in r. hand and her skirt in l. Her Doric chiton falls in a deep fold at the neck; two incised arcs indicate folds beneath her breasts. The support with engraved palmette design has two Erotes suspended from it. Two doves and a frontal siren with ring on her back grace the milled edge of the disc. Because of the apparent difference in the curve of support and disc, it has been suggested that the disc did not originally belong to this caryatid. (SD)

WAG *Handbook of the Collection* (Baltimore, 1936), 26, ill.; Poulsen, 19–20 (1a) relates it to Karlsruhe piece (K. Schumacher, *Sammlung antiker Bronzen* [Karlsruhe, 1890], pl. 24); D. K. Hill, WAG *Bulletin*, 4:7 (1952), 2, ill.; L. O. K. Congdon, "Greek Caryatid Mirrors; technical, stylistic, and historical considerations of an archaic-early classical series," unpublished Ph. D. thesis, Harvard University (April 1963), no. 55. On Erotes cf. A. Greifenhagen, *Griechische Eroten* (Berlin, 1957).

Lent by The Walters Art Gallery, Baltimore (54.769).

89. Artemis

Arcadian, c. 470 B. C.; H: 0.155, H. of figure: 0.138, W: 0.064; dark green patina with some rust brown and white areas. Allegedly from Lousoi; purchased by Metropoulos from a shepherd in Kalavryta, 1881.

Artemis stands on a nearly rectangular plate with protrusions for attachment to a base. The coarse working of the features — almond eyes, crude parallel incisions for hair, slit mouth — and short, stocky proportions point to the provincialism of the scarce Arcadian work of early Classical date. The figure once held the nocturnal torch in her r. hand and the soporific poppy in her l., but these attributes have been lost in modern times. Such Eleusinian attributes might also belong to Demeter. (SD)

Neugebauer, *Kat.*, II, 22–23, no. 13, pl. 14 (showing attributes), with bibl. and comparanda; G. Lippold, *Die griechische Plastik* (Munich, 1950), 104, n. 6; Charbonneaux, 71; H. G. Niemeyer, *Promachos* (Waldsassen, 1960), 59. For Classical Arcadian style, P. Lévêque, *BCH*, 77 (1953), 105–115.

Lent by the Staatliche Museen Berlin, Antikenabteilung (Misc. Inv. 7644).

90. Standing Maiden

Probably northeast Peloponnesian, c. 470 B. C.; H: 0.091;
solid cast, green patina; surface badly worn, deep scratches
on chest and back, r. arm broken off.

The maiden wears the Doric chiton with *apoptygma*
(overfold) of medium length. The r. arm, now mostly
missing, was extended and probably held a bird or bud.
Although major vertical folds of the garment are plastically treated, minor folds at the shoulders and those
curving toward the l. hand are incised. Her feet are
not articulated, but she stands on a small plinth. Although closely related to the mirror caryatid type (Nos.
87 and 88), she is smaller than most such figures and
there is no evidence of attachment of a support to her
head. (SD)

Casson, 14, no. 104; E. Langlotz, *ArchEph* (1937), 605, pl. 1;
Herbert, 119, no. 422, pl. 41. Cf. Poulsen, 19–27, esp. fig. 11,
caryatid from Munich.

Lent by the Warren Collection, Bowdoin College Museum
of Art (1913.33).

91. Girl Making an Offering

C. 450 B. C.; H: 0.10, W: 0.04; originally a mirror handle,
broken at top of head, lower part worn, surface nicked;
ends of fingers of l. hand missing.

The stiff, formal stance, shallow modelling of facial
features and hair, and columnar treatment of the skirt
link the piece with the style of the Olympia pediments.
She does not correspond to an established type; raising
the l. arm and holding the r. elbow close to the body
produce an unusual, compact form, scarcely interrupted
by the slight bend in the r. leg. Perhaps Argive. DGM
feels that the monumental simplicity as well as the
unusual headgear make it possible that she might be
Athena or perhaps Hera. (AR)

Nationalmusei Konstsamlingar (Stockholm, 1911), 38, no.
715; H. Brising, *Antik Konst i Nationalmuseum* (Stockholm,
1911), 37, pl. 15; O. Antonsson, *Antik Konst* (Stockholm,
1958), 36 ff., ill.

Lent by the Nationalmuseum, Stockholm (NM Sk 715); gift
of E. M. Erskine, 1881.

92. Athena with an Owl

Mid 5th cent. B. C.; H: 0.144; hollow cast, dark brown surface, some green and red spots.

Clad in an unbelted Doric chiton and a helmet topped by a sphinx, she originally held a spear in her l. hand. The bronze was apparently not tooled after casting, but small depressions on the back suggest working of the model with a gouge. D. K. Hill was uncertain in her catalogue whether it was a Roman version or a 5th century B.C. original, but Eichler and Niemeyer both subscribe to the earlier dating and Miss Hill appears now to agree. She compares the Elgin Athena in the British Museum. (SD)

Hill, 86, no. 185, pl. 38; F. Eichler, *Gnomon*, 23 (1951), 61; H. G. Niemeyer, *Promachos* (Waldsassen, 1960), 91, no. 2; D. K. Hill, *Fashions of the Past: Ancient Greek Dress* (Baltimore, 1964), ill. 12. For helmet with sphinx, de Ridder, II, 2, no. 1102, pl. 65. Extant replicas of the Athena Parthenos indicate that she, too, wore a sphinx-crowned helmet.

Lent by The Walters Art Gallery, Baltimore (54.766); purchased 1929.

93. Aphrodite with Dove

C. 450 B. C.; H: 0.107; solid cast, r. arm and bird cast separately, deep green patina with large red areas; some in-fill in upper r. arm, iron pin in head, square patch in r. shoulder (technical intro., fig. 5). Allegedly from Epidauros.

The unusual motif of the nude r. breast suggests that she may represent Aphrodite rather than a devotee. The iron pin indicates that the figure may have been intended as a mirror support, although her pose is more relaxed than customary for the type. The head may have been inspired by an image known now only through Roman copies (cf. W.-H. Schuchhardt, *Festschrift für C. Weickert* [Berlin, 1955], 67 ff., n. 13–15). A figurine probably imitating the same monumental prototype is in Berlin (Neugebauer, *Kat.*, II, no. 21, pl. 16). Less close is an Etruscan piece in the Petit Palais (Dutuit, I, 52–53, no. 84, pl. 79).

(SD)

Fogg Art Museum Acquisitions (1959–1962), ill. 31; G. M. A. Hanfmann, *AJA*, 66:3 (1962), 281–284, pls. 73–74, with bibl. and technical analysis; ——, *Classical Sculpture* (Greenwich, Conn., 1967), no. 143.

Lent by the Fogg Art Museum, Harvard University (1960.666); gift of Frederick M. Watkins.

94. Dancing Satyr

Mid 5th cent. B. C.; H: 0.067; black patina, surface worn.

This bearded satyr has slightly pointed ears, but no other animal characteristics. The l. arm is held behind the back. The rather complex pose is skillfully and convincingly handled. Beard and hair were finely incised in parallel strokes. The facial type, proportions and musculature are not unlike MFA 98.669 (Vermeule, no. 113, "Argive school of Polykleitos"). For the skip with knee raised high, MMA 23.160.51 (Richter, *Greek*, pl. 75 f.), Munich (Reinach, IV, 551:3). (SD)

Sale, Sotheby (June 13, 1966), 68, no. 160, ill., "probably Western Peloponnese."

Lent by The Pomerance Collection; acquired 1966.

95. Reclining Satyr

Greek (?), 450–400 B. C.; H: 0.041, L: 0.051, W: 0.020; dark green surface with red areas; missing feet, r. hand. Ex-coll. J. Lionberger Davis.

Reclining nonchalantly on a cushion, this satyr is akin to the banqueters (Nos. 43–45), and may also come from the rim of a vessel. The adept handling of the twisted pose suggests a date after 450 B. C.; the stocky, muscular frame recalls an Argive workshop. Satyrs as symposiasts are, however, more common in Etruria, adorning lamps, tripods, and vessels. Earlier examples in similar poses are Käppeli, no. B12, "Etruscan"; C. Smith, 11, no. 25, ill., "Ionian"; Babelon-Blanchet, no. 414, "Etruscan." (SD)

CAMSL *Bulletin*, 1:5 (Jan.-Feb. 1966), 8, 9 ill. Cf. also R. Lullies, *Griechische Plastik, Vasen und Kleinkunst* (Kassel, 27 May–27 Sept., 1964), no. 17, ill.; E. Kunze, *OlBer*, VIII (1967), 236–250, pls. 114–117.

Lent by the City Art Museum of Saint Louis (95:65); gift of J. Lionberger Davis, 1965.

96. Youth

South Italian, late 5th cent. B. C.; H: 0.159; dark brown patina, some green underlay. From Cumae.

The youth stands at ease, his *contrapposto* stance betraying the influence of Polykleitos. Both hands are pierced, perhaps for athletic implements such as bow and arrow. K. Schefold thought the face, with broad, full mouth, sharp horizontal brows, large eyes, and incised pupils, Tarentine. Not unlike in features and modelling are an athlete in Dresden (Jantzen, *Bronzewerkstätten*, pl. 16) and a broad jumper in New York (Richter, *Br.*, 54, no. 81), both from Tarentum. (SD)

Handbook of the Collections in the William Rockhill Nelson Gallery of Art and the Mary Atkins Museum of Fine Arts (Kansas City, Mo., 1959), 25, ill.; *"Anatomy and Art," *Nelson Gallery and Atkins Museum Bulletin*, 3:1 (May 8–June 5, 1960), 17, no. 47.

Lent by the Nelson Gallery-Atkins Museum (56–79); purchased 1956, Nelson Fund.

97. Wrestling Youth

Mid 5th cent. B.C.; diagonal L: 0.086, H. as mounted: 0.067; smooth green patina, some pitting; lower l. arm missing. Allegedly from Dodona.

From a group; traces of his opponent remain along the inside of l. arm, l. chest, and r. fist. Neugebauer suggests the toes of r. foot should be flush with ground, placing the figure at an angle of 30° and changing the H. to 0.044. The distance between r. and l. hands would have been 0.013, enough for a human head. He proposes Herakles wrestling Acheloos, on analogy with vase paintings, although the combatants might simply be athletes. The triangular space between them would be too small for a hand, he feels, eliminating use as a handle, but use as an appliqué to lip or shoulder of a vessel is possible. Neugebauer cites stylistic parallels to other Dodona finds whose origin he feels is probably Corinth. (SD)

K. A. Neugebauer, *AA* (1937), cols. 496–510, figs. 1–3.

Lent by a private collection.

98. Dirce?

365–330 B.C.; H: 0.115, W: 0.101; half round, with large hollow area in center back. Allegedly from Piedmont. Ex-coll. Ancona, Milan; von Duhn.

On analogy with vase paintings and a sarcophagus relief A. Rumpf identifies the richly clad figure, seated on the ground with a serpent at her breast, as a goddess of the spring, perhaps Dirce; he suggests that she served as an appliqué to a vessel. Although she is patterned on Greek 5th century B.C. grave reliefs (cf. Vermeule, fig. 79), the rather coarse, summary workmanship places her with 4th century classicising sculpture of South Italy, probably Tarentum. (SD)

Richter, *Sculpture*, 80, fig. 211; A. Rumpf, *Concordia Decennalis* (Cologne, 1941), 41–46, ill., and bibl., reviews other widely divergent interpretations; Bruns, 63–64, fig. 43; G. M. A. Richter, *Ancient Italy* (Ann Arbor, 1955), 48, fig. 164.

Lent by the Staatliche Museen Berlin, Antikenabteilung (Inv. 30794); acquired 1920.

99. Lion

Probably South Italian, late 6th–early 5th cent. B. C.; H: 0.093; solid cast, green and blue patina; attachment hole under l. forepaw and r. hindpaw. Allegedly found on Monte Sannace near Gioia del Colle (Bari).

The artist has seen more of waterspouts than of lions. The more frightened than frightening face is surrounded by a raised ruff of mane; attached to it, but not articulated with it, is the artist's conception of a lion's body, with heavy paws and decoratively looped tail. He has none of the apotropaic fierceness of Etruscan lions (cf. L. Brown, 93 ff.). The linear stylization of the mane resembles lions from Greek Italy (cf. H. Jucker, *Bronzehenkel*, pl. 65 f.); surely his antecedents were the gentler lions of Greece. (JAS)

F. Jones, *Archaeology,* 7 (1954), 240; mentioned *Record of the Art Museum,* Princeton University, 13 (1954), 63, *Art Quarterly,* 17 (1954), 179; *Metropolitan, 1959–1960, 36, as comparison with no. 141, pl. 44. For Greek relations, H. Payne, *Perachora* (Oxford, 1940), pl. 39; Staïs, 295, no. 6229.

Lent by The Art Museum, Princeton University (53–83); acquired 1953.

100. Leaping Deer

5th cent. B.C.; H: 0.08, L: 0.08; solid cast; tip of tail perhaps missing. Found May 18, 1948, in excavation of sanctuary of Apollo, Kourion, Cyprus.

The sanctuary at Kourion honored Apollo Hylates ("of the woodlands"), and was surrounded, Aelian recounts, by a deer park. The young deer looks as though it has come to a sudden stop or just landed after jumping. The unusual pose affords a silhouette which plays off curves and angles with tense vitality. All four feet are attached to a rectangular plaque, from which protrude pins for joining it to a vessel. (SD)

ILN, 220 (5 April, 1952), 589, fig. 5. For a contemporary deer, very similar in modelling and mien, E. Kunze in *Collection Hélène Stathatos*, III (Strasbourg, 1953), 70–72, no. 18, fig. 26, pl. 9.

Lent by the University Museum, Philadelphia; allotted to the museum by the Department of Antiquities of Cyprus, 1954.

101. Standing Goat

Late 5th cent. B. C. (?); H: 0.153, L: 0.165; solid cast, dark green patina; half of r. and tip of l. horn, feet missing. Found in Sierre (Valais), Switzerland.

The long hair of forelock, goatee, and along the spinal column is indicated in delicate lines, although the areas are stylized in shape. Very similar beasts are in the MFA (*Detroit, 1947, no. 71, ill.), Musée Evreux (Reinach, II, 751:3), Palazzo Conservatori (H. S. Jones, ed., *A Catalogue of the Ancient Sculptures Preserved in the Municipal Collections of Rome — The Sculptures of the Palazzo dei Conservatori* [Oxford, 1926], 296, no. 37, pl. 118, WAG (Hill, nos. 260–261), Trieste (Jantzen, *Bronzewerkstätten*, no. 40, pl. 9), and Madrid (Thouvenot, no. 373, pl. 19). Deonna, Hill, Richter, and others have considered them mid to late 5th century B.C. Jantzen follows this dating but calls the Geneva and Evreux pieces works of Greek colonists in Provence; the Boston, Rome, and Trieste examples Tarentine, of just before mid-century. E. Thomas, however, published a similar goat as Roman, 1st century A. D. (*Römische Villen in Pannonien* [Budapest, 1964], 106, pl. 82),while H. Hoffmann feels the Boston and Geneva pieces to be Hellenistic. (SD)

Deonna, 298, no. 105, pl. 3, and bibl.; Richter, *Animals*, 26, fig. 128; Jantzen, *Bronzewerkstätten*, 35; *Basel, 1957, 126, no. 30.

Lent by the Musée d'art et d'histoire, Geneva, Switzerland (C 1165); purchased 1887.

102. Head of a Horse

Possibly Tarentine, 5th cent. B.C. or later; H: 0.13, L: 0.18, D: 0.06; solid cast, surface black with large green and red areas.

The Greeks' great admiration of the horse is evident in this spirited and sensitive equine head. Its naturalism, yet simplicity, are comparable to horse representations from the Parthenon frieze. Four rivet holes along the base of the neck may have provided for attachment to a separately cast body, a throne, or some other article of furniture (cf. Richter, *Furniture*, fig. 92, with forepart of horse; fig. 94, with feline head). (SD)

Bulletin of the J. Paul Getty Museum of Art, 1:2 (1959), fig. 9; Stothart, 18; J. Paul Getty, *The Joys of Collecting* (New York, 1965), 46–47, color ill.

Lent by the J. Paul Getty Museum, Malibu, Calif. (A 58.S–9).

103. Handle with Goat Protome

Ionian (?), 5th cent. B. C.; H: 0.047, diam. of ring: 0.024; solid cast, dark green patina; corrosion behind r. ear, l. horn missing, l. ear bent.

Head and forelegs of the jumping animal are draped over a ring; its skin ends in leaf-like upturn. In the ring below the muzzle is a hole for fastening the piece to a rim. DGM suggests the handle belonged to a late Classical kantharos. The sensitive, clean modelling and precise delineation of eyes, hoofs, and horns are Greek; the notion of a piece at once animal and handle is Achaemenid Persian. It probably originated in Asia Minor under Persian rule. (GMAH)

Unpublished. For kantharos shape: E. Pfuhl, *Malerei und Zeichnung der Griechen*, III (Munich, 1923), 3, fig. 618. Achaemenid handles: P. Amandry, *Collection Hélène Stathatos*, III (Strasbourg, 1963), 176, figs. 158 ff.; for Graeco-Persian animals: E. Porada, *The Art of Ancient Iran* (New York, 1965), 168, pl. 50; style, cf. Richter, *Greek*, fig. 76g. Ring with panther (Hellenistic?), Bieber, *Cassel*, 77, no. 275, pl. 47. The same concept: Hellenistic lamp handles, Fuchs, 29–30, no. 34, pl. 42.

Lent by the Collection of Dr. and Mrs. Renato Almansi; acquired 1966.

104. Walnut

H: 0.042; hollow cast, smooth dark green patina.

The small pore-like holes here and there are due to the presence of air bubbles in the wax model. A casting flaw has been repaired with a 7 mm. square patch. Neither the function nor the date of this unusual bronze is known to us. It may have been a votive deposit. (HH)

H. Hoffmann, *AA* (1960), 123, no. 38, fig. 60; —, *HambJb*, 6 (1961), 244. On the walnut in antiquity, *RE*, IX, 2508, s. v. Iuglans; cf. also V. Hehn, *Kulturpflanzen und Hausthiere in ihrem Übergang aus Asien nach Griechenland und Italien sowie in das übrige Europa* (Berlin, 1883), 318 ff.

Lent by the Museum für Kunst und Gewerbe, Hamburg (1960.3).

105. Mirror with Siren

C. 450–400 B. C.; total H: 0.265, H. of siren: 0.10; disc, pitted and partly encrusted, is joined to three supports cast with and rising from head and wings of siren; handle broken at bottom (?). Allegedly from Asia Minor.

The disc rests directly on the wings of a siren without an intermediate piece. With three-clawed feet the siren grasps a finial. She has a triangular face with gashed, pouting mouth, linear hair, and carefully incised feathers ending in a necklace-like border around the neck. Her large wings are spread slightly upward. The shape of the wings is closest to an Eastern Greek mirror in Munich and handle sirens found in Northern Greece and the Balkans. (GMAH)

Unpublished. For siren mirrors, J. Sieveking, *Antike Metallgeräte* (Munich, n. d.), pl. 21; E. Buschor, *Die Musen des Jenseits* (Munich, 1944), 55, frontispiece; Lamb, 158, fig. 1, pl. 60; *Clara Rhodos* 4 (1931), 126, fig. 119; E. Langlotz-M. Hirmer, *Ancient Greek Sculpture of South Italy and Sicily* (New York, 1965), 77, pl. 89; Jantzen, *Bronzewerkstätten*, pl. 6, fig. 24; *Basel, 1960, 222, no. 258, ill. p. 227; MFA 99.468. For wings cf. Diehl, 36, nos. B156, B157, pls. 17f.

Lent by The Schimmel Collection.

106. Kalpis Handle with Siren

Peloponnesian (?), 5th cent. B.C.; L: 0.160, max. W: 0.052; solid cast, dark brown and green patina.

From a hydria of kalpis type such as No. 108; the upper and lower oval attachment plates are incised with half palmettes. Her down-turned wings are atypical (cf. Diehl, nos. B 165 and B 166, pl. 18:6, and an example belonging to C. C. Vermeule). For a piece with similar fluted handle and incised ornament cf. Münzen und Medaillen Auktion 22 (May 13, 1961), no. 59, pl. 17. (SD)

Casson, 15, no. 123; Herbert, 118, no. 420, pl. 41; D. von Bothmer, *Gnomon*, 37 (1965), 603 (review of Diehl). The group of kalpis handles with sirens is discussed by Diehl, 34 ff., pls. 14–18.

Lent by the Warren Collection, Bowdoin College Museum of Art (1915.26).

107. Siren Handle

Mid 5th cent. B. C.; max. L: 0.18; solid cast.

The siren appears here in a delicate decorative pattern of reverse volutes and palmettes (broken above her claws) which bore a carefully considered relationship to her wings, the shape of the vase, and the pattern at the upper end of the handle. D. von Bothmer places this handle just after E. Diehl's B 139. It closely resembles one in the Metropolitan Museum (09.221.12), by analogy to which the decorative pattern can be reconstructed. (JAS)

D. von Bothmer, *Gnomon*, 37 (1965), 603 (review of Diehl). Cf. Diehl, 34 ff. For MMA handle, D. von Bothmer, *BMMA*, 13 (1954–1955), 197.

Lent by the Ella Riegel Memorial Museum, Bryn Mawr College (M–28).

108. Hydria

C. 450–425 B. C.; H: 0.40, max. diam.: 0.285; vase hammered, handles and base cast, metallic surface with irregular green corrosion which is somewhat abraded, small silver bosses under siren; missing parts of volutes below siren restored in stucco, two filled holes in body. Ex-coll. J. E. Taylor (sale, Christie's, July 1, 1912, 92, no. 367, "acquired in Rhodes, probably from the island of Chalke"); H. Oppenheimer (sale, Christie's, July 22–23, 1936, 41, no. 126, ill.); J. Brummer (sale, Parke-Bernet, May 11–14, 1949, 45, no. 185).

As its name implies, the hydria was used primarily for carrying water, the side handles for lifting and the vertical one for pouring; those of this shape are also called kalpides, although it is not certain whether the ancients applied the term kalpis to this specific group. Costly bronze hydriai were perhaps given to brides and were probably used only for special occasions or religious rites. Their function as containers for drawing lots, athletic prizes, and cinerary urns is attested. This elegant hydria has an egg-and-dart motif and beaded moulding at the lip; the handles are fluted, and a delicate tongue motif adorns their attachments and the foot. The siren at the base of the vertical handle is characteristic of a large group of 5th century B.C. hydriai (cf. Nos. 106–107). Although these sirens vary in details, a piece in the British Museum (Diehl, pl. 15:2) is virtually identical. Both stand on seven-leafed palmettes, have identical volutes beneath the wings, rolled coiffures with two strands hanging over the shoulders, incised feathers on their bodies, and a single row of wing feathers. Diehl judges this hydria later because while it has convex volutes on the siren handle, those of the side handles are concave. She does not name a workshop, but suggests Boeotia for related but less fine vessels. (SD)

*"Greek Art and Life," Fogg Art Museum, 1950, no. 15 (mimeographed catalogue); Diehl, 35 ff., 219, no. B 147; D. von Bothmer, Gnomon, 37 (1965), 603; the lid with ring handle which he describes is not at the Fogg Museum.

Lent by the Fogg Art Museum, Harvard University (1949.89).

109. Hydria

C. 400 B. C. (?), H: 0.425, max. diam.: 0.335; deep green patina bordered with brownish red on lower half, upper half dull gold color with patina removed. Ex coll. S. Pozzi (sale, G. Petit, June 25—27, 1919, 31, no. 430).

As with most hydriai, the body of this vessel was hammered metal, the foot and handles were cast separately and attached with rivets and perhaps solder. Simpler than the previous example, this hydria has similar egg-and-dart and beaded mouldings at the lip, but undecorated handles and base. Although a group of related vessels has been dated c. 460 B.C. (cf. Diehl, 31—32, pl. 9:2,3; 10:1,3; Vienna, London, Athens), D. von Bothmer places this example at the end of the century. (SD)

D. von Bothmer, *Gnomon,* 37 (1965), 603 (review of Diehl). For hydriai in general cf. E. Fölzer, *Die Hydria* (Leipzig, 1906); Diehl; and bibl. Nos. 108—110

Lent by the City Art Museum of Saint Louis (169:24); purchased 1924.

Drawing by Lucia Bogatay

110. Hydria

350–300 B. C., H: 0.464, max. diam.: 0.321, diam. of lip: 0.194, diam. of base: 0.143; blue-green patina on body with some modern retouching, brown-black on lip and inside of neck, traces of gilding under patina; surface apparently scraped on upper ²/₃ of vessel.

The slimmer, taller proportions with elongated neck characterize this vessel as late 4th century B.C. It belongs to a homogeneous group of which about twenty examples are known. Characteristic is the egg-and-dart motif of lip, deep fluting of handles ending in splayed, rounded forms, use of the Lesbian cyma (alternated pointed leaf and three-leafed palmettes) on the foot and a variant with rounded leaves on the attachments of side handles. The relief which adorned the area beneath the vertical handle is lost. On the lip, incised in punched dots, is ΧΑΡѠΝΙΔΑ ΧΑΙΡΕ, an ambiguous remark which can be read "Charonidas (or Charonis?), greetings," or "Charonidas, farewell," depending on whether the hydria was inscribed as a gift or as a burial furnishing. To the r. of this inscription and made by another hand are the letters ΔΕΙ, which may refer to the manufacturer, seller, or owner of the hydria. A. Steinberg suggests that, in addition to separately cast handles and foot, the rim may have been solid cast and attached to the hammered body, perhaps with solder. G. M. A. Richter thinks Attica was the place of origin for this class of hydriai, and E. Diehl seems to concur. (SD)

Picard IV:2, 1450, n. 1; H. Glasser, VMFA *Members' Bulletin,* 18:5 (Jan. 1958), Collections Supplement and fig. A; Diehl, 39–43, 222, 250, no. B 204, pl. 22–23; D. von Bothmer, *Gnomon,* 37 (1965), 604–605. Cf. C. Picard, *MonPiot,* 37 (1940), 94; G. M. A. Richter, *AJA,* 50 (1946), 361–367; D. von Bothmer, *BMMA,* 13 (1954–1955), 193–200. I am indebted to J. H. Kroll for epigraphical information.

Lent by the Virginia Museum of Fine Arts, Richmond, Va. (57–18).

111. Mirror Case with Woman's Head

400–350 B. C.; diam.: 0.17; gray-green patina. No fixture for joining the parts remains.

Hinged like a lady's compact, the mirror is composed of two parts: the lid with relief on the outside; the bottom with the mirror on the inside (where the powder would be), and decorated with concentric circles on the outside. The lady wears a simple rosette earring (the ear is obscured) and a necklace above the termination of her neck. The hair is plastically rendered, with additional fine incision. The eye is almost in profile, later than the transitional one in the MMA (Richter, *Br.*, no. 757, dates it 450–400 B. C., more likely than Züchner's date, 325–300 B. C.). The heavy lips resemble Corinthian examples, but A. Ramage points out that the straight, sharp nose, with almost complete lack of plastic modelling, bears the same comparison to the greater plasticity of mainland work as do South Italian coins to contemporary mainland coins. It is possibly from Magna Graecia or Tarentum; as listed by Züchner, examples are rare. (JAS)

Unpublished. For the coins: C. Kraay–M. Hirmer, *Greek Coins* (New York, 1966) 316, nos. 320–321, pl. 110. Lent by The Ella Riegel Memorial Museum, Bryn Mawr College (M–49).

112. Mirror Cover with Rape of Europa

C. 330 B. C.; diam.: 0.155; crusty green patina with blue flecks on inside; missing legs of Europa, hind legs and part of forelegs of bull; draperies on (viewer's) l. side restored. Allegedly bought in Athens, 1905, by C. Feuardent and restored by him. Ex-coll. C. Ravel, Marseilles; Swiss collector.

Europa half sits, half reclines on the back of the bull, which leaps over a cluster of waves in which a dolphin frolics. Her r. hand holds her billowing mantle. The mirror was attached on the inside at the bottom; a piece of rim is missing at the hinge. Grooves encircle the perimeter of cover and rim. K. Schefold sees the heavy figures and composition as Corinthian and the subject as a symbolic representation of blissful afterlife. W. Züchner cites only one other mirror with this subject, although deities astride animals are not rare (cf. Staïs, 286–289, nos. 7417, 7422 [Europa], 7423, 7608, 7675, and p. 285, ill; Züchner, figs. 22, 79, 81; pls. 3–6, 12). (SD)

*Basel, 1960, 92, 262, no. 345, ill. 261; Münzen und Medaillen Auktion 22 (May 13, 1961) 35, no. 63, pl. 19; *University Museum, 1964, no. 22. Cf. Züchner, 88, KS 146, pl. 4; on the subject cf. O. Jahn, *Die Entführung der Europa* (Vienna, 1870).

Lent by Dr. and Mrs. Robert Waelder; acquired 1961.

113. Relief Plaque with Satyr

4th cent. B. C., H: 0.124, W: 0.092; green patina. When purchased was (incorrectly) applied to hydria (No. 110); top cut down to fit hydria.

The slightly convex plaque is dominated by a satyr, who kneels on a rock on his r. knee and gazes off into the distance. At his l. lies his thyrsus, and at his r. stands a tree. A panther skin, knotted around his neck, and his equine tail billow out behind him. Different levels of relief are used to indicate various spatial planes between viewer and background. Note the recession of l. hand and daring fore-shortening of r. leg, with half of r. foot visible between the legs. Although the torso is heroic, the snub-nosed face is clearly a satyr's. The object may have been a cuirass shoulder guard or helmet cheek piece, less probably a hydria appliqué. (SD)

H. Glasser, VMFA *Members' Bulletin*, 18:5 (Jan. 1953), Collections Supplement, fig. D. Related lunging diago-nal poses and fluttering draperies in lower relief are characteristic of combat scenes such as the Siris reliefs and others of that group (Walters, no. 285, pl. 8; Lamb, 174–175, and bibl., pl. 77a, b; A. Rumpf, *RM*, 38–39 [1923–1924], 469 ff.) and mirror covers (cf. Züchner, 8, 10, 13 top, pl. 26). For the *aposkopein* gesture cf. I. Jucker.

Lent by the Virginia Museum of Fine Arts, Richmond, Va. (57–18/A); purchased 1957.

114. Vase in the Form of a Woman's Head

Northern Greek (?), c. 300 B.C.; H: 0.111, W. at base: 0.084; hollow cast, light green patina, nose slightly scraped. Allegedly from the region of Trikala, Thessaly.

The lady's hair is coiffured in a series of parallel tubular locks that spiral to the rear of the head where they merge under a corona of braids. The hinge for the cover of the vessel, which forms the top of the head, is cleverly concealed in the top of the braid. The head is tilted back and to the l.; the lightly incised, upturned pupils, and downcast, open mouth lend to it a pensive melancholy. A pair of chains is attached through loops affixed to two curls above each ear; a thin, spatula-shaped object, perhaps for applying the ointment or perfume in the vase, is fastened to the r. chain.

Greek female head vases of the late Classical period are fairly rare, although many comparable Etruscan vases are known (No. 226). A date of c. 300 B.C. is confirmed by the striking resemblance of the "melon" coiffure to that of the large late 4th century B.C. bronze female statue discovered at Piraeus in 1959 (S. Meletzis–H. Papadakis, *Le Musée archéologique national d'Athènes* [Munich, 1963], 8, figs. 78–79). (DGM)

Unpublished. Cf. Charbonneaux, 140, pl. 4:3.

Lent by the Collection of George Ortiz.

115. A and B   Two Horsemen

Iberian, 6th–5th cent. B.C.; A, H: 0.070, L: 0.063; B, H: 0.082, L: 0.076; solid cast, dark patina; some abrasion and chipping. Ex-coll. H. Obermaier, Madrid and Munich. Allegedly from La Mancha, Spain.

These charming votive horsemen are like miniature figures of Don Quixote and Sancho Panza. The larger (B) is bearded and wears a crested helmet; both sport "cavalier" hairdos — bangs with rolled-up edges. The smaller rider (A), bareheaded, with prominent "pop" eyes, sits lightly upon his colt-like steed, hefting with his r. hand a pike or long sword. His larger companion (B), astride a "plow horse," bends forward, hugging his lance to his r. side. These toy cavalrymen are the most vigorous of a series of horsemen from sanctuaries in Spain, which reflect in varying degrees the impact of Greek trade and art along the Spanish Mediterranean coast from the late 7th through the 5th century B.C., as well as possibly Punic influences. They probably come from different workshops, and are ultimately derived from such bronze and terracotta horsemen as No. 58. The provenance may be apocryphal. (DGM)

Mentioned Worcester Art Museum *Annual Report* (1957), 15. For Iberian bronze statuettes of horsemen, F. Alvarez-Ossorio, *Catálogo de los exvotos de bronce, ibéricos,* Museo Arqueológico Nacional (Madrid, 1941), pls. 77–79, 132. For Greek-Iberian contacts, J. Boardman, *The Greeks Overseas* (Baltimore, 1964), 220–221, P. Bosch-Gimpera, *Le Rayonnement des civilisations grecque et romaine sur les cultures périphériques,* 8e congrès international d'archéologie classique, Paris, 1963 (Paris, 1965), 111–118, pls. 1–2.

Lent by the Worcester Art Museum (1956. 96, 97).

116. Hunchback

Mid 3rd cent. B. C.; H: 0.066; eyes and teeth inlaid with silver, r. arm and foot missing, r. leg and l. arm bent out of place, crack in neck.

The body is emaciated, the back hunched grotesquely. He sits with legs crossed, holding the long phallus with his l. hand. His r. hand probably rested on the ground. The hunchback's sparse hair is tied into a knot at the back of the head. Such figures, combining the supposed apotropaic charm of Negroid race, hunched back, and phallus, were probably used as *porte-bonheurs*. A related figure, in Berlin, is seated on a rock (Neugebauer, *Kat.*, II, 69—71, no. 62, pl. 30); others are in Hildesheim and the Louvre. (HH)

U. Jantzen, *HambJb*, 3 (1958), 47 ff., figs 1—5; H. Hoffmann, *AA*, (1960), 122, no. 35, figs. 54—56; Hoffmann, 15, 39, fig. 47 A.

Lent by the Museum für Kunst und Gewerbe, Hamburg (1949. 40).

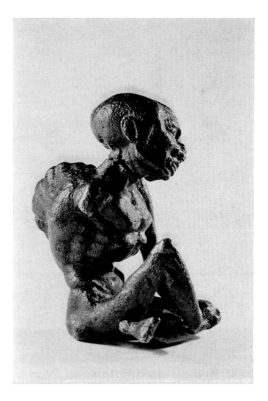

117. Dwarf Carrying a Vase

Alexandrian (?), 1st cent. B. C.; H: 0.081; figure and top flange of base solid, cast together; cylindrical portion of base hollow cast, with black incrustation; small hole in skull. Ex-coll. Sir Guy Francis Laking (sale, Christie's, 19—22 April, 1920, no. 413:1), Spencer-Churchill (sale, Christie's, 21 June, 1965, 132, no. 514, pl. 72).

Said in the *Iliad* to inhabit the borders of Ocean, pygmies were popular in the mythology and art of Hellenistic Egypt. Dwarfs from Nubia were brought to Pharaonic Egypt from the 6th dynasty (2420—2258 B.C.) or before. Bronze statuettes such as this were probably charms against the evil eye. The figure may carry a pointed alabastron or a one-handled vase. A very close figure in Amsterdam (Van Gulik, no. 15, pl. 30) and one from the Gréau collection (Reinach, II¹, 58:3) are said to carry amphorae. (SD)

'Pomerance, 83, no. 95, ill. On apotropaic use, A. J. B. Wace, *BSA*, 9 (1902—1903), 226—229; 10 (1903—1904), 103—114. For ancient literature, Perdrizet, 53—54; Van Gulik, 9—10 and bibl.; D. Levi in *Antioch*, III (Menasha, Wisc., 1941), 220—232; Fuchs, 17—18, no. 7, and bibl.

Lent by The Pomerance Collection; acquired 1965.

118. Comic Actor

400–350 B. C.; H: 0.09; gray-green patina; rivet holes in hands, feet missing.

The figure wears the typical garb of an actor in the Old Comedy — grotesque mask, short exomis over a well-padded body, tightly-wrapped legs, and phallus. A statuette of comparable size and stance, but wearing a Phrygian cap (Bieber, *Theater*, fig. 159), was the basis for modern restoration of the lower l. leg and two covered pans. The character represented was probably a kitchen slave. Nos. 119 A and B are of the same type. (SD)

J. W. Graham, *ROM Bulletin*, 22 (Sept. 1954), 4, fig. 2.
Lent by the Royal Ontario Museum, University of Toronto (953.171); purchased 1953.

119. A and B   Pair of Comic Actors

400–350 B. C.; H. of each: 0.075; A. has light green patina.

Like No. 118 they probably represent kitchen slaves, and held vessels on their outstretched hands. The character and costume persisted through Middle Comedy, which ended c. 330 B. C. Many similar figures have been found, most with grimaces like B: formerly in Berlin (*JPKS*, Beiblatt 57 [1936], 29 f., fig. 6); coll. G. Ortiz (*Basel, 1960, 262, no. 342, "Phrygian slave"); Mahdia (Fuchs, 21, No. 13, pl. 21). Closer to A is de Ridder, I, 73, no. 497, pl. 37. (SD)

A: Ars Antiqua, Auktion 3 (29 April, 1961). On actors in general, Bieber, *Theater*, and bibl.; *The Theater in Ancient Art*, The Art Museum, Princeton University (Dec. 10, 1951 – Jan. 6, 1952).
Lent by N. A. C. Embiricos; acquired 1961 and 1960.

120. Standing Comic Actor

Greek or Roman, 1st cent. B.C.; H: 0.118, W: 0.046; green patina. Allegedly from Syria.

Wearing the mask of a slave, the actor declaims his lines, his r. hand resting on his l. arm. His short-sleeved, short tunic with cloak folded over one shoulder is the costume of New Comedy, more closely related to everyday dress than the padded garments of Old Comedy. Very similar is a piece on a rectangular pedestal or altar, from the J. Sambon collection, now in the Museo alla Scala, Milan (Bieber, *Theater*, 104, fig. 403). The workmanship is summary. (SD)

Bieber, *Theater*, 104, fig. 404 a–c.

Lent by a private collection.

121. Mime

Alexandrian (?), 1st cent. B. C.; H: 0.173, W. at elbows: 0.056, support H: 0.168, W: 0.036; combination solid-hollow cast, brown patina with red-brown incrustation.

The lack of a mask identifies this bronze as a mime, rather than a comic actor. Physically deformed, or made up to look so, these entertainers were often itinerant, providing a vaudeville repertoire of playlets mimicking everyday situations. This figure's enormous phallus, bald pate, bulbous nose, misshapen cranium with four warts, and dejected expression were characteristic of the mime or buffoon, who appealed to the Hellenistic love of the grotesque. The support, which is hollowed out, and the base provide for attachment, perhaps to a piece of furniture. (SD)

Unpublished. A similar piece is in Lyons, Reinach, IV, 352:2. For the mimus cf. Bieber, *Theater*, 106 f., 248 ff., 159 f., with ill.; G. M. A. Richter, *AJA*, 17 (1913), 149–156; H. Goldman, *AJA*, 47 (1943), 22–34. Related terracottas are S. Mollard-Besques, *Les terres cuites du Louvre*, II (Paris, 1963), pls. 174–175.

Lent by the Collection of Dr. and Mrs. Irving F. Burton; acquired 1960.

122. Dancing Grotesque or Mime

2nd–1st cent. B. C.; H: 0.100; some green patina, silver inlay in eyes, pupils lost; lower arms and lower legs missing. Allegedly from Alexandria.

Engaged in a vigorous dance, the figure may have accompanied himself on *crotala*, castanet-like clappers of ivory or wood. He is bald except for a lock at the crown, and wears only a sash, tied about the waist. The contorted contours and exaggerated features embody Hellenistic love of caricature. (SD)

*Pomerance, 82, no. 94, ill. On mimes, cf. No. 121, and bibl. For the hairdo, Van Gulik, 6–7. Other dancers in twisted poses are J. Sambon, 42, no. 371, pl. 17; Perdrizet, 65–67, no. 102, pls. 29–31. DGM cites Menzel, *Trier*, 44, no. 92, pls. 42–43, for a Roman example of the type.

Lent by The Pomerance Collection; acquired 1961.

123. Old Man Posturing

Late Hellenistic; H: 0.078, W: 0.035; green patina; r. arm broken off below elbow, l. foot at ankle, garment broken behind head and nicked at r. side, face battered.

The old man stands on tiptoe on a pedestal; the weight is off his l. leg and the whole movement of the figure is upward and to its r. This is accentuated by the folds of the chiton, which clings to the body, and by the framing effect of the heavier himation. His mouth is open and his head tilted back. The impression is one of impassioned action — perhaps he is declaiming or doing a mime. The owner suggests that it was an attachment for a large bronze vessel. (AR)

Unpublished.
Lent by a private collection.

124. Priest or Votary of Isis

Greek or early Roman, 1st cent. A. D. (?); H: 0.08, W: 0.035; green-brown patina, rough green-gray incrustation removed. From Gaza.

The thin, bald figure wears a woman's fringed garment, bound under the armpits, with one corner brought over the r. shoulder and tied to the upper border in the "knot of Isis." The corresponding corner on the l. has become untied and hangs down in back. A head-cloth and sandals complete the costume. His gesture, expression, and dishevelment portray extreme despair; perhaps a priest or follower ritually re-enacts Isis' anguished search for the scattered limbs of her husband, Osiris, murdered by Typhon. Possibly he is an actor of pantomime, which would account for the feminine attire and dramatic gesture, but pantomime without masks is unknown. (SD)

H. Seyrig, *Syria*, 32 (1955), 44–48, pl. 5, with bibl. on Isis rites; for the Isis costume, H. Schaeffer, *Janus*, I (1921), 194–206.
Lent by a private collection.

125. Silenus

3rd–2nd cent. B. C.; H: 0.125; solid cast, dull green-brown patina; l. hand missing.

This elderly but truculent satyr, caught in a pose best suited for pie-throwing, wears only a cloth knotted around his waist. One can imagine his portrayal, provided with a suitable mask, of a cunning slave or other stock role in one of the situation plots of New Comedy or an uproarious South Italian farce of the *phlyax* type. His predecessors include members of comic choruses and characters from satyr plays in 5th century B. C. Athens. (DGM)

C. C. Vermeule, *CJ*, 56 (1960), 5 f., fig. 5, and *FA*, 15 (1960), no. 665. Cf. Bieber, *Theater*, figs. 295–299; on satyrs as actors, T. B. L. Webster, *Hesperia*, 29 (1960), 254–284; F. Brommer, *Satyr-spiele* (Berlin, 1959).

Lent by the Museum of Fine Arts, Boston (60.41). Gift of J. J. Dixwell by exchange.

126. Egyptian Priest

Probably from Egypt, late 3rd cent. B. C. (?); H: 0.090; solid cast, red-brown patina; surface worn.

The narrow garment, bound at breast level, with a heavy roll at its upper edge and a strong vertical fold between the legs, is typical for an Egyptian acolyte, perhaps a priest of Isis. His head is probably shaven, although there is a ridge at the back of the neck. His stick represents one of two poles by which a pair of priests carried cult images in processions. The interpretation is V. Müller's; K. Herbert identifies the object as an early Classical youth. (SD)

Casson, 14, no. 105; V. Müller, *Art in America*, 32 (1944), 19–25, figs. 3–5, with related terracottas; Herbert, 118, no. 419. For Egyptian priests, Perdrizet, nos. 82, 83, pls. 22, 20; Lamb, 198, pl. 80a; Hill, 64–65, no. 137, pl. 5.

Lent by the Warren Collection, Bowdoin College Museum of Art (1923.49).

127. Weeping Eros

Alexandria (?), 1st cent B. C.–1st cent. A. D.; H: 0.175; solid cast, two sockets in shoulder blades for attaching (missing) wings, with leading preserved.

Eros, wearing sandals and a sash knotted over the l. hip, leans against a pillar with garlands of fruit hanging over its front and back. His cloak is draped over his l. arm, behind his back, and over the support. Curls protrude from the cap covering the back of his head. A marble Eros in the Pitti Palace, Florence, and one in the Borghese Gallery, Rome, copy the same prototype of around 300 B. C. The bronze-worker, while keeping the wings of the original (omitted on most marble copies because they were susceptible to breaking off), has misunderstood the sash, which was originally a chain linking the l. hip to an ankle shackle. The motif of Eros weeping as he approaches Aphrodite for chastisement is taken over on a well-known Pompeiian wall painting. Joachim von Sandrart, in 1679, considered the work a symbol of penitence. (SD)

Unpublished. On other replicas and their meaning, L. Curtius, *Festschrift für James Loeb* (Munich, 1930), 53–62. For the tradition in the Renaissance, I. Panofsky, *Studies in Iconology* (New York, 1962), 129–170.

Lent by the Collection of Hon. and Mrs. Edwin L. Weisl, Jr.

128. Infant Herakles (?)

1st cent. B. C.; H: 0.622; hollow cast, lustrous shiny black patina with small green areas, mechanically cleaned, 1944; silver eyes and teeth; missing r. arm, lower l. arm. Allegedly found at Daib el Guirza, Fayoum.

Children were favorite subjects of Hellenistic sculptors, but a work of this monumentality and careful finish probably depicts a divine, not a mortal infant. Lacking wings (Eros), ivy crown (Dionysos), or other attribute, the infant Herakles has been postulated. The baby Herakles was famed for his strength in strangling the serpents; other deeds of the adult hero were transferred to his childhood in popular mythology. (SD)

S. Reinach, *GBA*, 16 (1927), 300–301, ill.; CAMSL *Bulletin* 13:2 (April 1928), 22–24, ill., and 28:4 (Dec. 1943), 41–44, ill., describing cleaning; *Detroit, 1947, 11, no. 85, ill. 43; D. K. Hill, *GBA*, 36 (1948), 200 n. 3, on representations of the infant Herakles.

Lent by the City Art Museum of Saint Louis (36:26); acquired 1926.

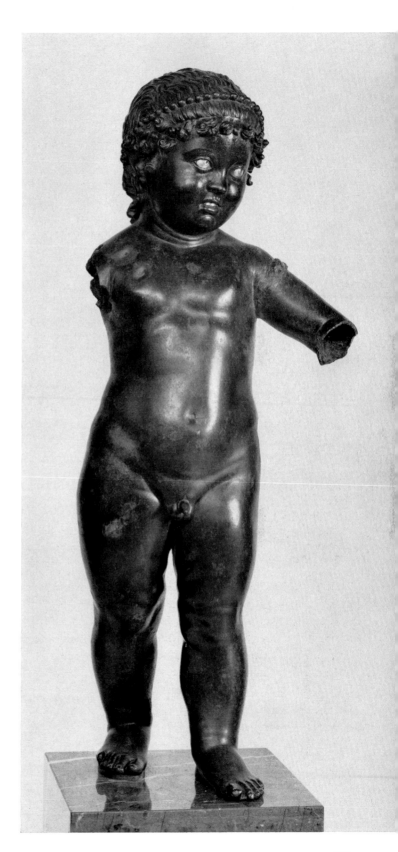

129. Poseidon

C. 250 B. C.; H: 0.060; solid cast, light brown patina, minute green traces.

This statuette is a miniature reflection of the monumental statue thought to be the "Isthmian Poseidon" created for Corinth by Lysippos, the best known copy of which is in the Lateran. The l. hand is pierced for a trident. Even on this diminutive scale his gnarled musculature and dense beard are carefully worked. The gaze is directed outward, as on coins of Demetrius Poliorcetes, not downward, as in the Lateran work. (SD)

Casson, 14, no. 107; Herbert, 119–120, no. 425, pl. 42. For the ascription to Lysippos and other replicas (esp. bronzes from Vevey and Kolhâpur), Picard, IV², 491 ff., figs. 202–207, 213–216; F. P. Johnson, *Lysippos*, (Durham, 1927), 142–147, pl. 24; cf. *Record of The Art Museum*, Princeton University, 23 (1964), 34.

Lent by the Warren Collection, Bowdoin College Museum of Art (1915.60).

130. Running Satyr

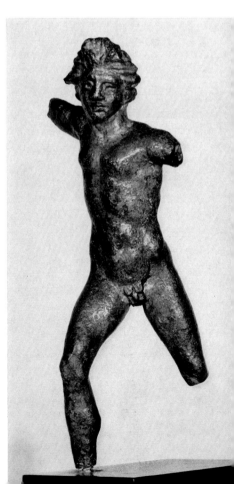

200–150 B. C.; H: 0.138; solid cast, dark brown and olive green patina; missing r. forearm, l. arm, lower l. leg, feet. Allegedly found in Egypt. Ex-coll. S. Pozzi (sale, G. Petit, 25–27 June, 1919, no. 413?).

Though not bearing the horns, tail, or goat's ears customarily associated with satyrs, the figure is related to such sylvan creatures as that in Chantilly by his unkempt hair and vigorous motion. The summary modelling and workmanship suggest an Alexandrian origin during the "dynamic phase" of Hellenistic art. An indentation on the crown of his head was possibly for an applied hairband; the eyes were probably inlaid. The satyr may be engaged in a foot-race or fight. (SD)

Reinach V¹, 52:6, "vendu à Paris le 7 juillet 1922, no. 88"; G. M. A. Hanfmann, *AJA*, 58 (1954), 228–229, figs. 17–19, pl. 40. For Chantilly satyr, C. Picard, *MonPiot*, 43 (1949), 58, figs. 1–3, pls. 6–7.

Lent by the Fogg Art Museum, Harvard University (1951. 106).

131. Portrait of a Barbarian or Ruler

2nd cent. B. C.; H: 0.195, W: 0.103; hollow cast, thin walls, rubbed and polished surface. Allegedly from Asia Minor.

The heroic portrait is based on a 5th century B. C. statue of Diomedes carrying off the Palladium from Troy, attributed to Kresilas. Arms and legs were made separately, and are now lost. Though the garment of the original is omitted, its modelling and even its angular jaw and slight beard are recaptured, Furtwängler claims. The facial features, soft, full bodily forms, moody expression, and impressionistic rendering of hair are typically in the Hellenistic tradition. G. M. A. Hanfmann suggests, however, that Antinous (favorite of Hadrian, died 130 A. D.) may be portrayed. (SD)

A. Furtwängler, *Masterpieces of Greek Sculpture* (London, 1895), 155; Neugebauer, *Führer*, 27. Cf. C. Clairmont, *Die Bildnisse des Antinous* (Schweizerisches Institut in Rom, 1966), nos. 1, 4, 13, 28.

Lent by the Staatliche Museen Berlin, Antikenabteilung (Misc. Inv. 7419).

132. Ruler Portrait

H: 0.238; green patina with small red areas, scraping overall except top of head and drapery, where stony deposit remains; missing l. foot, toes of r. foot, r. index finger. Allegedly found in Egypt. Ex-coll. Matossian, Lépine.

The idealized ruler has long arms and a small head. His r. hand probably held a staff; the l. supports a sword pointed toward the elbow. Masses of hair protrude beyond his leafy garland. Both his stance and the gripping of the sword hilt are characteristic of portraits of Alexander the Great. E. Buschor identifies the piece with Alexander and compares the Loeb Poseidon (Sieveking, 41–47, pl. 17–18), now in Munich; J. Charbonneaux relates the Jameson Poseidon, in the Louvre, to these two, noting the fine surface finish and bulging muscles of all three. The pose is used for other rulers, however, and the sword motif occurs in a Dioskouros statuette (Hill, no. 47, pl. 10). (SD)

Reinach, V, 311:5–6; Hill, 53–54, no. 110, pl. 27; E. Buschor, *Das hellenistische Bildnis* (Munich, 1949), 27, fig. 16; J. Charbonneaux, *MonPiot*, 46 (1952), 37; G. M. A. Hanfmann, *AJA*, 58 (1954), 229.

Lent by The Walters Art Gallery, Baltimore (54.1045); purchased 1930.

133. Boxer on Corinthian Capital

1st cent. B. C. or later; total H: 0.27, H. of figure: 0.142; figure olive green with some green crystals, stand dull green with iron rust stains.

The boxer wears leather gloves secured at mid-forearm with two bracelets, over which are placed hard leather or metal knuckle guards, bound to the bracelets by crossed leather straps. The l. hand holds a sponge. He stands atop a short pipe crowned by a three-faced Corinthian capital. Remains of three iron pins on the platform may have held hooks or chains, from which lamps or implements for symposia were hung. Hellenistic realism is evident in the sensitive modelling of the battered face, comparable to that of the seated bronze boxer in Rome (Bieber, *Hellenistic*, fig. 769). (SD)

Hill, 69, no. 146, with bibl., pl. 31 and frontispiece; D. K. Hill, *Apollo*, 84 (Dec. 1966), 453–454, fig. 1.
Lent by The Walters Art Gallery, Baltimore (54.1006); purchased 1924.

134. Suppliant Barbarian

Hellenistic Greek or early Roman; H: 0.130; light green surface with casting bubbles, silver eyes, pupils perhaps originally inset with jewels. Ex-coll. Bardini, A. Sambon (21, no. 73, pl. 14).

About to kneel before his conqueror, the barbarian wears trousers *(bracae)* and a long-sleeved shirt over which is a short-sleeved, belted tunic. Soft boots with ties and a pointed cap decorated with incomplete circles round out the costume. His small head is ringed with heavy curls; the eyes gaze upwards. Although identified as a Mithraic deity, Attis or Mên, he lacks appropriate attributes. D. K. Hill sees a resemblance to Alexander portraits, and feels that a human figure is intended. P. Bienkowski includes it in a group of bronze appliqués of unknown use. The unbalanced pose, Hill suggests, requires a complement — perhaps the conquering emperor. (SD)

Reinach, V, 221:7; Bienkowski, 62 f., no. 6; Hill, *JWalt*, 7–8 (1944–1945), 77 f., figs. 1, 3, p. 74; Hill, 61, no. 123, pl. 26; M. J. Vermaseren, *Corpus inscriptionum et monumentorum religionis mithriacae*, II (The Hague, 1960), 395, no. 2371, "not Mithraic."

Lent by The Walters Art Gallery, Baltimore (54.2293); purchased, 1944.

135. Aphrodite Removing Her Sandal

Alexandrian (?), c. 170–150 B. C.; H: 0.215; green patina with red areas.

Removing her sandal preparatory to the bath, Aphrodite extends her l. arm, which has just dropped the other sandal, for balance. The momentary quality and involvement with three-dimensional space are Hellenistic innovations. Her fresh, breathless expression suggests the jockey from Cape Artemision (Bieber, *Hellenistic*, fig. 645); the coiffure is reminiscent of the Capitoline and Medici Aphrodites. Her relatively long arms, large hands and feet, and small head reflect a late canon of proportions; the style hovers between the "baroque" and "rococo" phases of Hellenistic art. Over seventy representations of the theme are known, particularly close being Käppeli, B 21, said to be Roman. (SD)

*Santa Barbara, 1963, 9, no. 32, ill.; Stothart, 17; *Bulletin of the J. Paul Getty Museum of Art*, 1:2 (1959), 15–17, fig. 11; J. Paul Getty, *The Joys of Collecting* (New York, 1965), 64, color ill. Cf. Bieber, *Hellenistic*, 144, figs. 606–607.

Lent by the J. Paul Getty Museum, Malibu, Calif. (A58.S–3); purchased, 1958.

136. Hygieia

Late Hellenistic or early Roman, c. 2nd–1st cent. B.C.; H:0.084; hollow cast, green patina. Allegedly from Smyrna.

Hygieia, daughter of Asclepius, stands clad in a sleeveless chiton under a bell-shaped, tightly wound himation. She holds a serpent, one of Asclepius' healing creatures, in her r. hand and perhaps a phiale in her l. The stance and workmanship of this exquisite miniature, probably Hellenistic, recall Tanagra figurines; the complex drapery and proportions, however, are close to late Hellenistic statues. This figure was possibly dedicated at Pergamon or in another Asclepeion on the western coast of Asia Minor during the later 3rd or 2nd century B.C., when Pergamon ruled this area. (DGM)

S. N. Deane, MFA *Annual Report* (1906), 59; —, *AA* (1907), col. 395. Cf. Babelon-Blanchet, 252 f., no. 603; Reinach, II, 664:3. For late Hellenistic draped female figures, Bieber, *Hellenistic*, figs 499–501 (muses), 510–512, 514–515 (mortals) (2nd cent. B. C.).

Lent by the Museum of Fine Arts, Boston (06.2372).

137. Schoolboy

Late Hellenistic or Roman, c. 100 B. C.–200 A. D.; H: 0.195; solid cast, green and brown patina, some incrustation. Probably from Syria.

Rhetoric was one of the principal subjects studied by well-born youths in the late Republic and early Empire; this wide-eyed, pouting boy, clad in an enveloping cloak and wreath, may be declaiming or standing after winning an award in oratory or poetry. The spool-shaped base serves as his rostrum. His form is attenuated; the back of his robe is almost flat, with a filled hole at hip level. He recalls the "serious youth" in New Comedy, as in a terracotta figurine from Myrina, in Athens (Bieber, *Theater*, 94, n. 30, fig. 338), as well as the Lateran Sophocles. (DGM)

Reinach, V², 351:2, "vente à Paris, 7 juin 1922, n. 114"; C. C. Vermeule, *CJ*, 57 (1962), 148–149, n. 13, fig. 4; D. Adlow, *Christian Science Monitor* (Sept. 6, 1962), 7. Cf. also No. 260 and G. M. A. Hanfmann, *Record of the Museum of Historic Art, Princeton Univ.*, 2 (1943), 4–11.

Lent by the Museum of Fine Arts, Boston (60.530); gift of Edward Robinson by exchange.

138. Standing Zeus

Graeco-Roman, c. 1st cent. B. C.–2nd cent. A. D.;
H: 0.118; red, green, and brown patina, lower r. arm
and hand, scepter from l. hand missing.

This standing, bearded divinity, clothed in chiton,
long himation and sandals, could almost as easily
be Serapis or Asclepius as Zeus, so generalized
have his attributes become. As C. C. Vermeule
remarks, the artist may have transformed a standing Serapis back into Zeus by omitting the *modius*
(corn measure, see Nos. 271, 272) and probably sub-
stituting a thunderbolt for a patera in the r. hand.
Called "Graeco-Roman" because of the absence
of criteria by which a more precise date might be
determined, the type became the sculptural common denominator of Olympian divinity for votive
figurines and cult statues throughout the Roman
empire during the first two centuries A. D. (DGM)

C. C. Vermeule, *CJ*, 55 (1960), 201, fig. 9; *FA*, 15 (1960),
no. 671. Cf. Bieber, *Hellenistic*, 180–181, figs. 770–778.

Lent by the Museum of Fine Arts, Boston (59.298),
John Michael Rodocanachi Fund.

139. Cloaked Man

2nd–1st cent. B. C.; H: 0.118; dark green patina,
copper inlaid border of cloak and hood; hood broken 0.02 below peak and repaired.

The bearded man is enveloped in a short cloak
rising to a peaked hood. Both hands are covered,
the r. seeming to grasp the cloak, the l. holding
an indistinct object. The tall cap and cloak are
paralleled in bronzes of fertility genii which
appear first in the Hellenistic age. His asym-
metrical glance and breathing mouth point to
Pergamene influence, but style and expression
are much softer. DGM compares contemporary
terracottas from Kyme. (GMAH)

Kouchakji Frères (sale, American Art Association,
8–9 March, 1918, no. 322, ill., and earlier bibl.); for
gods, genii, mortals wearing hooded cloak, W.
Deonna, *Latomus*, 21 (Brussels, 1955), 102, 111, figs. 29
(silen), 40 (cap).

Lent by Thomas T. Solley, Bloomington, Ind.

140. Archaistic Kore

1st cent. B. C.; H: 0.145, W: 0.055; light red-tan bronze, pitted, eyes and meander garment border inlaid with silver; cleaned 1965. Ex-coll. J. Pierpont Morgan; Belle da Costa Greene.

The tendency to imitate Archaic works appears in Greece from the 5th century B. C. on. This delicate kore is typical of the sophisticated archaism of late Hellenistic and Augustan times. In paraphrasing the Archaic maiden type the artist exaggerated the intricate linear folds and zigzags of drapery and schematized them into an affected linear pattern. He also combined two types of earlier coiffures. The missing r. hand would have held a flower or fruit. The recent cleaning (1965) has shown the superb skill of the sculptor and live plasticity of the piece, and has proved its "twin" in the British Museum (Walters, no. 192; Lamb, pl. 88a) to be a modern imitation. (GMAH)

Collectors' Choice, Denver Art Museum (June 4–29, 1958), no. 37, ill. (incorrectly dated 6th cent. B. C.). Similar archaistic bronze and marble korai, including another modern imitation, in silver, Richter, *D. O.*, 29–32 and bibl., pls. 12 f. For the archaistic style in general, E. B. Harrison, *Agora*, XI, 50–67.

Lent by the Eric de Kolb Collection.

141. Cerberus

4th–3rd cent. B.C.; H: 0.054, L: 0.045; solid cast, green patina; forepaws, l. hind leg, tip of l. animal nose missing.

Cerberus, the three-headed guardian of Hades, was associated with Serapis, particularly in a statue by Bryaxis. As in Macrobius' description of it (*Saturnalia*, I, 20, 13), the central beast is a lion, whose forelegs are entwined with snakes. The lateral heads, rather than a tame dog and ferocious wolf, seem here to be two identical canines with pointed muzzles. Stippling indicates short hair, with coarser, deeper strokes characterizing the shaggy ruff; the overall workmanship is coarse. The tail was apparently omitted. (SD)

Casson, 14, no. 101; Herbert, 119, no. 424, and bibl. Similar small Cerberus statuettes are Walters, 174, nos. 948–950; Babelon-Blanchet, 340, no. 790; de Ridder, *de Clercq*, 254, no. 369, pl. 56:3, and bibl.; Reinach, II, 698:5, 699:3, III, 205:1; Berlin, A. Michaelis, *JHS*, 6 (1885), 292–294; Froehner, *Gréau*, 171, no. 850.

Lent by the Warren Collection, Bowdoin College Museum of Art (1923.45).

142. Pantheress Looking up from Her Prey

Late 4th–3rd cent. B.C.; H: 0.046, L: 0.068; solid cast; part of tail missing. The oxide crust which covered the bronze when acquired contained traces of textile material.

The pantheress is represented as glancing up from her prey, perhaps alarmed by impending danger. The piece is therefore part of a two-figure composition; judging by the fact that the beast stems her r. rear leg against her prey, the latter must have been a large animal, such as a donkey (cf. K. Parlasca, *Die römischen Mosaiken in Deutschland* [Berlin, 1959], pl. 91:4). The fur is finely engraved. The object is a rare example of Hellenistic animal sculpture. (HH)

H. Hoffmann, *AA*, (1960), 112 ff., no. 34, fig. 53; —, *HambJb*, 6 (1961), 240; Hoffmann, 15, 39, fig. 47B.
Lent by the Museum für Kunst und Gewerbe, Hamburg (1960.2).

143. Bull

Hellenistic Greek or Roman; H: 0.072; dark green patina; hole in neck for Apis headdress.

Although basing his conception upon observation, the sculptor has reduced such details as the tuft at the tip of the tail, the forelock, and folds of skin at the neck to a series of schematized gouges. Leg joints and hooves are also summarily handled, suggesting provincial workmanship. The looped tail occurs often in examples of the type. (SD)

Unpublished. Cf. No. 283 and bibl.; *Fogg, 1954, 32, No. 235, pl. 73.

Lent by the Estates of Audrey B. and Stephen R. Currier.

144. Recumbent Kid

2nd cent. B. C. (?); H: 0.057; dark green patina.

Curving, incised lines indicate the kid's long hair. The tilt of the head, oversized ears and round eyes provide a comic effect. This statuette may, like its Archaic and early Classical predecessors, have been mounted on the rim of a large vessel. (SD)

Unpublished. For the treatment of the goat in ancient art, Richter, *Animals*, 25–27, figs. 120–135.

Lent by the Estates of Audrey B. and Stephen R. Currier.

145. Bull Protome

Hellenistic, imitating Classical model (?); H: 0.11, max. W: 0.082, H. of head: 0.055; cast in one piece, head cast hollow, gray-green patina, iron oxide between horns mostly removed in 1967 cleaning.

The upright rod may have been intended for insertion into a chariot railing, the rings serving as rein guides. The trefoil shape is distantly derived from the three wing-like plates by which Urartean bull's head protomes were riveted to bronze cauldrons. Roman objects of related form but inferior size and quality were probably votive. The unevenness of the neck edge and other defects suggest an imperfect casting. (DGM)

D. G. Mitten, *Fogg Art Museum Acquisitions 1965,* 136–140, ill., with Roman comparanda. Cf. P. Amandry, *The Aegean and The Near East; Studies Presented to Hetty Goldman* (New York, 1957), 236–261; —, *Annales de l'Est, Mémoires,* 19 (Nancy, 1958), esp. pl. 7.

Lent by the Fogg Art Museum, Harvard University (1964.145).

146. Mina Weight

C. 350–250 B.C.; H: 0.067, L: 0.071, Th. at edge: 0.009; solid cast, gray-green patina.

The rectangular weight bears a facing bull's head in relief. The inscription reads: ΔΑΜΟΣΙΑ ΑΓΟΡΑΝΟΜΕΟΝΤΟΣ ΜΕΝΕΞΕΝΟΥ, "Public (Mina), (Authority of the) Market-inspector, Menexenos." Allowing a loss from wear and cleaning, the weight, 413.3 gm., corresponds to the common Attic

standard (mina variously calculated from 431 to 458 gm.). The object is probably to be attributed to Phocis in central Greece on the basis of dialectical variations in the inscription and the bull's head symbol, which is the primary civic badge on all coinages of Phocis. Herbert's attribution to Cnidus is weakened by dialectical considerations and by the fact that a bull's head was used only sporadically, and then only as a secondary device, in Cnidian Hellenistic coinage. (J. H. Kroll)

Casson, no. 100; S. Casson, *AJA,* 39 (1935), 516–517, fig. 6, interprets punching of circular characters as showing artist's lack of confidence at cutting them freehand; K. Herbert, *AJA,* 66 (1962), 382–383, pl. 104:4; Herbert, 119, no. 423. Attribution to Phocis will be discussed in a forthcoming note by J. H. Kroll.

Lent by the Warren Collection, Bowdoin College Museum of Art (1923.14).

147. Mule's Head from a Fulcrum

Probably 2nd cent. B. C.; H: 0.107, L: 0.106; green patina, blackish where rubbed, silver inlay on harness; back filled with lead which is covered by piece of sheet bronze from the *kline*. Allegedly from Adana, Turkey.

The ends of *fulcra* (head boards) of both Hellenistic and Roman reclining couches *(klinai)* were decorated at the top by a finial, usually the head of an animal, and at the bottom by a circular medallion (see drawing). The two ornaments were connected by a curving metal frame and a metal sheet behind the frame, part of which still remains here. The area in front of the sheet metal was inlaid. Below the mule's neck a heavy collar, decorated with a swastika meander, holds an animal skin. The sensitive realism of the head indicates close observation of nature; the soft muzzle, organic structure of bone, muscle and folds of skin on the curving neck are carefully characterized. (JAS)

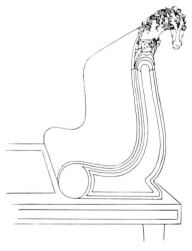

Drawing by Suzanne Chapman

Unpublished. Cf. Richter, *Furniture*, 107 f., fig. 543; H. Hoffmann, *AJA*, 61 (1957), 167 ff. His suggestion that *fulcra* can be dated by the sharpness of curve and observations on workmanship bear out the owner's assertion that this piece is Greek. Cf. Nos. 302, 303.

Lent by the Collection of George Ortiz.

148. Votive Boat (Lamp?)

4th cent. B. C.; H: 0.076, L: 0.13; combination solid-hollow cast, green patina.

L. Casson (by letter) diagnoses the curved end as stern and the stubby projection at cut-water as a traditional constructional feature, the "projecting forefoot." A boar's head is incised on one side of the projection, a branch on the other. Casson points out that the connection between boar's head and bow projection is well established (C. Torr, *Ancient Ships* [Cambridge, 1894], 65). The bow seems to form a spout; the forked upright may be intended for suspension if the ship functioned as a lamp. (GMAH)

Unpublished. For the ship type, L. Casson, *The Ancient Mariners* (New York, 1959), 216, pls. 9b, 12–15; —, *Illustrated History of Ships and Boats* (New York, 1964), ill. 57; for a Greek dedication to Athena (military?), Staïs, no. 7083, ill.; for a Geometric ship rhyton, G. Kirk, *AJA*, 55 (1951), pl. 34; for boat from Isthmian sanctuary of Poseidon, O. Broneer, *Hesperia*, 28 (1959), 328, fig. 5 (probably late 6th cent. B. C.); cf. also Cincinnati Art Museum *Bulletin* 7 (1965), ill.

Lent by the Seattle Art Museum, Norman Davis Collection (Cs6.14); acquired 1962.

149. Handle Attachment with Herakles Head

Late 4th cent. B.C.; H: 0.098, W: 0.058; solid cast.

One of a pair. The holes are for the swinging handles of a situla; the back is gently concave for application to the pail. Herakles wears a lion skin on his head, its mouth framing his forehead, and its forepaws knotted under his chin. The mane forms a series of flame-like tufts around his head. Related are a bronze in the Louvre (de Ridder, I, 72, no. 491, pl. 37) from Dodona and a silver situla with attachment found at Pilaf Tepé, Thessaly (C. Edmonds, *JHS*, 20 [1900], 23–25, pl. 5); expression and stylization of the beard are close to a Herakles in the Louvre (de Ridder, I, 34, no. 186, pl. 19). (SD)

Unpublished.

Lent by the Museum of Art and Archaeology, University of Missouri (58.2).

150. Silenus Head

Provincial work; H: 0.114, W: 0.075, Th: 0.049; hollow cast, back open, leaves and berries cast in one piece with rest of head, olive green patina; nose flattened in antiquity. Allegedly found near Ancona. Ex-coll. Tyszkiewicz, J. H. Fitzhenry.

Behind the small, forward-pointed ears are semicircular cutouts which allowed a cylindrical member to pass through the head. Three rings, on the top of the head and below the cutout on each side, were cut off between 1898 and 1904. On the back a rim of bronze bears ancient solder. The head was probably soldered to a piece of furniture and riveted through the loops. A handle ring may have gone through the cutouts. Fuchs, pl. 50, shows a charcoal box ornamented with similar plastic heads. Cf. also No. 213 with ring. (SD)

Froehner, *Vente Tyszkiewicz*, 53, no. 146, pl. 11; *Burlington, 1904, 66, no. D120, pl. 70; Casson, 16, no. 130; Herbert, 120, no. 426, pl. 42.

Lent by the Warren Collection, Bowdoin College Museum of Art (1915.50).

151. Head of Medusa

3rd–2nd cent. B. C.; H: 0.13, W: 0.145; solid cast, reddish brown with traces of bright green patina; l. wing feather on top of head broken off.

Undulating waves of hair frame the face, turning into two snakes under the chin. The mouth (pierced through) is open; eyes are turned upward, pupils hollowed and iris incised, in the agonized expression associated with the atelier of Skopas. A feathery wing was on each side of the large, heavy curl on the forehead. The horror of the ancient myth is de-emphasized; the face is almost beautiful. (JAS)

Unpublished. Cf. de Ridder, no. 803, pl. 55; Ucelli, 205 ff., figs. 228, 229. For marble Roman copy, A. Furtwängler–H. Urlichs, *Denkmäler griechischer und römischer Skulptur* (Munich, 1904), 39 f., pl. 13; for meaning, *OCD* (Oxford, 1949), 391 (s. v. Gorgo); E. Goodenough, *Jewish Symbols of the Graeco-Roman Period*, VII (New York, 1958), 225 ff., with earlier bibl.; for transformation of Medusa-Sol in late Empire, M. J. Vermaseren, *Latomus*, 28 (1957), 514 ff.

Lent by Mr. and Mrs. Joseph Ternbach.

ΝΙ ΚΑΣΙΜΑΧΑ ΑΝΕΘ ΗΚΕ

152. Poppy with Votive Inscription of Nikasimacha

3rd–2nd cent. B. C.; H: 0.048, W: 0.075; hollow cast, dark green patina; deep modern gouge above the letters E and Λ, on underside remains of an iron rod.

The fruit bears a carefully incised inscription: ΝΙΚΑΣΙΜΑΧΑ ΑΝΕΘΗΚΕ. Peter Herrmann kindly supplied the following epigraphic information (trans.): "On account of the alpha with broken cross-bar, and especially on account of the theta, which is smaller than the other letters, I should date the inscription in the 3rd or possibly 2nd century B. C. The name Nikasimacha appears to be Doric or northwestern Greek; it is not, however, documented elsewhere." The poppy is the attribute of Demeter, Aphrodite, and Artemis. One thinks at once of the Artemis from near Lousoi (No. 89), who once held a similar fruit on a long stem. E. Langlotz, who saw the bronze shortly after it was acquired by the Hamburg museum, thought it might have come from Lousoi. See also L. Robert, *Coll. Froehner, Inscriptions grecques* (Paris, 1936), no. 29, pl. 13; *RE*, XV, 2433 ff., s. v. Mohn. I am grateful to Prof. R. E. Schultes of Harvard for identifying the object as a poppy. Other authorities had previously suggested that it might represent a pomegranate. (HH)

H. Hoffmann, *HambJb*, 8 (1963), 211.

Lent by the Museum für Kunst und Gewerbe, Hamburg (1961.33).

Etruscan Bronzes

Plate IV, No. 203   Oval Toilet Box (Cista)

ETRUSCAN
BRONZES

The copper deposits of the Catena Metallifera, the ore-rich mountain chain in western Italy, gave the Etruscans and their Villanovan predecessors great opportunities to develop a bronze industry. How well they utilized them is best seen in the overwhelming displays of the Museo Villa Giulia in Rome, where case after case is filled with bronze armor, bronze utensils, bronze figurines, and even furniture of bronze. The prehistoric Iron Age culture of Tuscany and the Po valley, named "Villanovan"[1] after a site near Bologna, is allied with prehistoric Europe in its taste for fusing figure and ornament in the geometric manner, yet with a bent toward baroque enrichment of which the "open-work" bridle bits (Nos. 153–154) are superlative examples. This tradition of exuberant adornment of vessels and furniture persisted after the Etruscans (c. 700–100 B.C.) began to imitate first the arts of the Near East and then, consistently and closely, those of Greece. Vase handles, toilet boxes, candelabra, and supports sprout figures and plant forms with an uncontrolled vitality which distinguishes the Etruscan products through the ages[2] from the more precise, architectural use of the same elements in Greek bronzes (Nos. 184, 191, 197, 199, 203–210, 219, 221, 224).

Bordering the central, focal area of the Etruscan city states and their workshops there developed, to the north and east, Italic and other regional styles of bronze-working which retained some of the prehistoric types and traditions but modified them by refracting the Greek and Etruscan figurative models in a fantastic mood. Something of this process is seen in the wonderful discs from Italic armor (No. 158 A–C). The "art of the situla" flourished at a somewhat later date from Etruscan Bologna and non-Etruscan Este all the way into the Balkans.[3]

The way in which the Etruscans followed and adopted Greek models is a highly diversified development, and the line between Greek and Etruscan is sometimes hard to draw. Greek artists undoubtedly came to Etruria (No. 203, pl. IV); Greek colonies began on the Gulf of Naples and in Campania, a region of which parts occasionally came under Etruscan rule. The bronzes of these areas show an interplay of Etruscan and Greek elements (Nos. 84, 165). On the other hand, Greek authors' praise of Etruscan lamps and "of everything of bronze that adorns the house, for whatever use" (Kritias in Athenaeus I:28 b)[4] and the scattered finds

1. Traditional scholarly opinion makes "Villanovans" Indo-European speakers, distinct from non Indo-European Etruscans; some recent views consider them Etruscans in an earlier cultural phase. See Hencken, and H. Hencken, *Antiquity*, 40 (1966), 205.
2. For up-to-date bibl. on bronzes: E. H. Richardson, *The Etruscans* (Chicago, 1964), 259; Mansuelli, 243–245; *Santa Barbara, 1967; *Worcester, 1967. For armor: A. M. Snodgrass, *JHS*, 85 (1965), 116. Vessels: M. G. Marunti, *StEtr*, 27 (1959), 65; M. Zuffa, *StEtr*, 28 (1960), 165, pls. 19–46.
3. *Mostra dell'arte delle situle dal Po al Danubio* (Florence, 1961). J. Kastelic, *Situla Art* (New York, 1965).
4. K. O. Müller and W. Deecke, *Die Etrusker*, II (Stuttgart, 1877), 258. This work is still unsurpassed as collection of ancient literary sources. For various facets of modern research on the Etruscans, see M. Pallottino, *The Etruscans* (Pelican A 310, Aylesbury, England, 1955). Well-selected bibliographies in E. H. Richard-

of Etruscan bronzes and pottery[5]) in sanctuaries of the Greek mainland, the Greek islands, and Asia Minor show that sea-borne contacts could mediate artistic stimulation even from remote Greek centers. The contacts with Greek *toreutike* thus took place on many levels of intensity, from the Greek bronze-worker who came to settle in a coastal city like Caere where Greeks made dedications inscribed in Greek, to a village coppersmith who imitated something which was adapted from a Greek model in a major center. It is at the top level where contact was closest; hence it is more difficult to place with assurance the finest pieces: the Getty Zeus, the Minneapolis kouros and the Getty kore have been assigned by some scholars to Greek, by others to Etruscan masters (Nos. 164, 167, 56).

The major phases of Greek art — Archaic, Classical, and Hellenistic — are all reflected in Etruscan bronzes, but there has been much discussion as to whether Etruscan sculpture was *retardataire,* whether after the Archaic (600–500 B.C.) period it tended to lag behind the stylistic development in Greece. It can be documented in other branches of Etruscan art that a masterpiece close to the Greek in style was copied in an ever-coarsening series of imitations which continued to be made for a long time. A similar situation seems to have prevailed for some types of bronzes; the Fogg Turan (No. 168), for instance, seems to stand close to the beginning of a series of crowned women, and the warrior (Nos. 163, 173) and Herakles (No. 183) types are known in a long series of mass-produced replicas.[6]) How this diffusion took place, and how long it lasted for the various types, remains to be worked out.

At its end, Etruscan bronze work merged into the central Italian Hellenistic *koine,* a sort of Italo-Greek provincial artistic dialect (third to first century B.C.). After c. 400 B.C. one part of Etruria after another fell under the sway of Rome, and while the artistic traditions appear to be Etruscan, the artists may have been Italic or Latin. One of the few Etruscan lifesize bronze statues extant[7]), the Mars of Todi (fourth century B.C.) in the Vatican, bears an inscription in Umbrian, and the Praenestine toilet boxes have inscriptions in Latin (No. 208) beginning not

son, n. 2 *supra,* and *Santa Barbara, 1967. Major vehicle of research is *Studi Etruschi* (Florence) for articles on language, religion, and technical aspects of bronzes, as well as a series of articles on "Materials for a Corpus of Etruscan Bronze Figurines": U. Fogolari, *StEtr,* 21 (1951), 343; 22 (1952), 287; 23 (1954), 383 (Verona); F. Maetzke, *StEtr,* 25 (1957), 489 (Chiusi); A. Mazzolai, *StEtr,* 26 (1958), 193 (Grosseto).

5. E. Kunze, *Studies Presented to David M. Robinson,* I (G. Mylonas, ed., St. Louis, 1951), 736.

6. Well-illustrated in Fogolari's, Maetzke's and Mazzolai's articles, n. 4 *supra.* Such series also include draped sacrificing men.

7. Etruscan bronze statues were celebrated. The Romans were accused of having attacked Volsinii to carry off its 2,000 statues (Metrodoros of Skepsis in Pliny, *Natural History* 34:34). A head from Bolsena: S. Haynes, *StEtr,* 33 (1965), 523, pl. 121. In addition to pieces previously known: A. J. Vostchinina, *StEtr,* 33 (1965), 317, pls. 71–74, reclining half-lifesize youth from Perugia, c. 350–300 B.C. For unusual Archaic half-hammered, half-cast statues, S. Haynes, *Antike Plastik,* IV, ed. W. H. Schuchhardt (Berlin, 1965), 20–24.

later than the second half of the fourth century B. C.[8] On the other hand, the bronze statue of the "Arringatore" in Florence, often considered the very exemplar of Roman Republican portraiture, bears an Etruscan dedication — as late as the first century B. C.[9]

Only a careful comparative study, which systematically considers both the epigraphic pecularities of inscriptions found not infrequently on Etruscan bronzes and the stylistic character of the pieces[9a] can form a firm basis on which to distinguish Etruscans from Romans.

Interest in Etruscan bronzes goes back to the Renaissance. The celebrated Chimera of Arezzo was found in 1553 and restored by Benvenuto Cellini.[10] In the seventeenth century Baroque draftsmen who worked for the antiquarian Cassiano dal Pozzo (1589–1657) drew Etruscan bronze warriors and mirrors.[11] The patriotic Etruscomania of the eighteenth century resulted in much publication of relevant material, but interest was directed to subject matter; this trend reached its culmination in such huge collections as that of Etruscan mirrors initiated by Eduard Gerhard in 1840.[12] The question of the meaning of Etruscan bronzes is as yet unresolved: we are often still unsure which Etruscan divinities are represented and what they mean (Nos. 163, 168, 170, 179, 184, 195); or why Greek legends seem peculiarly twisted or misunderstood (Nos. 192, 193, 203, pl. IV, 206, 210, 216, 217); but much progress has been made, and at least the outlines of the Etruscan pantheon and of Etruscan adoption of Greek gods and heroes are emerging.[13]

This research and, indeed, all research on Etruscan bronzes is handicapped by lack of information on the use of bronzes in Etruscan sanc-

8. Mars of Todi: *Kunst und Leben der Etrusker (Cologne, 1956), no. 414, pl.48 (H. Jucker) with bibl.; Giglioli, pls. 250 f. Cistae: G. A. Mansuelli, StEtr, 21 (1951), 401; *Santa Barbara, 1967, 76; L. B. Warren, AJA, 68 (1964), 35, with bibl.
9. Arringatore: Hanfmann, Roman, 81 f., fig. 48.
9a. J. Heurgon in Studi in Onore di Luisa Banti (Rome, 1965), 178–189.
10. L. Brown, 155, pl. 57. B. Cellini, Vita, II (Florence, 1829), 87.
11. C. C. Vermeule, TransPhilAs, 66:2 (1966), 25, 41, figs. 71 (mirror), 156 f. and 50:5 (1960), 28, fig. 94. cf. D. K. Hill, AJA, 69 (1965), 120, pl. 30:13–14, handle in Bologna.
12. Survey of Etruscan discoveries and studies of Etruscology: P. Ducati, Etruria antica, II (1926), 144–161; major Etruscologists: *Kunst und Leben der Etrusker (Cologne, 1956) 39–45, notably: T. Dempster (1579–1625), Athanasius Kircher (1601–1680). For Museo Kircheriano bronzes: E. De Ruggiero, Il Museo Kircheriano (1878) and G. Q. Giglioli, StEtr, 22 (1952), 68. Other major publications of Etruscan materials were made by A. F. Gori (1661–1757), F. Inghirami (1772–1846), L. Lorenzi (1732–1810), G. Micali (1769–1844); cf. StEtr, 29 (1960), xxxix.
13. J. Bayet, Herclé (Paris, 1926). F. De Ruyt, Charun (Brussels, 1934). Ulisse (pseudonym), Figure mitologiche degli specchi etruschi (Rome, 1929–1930). G. A. Mansuelli, StEtr, 20 (1948–1949), 59, systematic survey of gods, heroes, legends on Etruscan mirrors. R. Enking on Lasa, Culsu, Vanth: RM, 57 (1942), 1; 58 (1943), 48. G. Camporeale, StEtr, 26 (1958), 3, Tityos; 28 (1960), 233, Thalna. R. Herbig, Götter und Dämonen der Etrusker (Mainz, 1965). R. Hampe–E. Simon, Griechische Sagen in der etruskischen Kunst (Mainz, 1964). On the literary and linguistic side: C. O. Thulin, Die etruskische Disciplin (Göteborgs Högeskolas Årsskrift, Göteborg, 1905–1909). E. Fiesel, Die Namen des griechischen Mythos im Etruskischen (Göttingen, 1928). General: G. M. A. Hanfmann, OCD, s. v. Religion, Etruscan. A. Grenier, Les religions étrusque

tuaries[14]) and cities. Hundreds if not thousands of Etruscan bronzes in European and American museums, especially figurines, have come without any information about the circumstances under which they were found. What information was available came chiefly from finds in graves and was instructive only regarding sepulchral use of bronzes. Some light is shed on their use in the domestic sphere by paintings and reliefs in Etruscan mausolea, where bronze vessels and furniture are depicted in symposium scenes, for instance in the famous Tomb of the Lionesses, Tarquinia; candle holders like No. 219 and stands like Nos. 220–221 in the "Golini I" Mausoleum of Orvieto; and Etruscan armor portrayed suspended on the walls in the famous reliefs of the Tomb of the Reliefs in Caere.[15]) A carefully recorded find of a sanctuary with bronze votives is rare and always important. In the early 1930's the discovery of a small sanctuary demonstrated the manner in which some popular types of bronze votives were displayed, and provided an important indication for the relatively late date of the elongated women and warriors (cf. Nos. 163, 180).[16])

The arts of Italy have always tended to be strongly regional, and this is true of Etruscan bronzes as well, but only in the last and present generations have scholars like K. A. Neugebauer, P. J. Riis, L. Banti, G. A. Mansuelli, S. Haynes, and E. H. Richardson begun to organize the material and to distinguish regional centers.[17]) It is possible to place some fine Archaic reliefs with probability in a south Etruscan center (Caere); some late Archaic and Classical tripods, candelabra, and related products in Vulci (Nos. 173, 178, 188, 192, 197); and some bronze implements and figurines in Chiusi (Clusium), (Nos. 160, 170, cf. 164). More tentative attributions have been made to other regions ("North Etruscan") and centers (Bologna, Perugia, Fiesole, Spina, Numana) in Etruria and neighboring regions. Praeneste has been long recognized as probably the major

et romaine (Paris, 1948). Of great importance for religion and language are the recent discoveries of gold plaques inscribed in Etruscan and Punic attesting to a cult of Punic Ashtart at Pyrgi, port of Caere, J. Heurgon, *JRS,* 56 (1966), 1. 14. Bronze plaque inscribed in Etruscan was found in the sanctuary of Pyrgi: M. Pallottino, *StEtr,* 34 (1966), 177. A frieze in gilded bronze decorated the temple of Diana at Nemi, M. Moretti, *Museo Villa Giulia* (Rome, 1963), fig. 164. The representation of a liver cast in bronze and found near Piacenza is one of the major documents for Etruscan religion. For votive figurines see no. 16, *infra.*

15. Giglioli, pls. 111:2, 245, 341–343. Helmets of type of No. 227 are represented on the ends of a terracotta urn in Worcester, Richardson, n. 2 *supra,* pl. 45. See J. Heurgon, *La vie quotidienne chez les Etrusques* (Paris, 1961).

16. P. Mingazzini, *NSc* (1932). Bronzes from sanctuary at Satricum, (6th to 5th cent. B. C.): N. Bonacasa, *StEtr,* 25 (1957), 549, figs. 1–26, from that of Diana, Nemi, Moretti, n. 14 *supra,* 235; S. Haynes, *RM,* 57 (1960), 45, pls. 18–20.

17. The most comprehensive attempt, which includes all sculpture, is P. J. Riis, *Tyrrhenika* (Copenhagen, 1941). Literature in Richardson and *Santa Barbara, 1967, supra n. 2. Mrs. Richardson is at work on a definitive study of bronze figurines. Some of her results appear in *MAAR,* 27 (1962), 159–198 and in *The Etruscans* (Chicago, 1964). Caere: L. Banti, "Bronzi archaici etruschi: i tripodi Loeb," *Tyrrhenika: Saggi di studi etruschi* (Milan, 1957). The gigantomachy reliefs: G. M. A. Hanfmann, *ArtB,* 19 (1937), 494, were probably made in a

center of graven toilet boxes; Rome was another. The complex problem of dating and grouping the figured mirrors has been tackled by J. D. Beazley, R. Herbig, G. Mansuelli and others.[18]

The paucity of comprehensive modern publications making parts of this material available with sufficient illustrations in a form convenient for research has impeded progress. To assist toward this end is one of the purposes of the present exhibition. Its other aim is to help the collector. The twentieth century has shown in recurrent surges of enthusiasm that Etruscan art appeals to its sensibilities. D. H. Lawrence's romantic notion that Etruscans were unregimented, mysterious, and "vital"[19] motivated the surge in the twenties and thirties; recognition of "primitive, essential" form as in the celebrated comparison of elongated (mass-produced) Etruscan figurines with sculptures by Giacometti did much for the Etruscan revival of the fifties. Our aim is not to rediscover modern art in ancient Etruria, but to present in select examples an art which, while always technically competent in the congenial medium of bronze, yet displays a great variety of artistic achievement in the interplay of form, function, and spirit of its works. Hopefully, the exhibition may thus also contribute to a more discriminating assessment of the different levels of artistic achievement among Etruscan bronzes.

George M. A. Hanfmann

coastal center rather than Bomarzo. Vulci: K. A. Neugebauer, *AA* (1923–1924) 302. M. Guarducci, *StEtr*, 10 (1936), 181. G. Fischetti, *StEtr*, 18 (1945), 9–27. Chiusi: K. A. Neugebauer, *RM*, 51 (1936), 181, pls. 24–26. R. Zandrino, *StEtr*, 22 (1952), 329, figs. 1–3. E. Homann-Wedeking, *RM*, 58 (1943), 88; for those in Chiusi museum: G. Maetzke, *StEtr*, 25 (1957), 489, figs. 1–62. P. J. Riis, *StEtr*, 26 (1958), 31, kore from Rimini, Numana? F. Messerschmidt, *RM*, 57 (1942), 151, 169, figs. 4, 20, 27, pls. 15 ff. and R. Zandrino, *ibid.* 236, figs. 1–12, pls. 23 f. (3rd and 2nd cent. B.C.). P. A. Arias, *StEtr*, 52 (1952), 69. D. K. Hill, *AJA*, 69 (1965), 115, pls. 27–30 (4th cent. workshop). Attributions to Spina and Umbria (geometricized warriors and "Minervas"): E. Richardson, *MAAR*, 27 (1962), 196 f. Cf. also the remarks by Mansuelli, 225–231, on Arezzo, Caere, Capua, Cortona, Bologna, Marzabotto, Populonia, Spina, Tarquinia, Vetulonia, Vulci.
18. J. D. Beazley, *JHS*, 59 (1949), 1. G. A. Mansuelli, *StEtr*, 19 (1946–1947), 9–137, figs. 1–5 (chronology and attributions). R. Herbig, *StEtr*, 24 (1955), 183 and *Festschrift B. Schweitzer* (R. Lullies, ed., Stuttgart, 1954) and the literature in *Santa Barbara, 1967.
19. D. H. Lawrence, *Etruscan Places* (London, 1932).

153. Horse Bit

Villanovan, 9th–7th cent. B. C.; H: 0.16, W. loop to loop of snaffle including pendants: 0.19.

The cheek pieces consist of a colt on the back of a large horse, a duck and colt underneath; idol?-shaped pendants hang from fore and hind feet. Named after their cemetery near Bologna, the "Villanovans" of the Po valley and Tuscany first mined on a large scale and produced much bronze work. "Bronze bits and cheek pieces were included in a dead man's equipment so that he could command the use of horses in the next world" (Trump). Concern with horses, geometric style, and many motifs link Villanova to the Iron Age cultures of Hallstatt, Danube, Caucasus, and Iran. The two-piece flexible horse bit was an invention of these early Iron Age cavalrymen. Interweaving ambiguously geometric function and animal form, Villanovan artists use humorous fancy in position and scale of animals in a style less strict than Greek, less dynamic than Iranian. L. Pomerance cites a close parallel in the Museo Archeologico, Florence. (GMAH)

*Pomerance, 104, no. 118, with bibl. For an up-to-date sketch of Villanovan culture, D. H. Trump, *Central and Southern Italy before Rome* (New York, 1965), 173, fig. 60. For characterization of Villanovan geometric style, Mansuelli, 31–36. On flexible bits, C. F. A. Schaeffer, *Préhistoire,* 6 (1938), 49 ff.; G. M. A. Hanfmann, *AJA,* 56 (1952), 37, n. 57; H. Hencken, *AJA,* 61 (1957), 1–4; H. Müller-Karpe, *Beiträge zur Chronologie der Urnenfelderzeit nördlich und südlich der Alpen,* Römisch-Germanische Forschungen, 22 (Berlin, 1959), *passim.*

Lent by The Pomerance Collection.

154. Horse Bit

Villanovan, 8th–7th cent. B. C.; H: 0.114, W: 0.187, L. of large horses: 0.127. Found at Villanova.

The type is close to No. 153, although a second duck replaces the small colt beneath the large horse, and any pendants are now lost. For further discussion of such bridles see Hencken, 267 ff., fig. 251; G. Kossack, *Studien zum Symbolgut der Urnenfelder- und Hallstattzeit Mitteleuropas*, Römisch-Germanische Forschungen, 20 (Berlin, 1954), 55–56; L. Laurenzi, *Civiltà del Ferro*, Documenti e Studi, 6 (Bologna, 1960), 5–71. (SD)

Mentioned *Art Quarterly*, 27:2 (1964), 207.
Lent by the Seattle Art Museum, Norman Davis Collection (Cs6.17); acquired 1963.

155. Horse

Italic, 8th cent. B. C.; H: 0.08, L: 0.111; red-brown surface, some green on mane; modern hole in belly now filled with copper. Ex-coll. H. Harris.

Although related to the horses of bits Nos. 153 and 154, its stylization is perhaps even greater, and having four legs, it is conceived as a free-standing sculpture. The owner considers it a forerunner of the bits, probably Villanovan, and possibly once on a votive chariot. (SD)

Unpublished.
Lent by the Collection of George Ortiz.

156. Ladle or Cup

Villanovan, 8th–7th cent. B. C.; H: 0.15 (with handle), diam. at mouth: 0.145; bowl hammered, handle cast, attached with two rivets; repair at one side of bottom. Allegedly found at Vulci in same tomb as No. 157.

Bowl: on bottom raised dots in concentric circles divided by double rows of dots; cross in center; zigzag dots on rim. Handle: dots and zigzags forming inverted T pattern; "double bird" in inner circle; horse heads topping outer circle. The bowl follows a Near Eastern type; the taste for bold "baroque" handles, already manifest in Bronze Age Italy, is a triumph of Iron Age zoomorphic style, with a teasing suggestion of animal bodies in its two circles. The vase type is represented in 8th century B. C. Villanovan Tuscany, but continues into the 7th century B. C. (GMAH)

Unpublished. Cf. Hencken, 408, fig. 403, and bibl. For bowl type, R. W. Hamilton, *Iraq*, 27 (1966), 3, figs. 2–3 (Assyrian, 9th–7th cent. B. C.); for handle, D. Randall-MacIver, *Villanovans and Early Etruscans* (Oxford, 1924), 141, pl. 26:8.

Lent by the Museum of Art and Archaeology, University of Missouri (65.15).

157. Situla

Villanovan, 8th–7th cent. B. C.; H: 0.195, max. diam.: 0.155, diam. of mouth: 0.16, diam. of bottom: 0.102; body hammered and riveted in three pieces, handles cast; one side restored, piece of rim broken, one handle lost. Allegedly found in the same grave at Vulci as No. 156.

The vessel has four vertical rows of ornamental rivets and one horizontal row of (functional?) rivets above the base. Attachments for the handles are riveted to the rim. One of its two twisted spiral handles is preserved, with a double spiral pendant hanging from each end; two more pairs hung from the rim on the cross axis (three are preserved). The steepwalled pail is a favorite shape of the Italian Iron Age. This is its early simple form; datable examples occur in early Etruscan burials from c. 700 B. C. on. A later series displays elaborate figurative decoration; the art of a whole area in northern Italy and the southeastern Alps has been termed "art of the situla." (GMAH)

Unpublished. Cf. Hencken, 262 ff., fig. 264b; G. von Merhart, *Festschrift des Römisch-Germanischen Zentralmuseums in Mainz*, 2 (Mainz, 1952), 1 ff.; D. Randall-MacIver, *Villanovans and Early Etruscans* (Oxford, 1924), 24 ff., pls. 7:3, 10; H. Müller-Karpe, *Beiträge zur Chronologie der Urnenfelderzeit nördlich und südlich der Alpen*, Römisch-Germanische Forschungen, 22 (Berlin, 1959), 80, 84, 98; W. Lucke–O.-H. Frey, *Die Situla von Providence*, Römisch-Germanische Forschungen, 26 (Berlin, 1962); M. V. Giuliani-Pomes, StEtr, 23 (1954), 149 ff. and 25 (1957), 39 ff. For the later development, J. Kastelic, *Situla Art* (New York, 1965).

Lent by the Museum of Art and Archaeology, University of Missouri (65.16).

158. A – C   Bronze Discs

Samnite or Picene, late 7th–6th cent. B. C.; hammered over wooden core, blue-green patina; traces of reinforcing rings around edge of back (iron, A and C; copper, B), bronze nails around edges backed by small iron plates. CAMSL *Bulletin*, 9:1 (1924), 8–9, ill.; O. Brendel, *AJA*, 47 (1943), 194 ff., figs. 1–3, with parallels; (A) *Detroit, 1947, 8, no. 34, pl. 22; *Walters, 1958; *Worcester, 1967, no. 6. For warrior with three discs on breastplate, *CAH*, vol. of plates IV (1934), 74, fig. a; for Greek models, F. Matz, *Geschichte der griechischen Kunst* (Frankfurt, 1950), pl. 92 (Argive), 182 (Cycladic) (c. 650 B. C.).

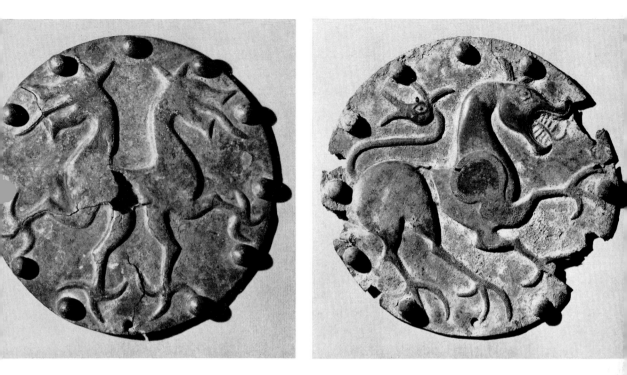

A   diam.: 0.305

Two running women nude except for belts and engraved ornaments (Brendel: muscles) around neck, elbows, knees; two heads growing out of plants; two roaring lions with spiral tails and horns (manes?, wings?). The rivets used to fasten the disc onto felt or leather are driven through the women's heads. Such discs were worn on leather straps and cuirasses as protective armor by Picene and Samnite warriors of eastern and central Italy; but because of its size, Brendel considers this disc part of a shield. The bizarre provincial Iron Age style is modelled on Archaic Greek figures; the women may ultimately derive from Greek gorgons. The representations are to ward off bad luck. The majestic size and quality of the human figures are exceptional.

B   diam.: 0.203; center repaired, cleaned 1943.

"Double horse", tongue sticking out, legs ending in three undulating claws. Part of same armor as A and C. The fantastic wavy stylization was a favorite device of central Italian provincial vase and metal engravers.

C   diam.: 0.228

Either front or back plate of same set as A and B. Toothy monster to r., three-clawed feet, tail ending in horned (?) animal head. Fine incision on ears, necks, claws, shoulder muscle. Perhaps a distant reflection of Greek representations of lion-headed, dragon-tailed chimaera (cf. Brendel, 194(b), fig. 2, with parallels). Very close is de Ridder, II, 176, no. 3450, and bibl., pl. 116. (GMAH)

Lent by the City Art Museum of Saint Louis (A – 51.22; B – 52.22; C – 53.22); acquired 1922.

159. Striding Kouros

550–500 B.C; H: 0.165; solid cast, casting tenons under feet preserved. Ex-coll. V. Simkhovitch.

The figure steps forward, his r. arm upraised to hold a spear; his extended l. probably carried a shield. His angular silhouette is stylized into a series of scallops. E. Richardson thinks it a provincial but good example of the Ionian style in Etruria, corresponding to the Greek "Anavysos-Ptoon 12" group, as defined by G. M. A. Richter (Kouroi, 113–125, esp. 135, no. 158, figs. 470–473 [Baker] and 142, no. 175, 515–517 [Berlin]). (SD)

*Schimmel, no. 40, ill.; *Worcester, 1967, no. 9.
Lent by The Schimmel Collection.

160. Kouros

Late 6th cent. B.C.; H: 0.46. Probably from around Chiusi.

Although the standing nude youth was a popular Archaic Greek type, the elongation, affected hand gestures, small head, and heavy thighs show Etruscan modification of the model. Decorative concerns outweigh attempts at naturalism. The musculature of the attenuated torso has been stylized into a linear pattern; the pubic hair is regularized into a three-lobed form. A rectangular opening in the back served to affix the piece to a support. Because of its exceptional size and quality, the statuette helps one visualize the renowned monumental Archaic statues of Etruria, now lost to us. (SD)

Neugebauer, *Führer*, 20, pl. 12; Giglioli, 126:3; Hanfmann, pl. 15; H. Jucker, *Kunst und Leben der Etrusker* (Cologne, 1956), 116, no. 282, fig. 17; Mansuelli, 92, fig. 32.

Lent by the Staatliche Museen Berlin, Antikenabteilung (Fr. 2159).

161. Standing Woman

Early 5th cent. B. C.; H: 0.167, W: 0.046, D: 0.044; solid cast, dark green patina, some light green areas and flaking; largely repatinated. Ex-coll. A. Loewi, North Italian private collection.

Standing on a rectangular plinth, she grips a panel of her chiton in her l. hand, a small egg (?) between thumb and forefinger of her r. Her dress has zigzag trim at the neck, a row of punched dots below. She also wears a stephane with punctate borders, and high-laced pointed shoes. The piece is very like a statuette found at Marzabotto; R. Teitz suggests that they may come from the same workshop. (SD)

E. Homann-Wedeking, *RM*, 58 (1943), 87–105, pls. 9–10 (on the basis of patina and stylistic details, he doubts the authenticity of this piece and one then on the Roman art market, and questions a third, then at a German dealer's); Worcester Art Museum *News Bulletin*, 14:2 (1948), 6–7, ill.; *Worcester, 1967, no. 29.

Lent by the Worcester Art Museum (1948.13).

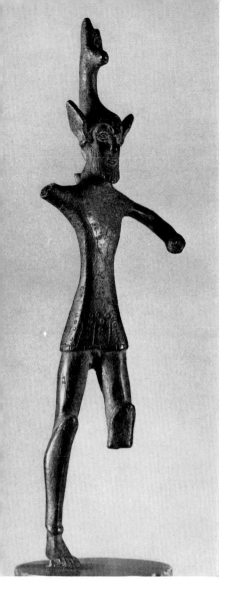

163. Striding Bearded Warrior

Early 5th cent. B. C.; H: 0.191; green-brown patina; r. arm and lower l. leg missing. Ex-coll. A. Kann, Paris (sale, American Art Galleries, N. Y., Jan. 6–8, 1927, no. 81).

This type of elongated warrior is common among Etruscan bronzes of the 5th century B.C. He would have held a spear poised for the throw in his r. hand and a shield on his l. arm. He wears an Attic helmet with upturned cheek pieces, a cuirass ending in rectangular flaps (pteryges), and greaves. The helmet appears to have had a high crest with zoomorphic support (cf. No. 38). Punctate ornaments adorn helmet and body armor; other details of costume and the beard are indicated by coarse striations. Whether a warrior god or mortal combatant is represented remains controversial. (SD)

E. Richardson, MAAR, 21 (1953), 100, fig. 13; Bulletin of the Allen Memorial Art Museum, 11:2 (1954), pl. and no. 5, 16:2 (1959), 109, no. 180, 16:3 (1959), ill. 164; *Walters, 1958; *Worcester, 1967, no. 38. On the development of Etruscan warrior images, E. Hill (Richardson), JWalt, 7–8 (1944–1945), 105–124. In MAAR, 27 (1962), 195 ff. she discusses the recurrence of a Geometric idiom in the 5th cent. B. C., originating perhaps at Spina and developing into a "Mannerist Geometric" school in Umbria.

Lent by the Allen Memorial Art Museum, Oberlin College, Oberlin, Ohio (43.116).

162. Reclining Banqueter

Late 6th cent. B. C.; H: 0.06, L: 0.115; gray-green patina, scattered incrustation.

This reclining banqueter probably comes from the rim of a large vessel, like his Greek counterparts, Nos. 43–45. His garment has a decorated hem and allover pattern of punched circles joined by engraved lines. This distinctive ornament, the garment border, elongated hands and feet, and hair style are reiterated in a banqueter in the Metropolitan Museum, probably from the same vessel. (SD)

Mentioned Art Quarterly, 16:2 (1953), 145; *Santa Barbara, 1967, 40, no. 44, color ill.; *Worcester, 1967, no. 31, and bibl. For MMA piece, G. M. A. Richter, BMMA, 25 (1930), 134–135, fig. 1, refering to a "similar figure . . . in a private collection" (this piece?). Cf. E. Homann-Wedeking, RM, 58 (1943), 87, n. 1.

Lent by the California Palace of the Legion of Honor (1952.26); gift of Arthur Sachs.

164. Bearded Figure (Zeus?)

500–480 B. C.; H: 0.19; dark green patina with red areas; lower r. arm and both legs below knees missing. Allegedly found at Piombino (Populonia).

The perforated hand held an attribute — perhaps a thunderbolt or staff. His himation with zigzag border is draped over l. shoulder and arm. The muscular upper torso, in its developed but stylized anatomy, parallels contemporary Greek works such as the Miletus torso (Louvre). J. Charbonneaux considers it Greek, comparing a Zeus Lykaios and Zeus from Olympia in Athens (Lamb, pls. 26c, 28c). However, the treatment of hair, mustache, beard with an extra tongue-shaped "flap" beneath the lower lip, small full mouth, prominent eyebrows, and protruding almond-shaped eyes recur in a Dionysos in Modena and reclining banqueter in the British Museum, considered Chiusine by Homann-Wedeking after Neugebauer. Not unlike are two draped youths, the Hirshhorn kouros (*Worcester, 1967, no. 47) and Walters, 70, no. 509, pl. 16. (SD)

Stothart, 11, pl. 2; J. Paul Getty, *The Joys of Collecting* (New York, 1965), 49, color ill., and bibl. (text by J. Charbonneaux); *Santa Barbara, 1967, 39, no. 42; *Worcester, 1967, no. 44. Cf. E. Homann-Wedeking, *RM*, 58 (1943), 87–91, pl. 7; K. A. Neugebauer, *RM*, 51 (1936), 194 ff.

Lent by the J. Paul Getty Museum, Malibu, Calif. (A55.S–6).

165. Seated Nymph

Etrusco-Campanian, c. 480–470 B. C., H: 0.065; solid cast, dark brown surface.

The nymph, clad in chiton and himation and with a rosette diadem in her hair, is seated, the upper part of her body turned in three-quarter view. She raises her l. hand as if in greeting (or perhaps alarm). As first noted by H. Cahn, the figure was originally supported by a satyr, who carried her on his shoulder; a closely related but mirror reverse group is in the Metropolitan Museum (Richter, *Br.*, 42–43, no. 61). (HH)

Münzen und Medaillen Auktion 18 (Nov. 29, 1958), no. 23, pl. 8; H. Hoffmann, *AA* (1960), 107, no. 31, figs. 49–50; —, *HambJb*, 6 (1961), 237 f.; Hoffmann, 38, fig. 42A.

Lent by the Museum für Kunst und Gewerbe, Hamburg (1958.38).

166. Striding Youth

500–470 B. C.; H: 0.125, W: 0.05; solid cast, brown patina; r. arm apparently bent inward, nose flattened; left hand missing. Ex-coll. G. Ortiz.

He strides forward on l. leg; his himation is draped over the l. shoulder, leaving the r. shoulder bare, and thrown over his back. Two diagonal folds encircle his r. side, while a series of deeper folds rises from r. knee across the torso and over the l. shoulder. Beneath this, his cloak (*tebenna*) is tightly draped with deeply cut ripples on the l. side. His felt cap has a lancet pattern imitating hair; the hair emerges in short careful strokes at the base of the neck. He clutches a bird with head broken off (or a flower) with his r. hand. The piece shows knowledge of early Classical Greek art translated into a very original style. (GMAH)

Unpublished.

Lent by the Eric de Kolb Collection.

167. Kouros

C. 470–460 B. C.; H: 0.177; solid cast, green
(malachite), red (cuprite), black (sulfate?)
surface, pitted and worn; arms missing, were
pegged in and soldered; cleaned 1966. Ex-
coll. G. Stroganoff.

The head on massive neck is bent forward
and to his l. The l. shoulder is drawn
back, l. leg with oversized buttock is set
forward. A tunic appears at neck. The
round-cut cloak (early toga) has in front
two vertical plaits with swallow-tail folds,
one of which falls on his l. thigh and is
flung back over the shoulder. The hair
and the cross pattern on the garment hems
are rendered with great precision. On the
exposed sides ribs are shown in straight
lines, and two muscles of the neck are
rendered. A ribbon divides the hair, which
is undercut in front; a rectangular lock
hung down in front of each ear. Sex is
summarily indicated under the cloak.
This important piece was described as
Greek, 480 B. C., by L. Pollak; Italo-
Etruscan under Sicyonian influence by
E. Langlotz; and Vulcian by P. J. Riis.
Big in form, exact in detail, it belongs to
a group of larger Etruscan bronzes which
come very close to their early Classical
Greek models. (GMAH)

L. Pollak-A. Muñoz, *Pièces de choix de la
collection du Comte Grégoire Stroganoff à
Rome*, I (Rome, 1912), 19, pl. 20; P. Arndt-
W. Amelung, *Photographische Einzelaufnah-
men antiker Skulpturen*, 12 (Munich 1931),
col. 63, nos. 3509–3510; Langlotz, 179, n. 15;
Riis, 90, pl. 18:3. For hair cf. H. Niemeyer,
Antike Plastik, III, pls. 17, 20, 35.

Lent by The Minneapolis Institute of Arts
(47.39).

168. Turan

450–430 B. C.; H: 0.203; solid cast, spotty green and red patina, owing to sporadic re-patination and overcleaning; cleaned, modern filling removed 1967. Allegedly found at Piombino (Populonia).

Turan, Etruscan equivalent of Aphrodite, goddess of love, holds a pomegranate, symbol of fertility, in her l. hand. Her divinity is established by the elaborate garland of metal leaves *(ampyx)* in her hair. She wears the typically Etruscan heavy necklace and upturned shoes. Details of hair and elaborately-draped costume are painstakingly rendered. The monumentality of conception bespeaks an artist in close contact with Greek traditions. For others of the type see Giglioli, 223:2–3, and No. 170. (SD)

G. M. A. Hanfmann, *Archaeology*, 9:4 (Winter 1956), 230–232, ill. 231 and cover; Fogg Art Museum *Annual Report* (1955–1956), 44, ill. 45, 60; Hanfmann, 7, pl. 28; *Walters, 1958; *Worcester, 1967, no. 59. The Greek model, a forerunner of "Kore Albani" (G. Lippold, *Die griechische Plastik* [1950], 157, pl. 56:1), is reflected in Greek bronzes: Charbonneaux, 116, pl. 23:2 (Attic, 440 B. C.); Neugebauer, 71, 130, fig. 38 (Thessaly, 450? B. C.).

Lent by the Fogg Art Museum, Harvard University (1956.43).

169. Woman Carrying Skyphos and Grapes

C. 480–470 B. C.; H: 0.107; solid cast, light olive green patina.

Her undergarment is a pleated chiton with elbow-length sleeves, whose tie strings are visible at the sides; over it she wears a woolen skirt with shorter sleeves. In her l. hand she holds a round-bottomed skyphos, and in her r. a bunch of grapes rendered with circular punch. Her carefully worked hair is dressed in the contemporary Greek mode, rolled under in back and held by an annular fillet. (HH)

Unpublished.
Lent by a Swiss private collection.

170. Goddess or Votary

C. 450–430 B. C.; H: 0.122; solid cast, even medium green patina, iron traces on back (below r. buttock); hands and feet missing.

Similar to No. 168 but of slenderer build, the figure has a more strongly bent r. leg. Her undergarment is incised in irregular vertical lines; the r. breast is visible beneath it. Draped diagonally across the chest, the cloak falls in plastic folds in front and back. Her necklace is beaded in front, plain in back. Somewhat schematic lines and cross-hatching adorn the garment borders. The piece seems a step farther from the Greek model than No. 168, and slightly later. Perhaps Chiusine. (GMAH)

Unpublished. Cf. *Pomerance, 190, no. 125.
Lent by the Eric de Kolb Collection.

171. Goddess or Votary

Late 5th–4th cent. B. C.; H: 0.389; body solid cast or filled, head and arms hollow, surface polished, bright green, some blue crystalline patina; missing head, two fingers of l. hand; crack at r. wrist, dent in r. back. Ex-coll. Bardini (sale, Christie's, June 5, 1899, 35, no. 191, pl. 3).

Richly dressed in chiton, himation, laced pointed shoes, necklace (torque) with bulla, and two bracelets, the lady represents a worshipper or goddess. Intricate tooling delineates details: a three-dot cluster recurs over the himation, zigzags and diagonal hatchings along its edges, rectangular grid on band over the r. shoulder, dots along the shoulder seam of the chiton and a corded pattern at the neck. Unusual are the prominent breasts. D. K. Hill suggests Walters, 91, no. 613, pl. 14, as a parallel. (SD)

Reinach, III, 197:2; Hill, 107, no. 240, pl. 46; G. Fogolari, *StEtr*, 23 (1954), 389, n. 30; *Worcester, 1967, no. 69.

Lent by the Walters Art Gallery, Baltimore (54.99).

172. Warrior Doffing Helmet

450–400 B.C.; H. of figure: 0.138, H. with base: 0.153, surface blackened by fire.

Doffing his helmet and holding a round shield, the warrior stands on a profiled double ring base decorated with a tongue pattern in relief. The object may be a candelabrum finial. He wears a cuirass decorated on the chest with two antithetical scrolls in relief. The crest of his Corinthian helmet is finely striated and parted in several divisions. The shield, now lacking its emblem, has a fine chevron pattern on the inside. The artist knew contemporary Greek sculpture well and may have been a Greek working in Etruria (cf. G. M. A. Richter, *ASAtene*, 24–26 [1946–1948], 79 ff.) or perhaps a South Italian craftsman. (HH)

Unpublished. The armor resembles that of a warrior from a candelabrum group from Locri, Jantzen, *Bronzewerkstätten*, 5, fig. 148, pl. 36.

Lent by a Swiss private collection.

173. Warrior

C. 450–420 B.C.; H: 0.135, W: 0.062; solid cast, green-brown patina, traces of cuprous oxide.

The warrior stands at ease wearing an Attic helmet with long crest and upturned cheek pieces, short chiton, and cuirass with a scale design and terminating in two rows of cross-hatched *pteryges*. The figure corresponds so closely to a candelabrum figure found at Marzabotto (Giglioli, 252:1,3) that it may have been cast from the same mold. Probably Vulcian. (SD)

Fogg Art Museum *Acquisitions* (1959–1962), 31, 142; *Worcester, 1967, no. 64; forthcoming publication in *Art Quarterly* by S. Doeringer, in *StEtr.* by S. Doeringer and G. M. A. Hanfmann. Cf. E. Hill (Richardson), *JWalt*, 7–8 (1944–1945), 105 ff.; —, *MAAR*, 21 (1953), 116 ff.; F. Messerschmidt, *RM*, 42–43 (1927–1928), 147 ff.

Lent by the Fogg Art Museum, Harvard University (1961.143).

174. Youth Leaning on a Stick

C. 450 B.C.; H: 0.083; smooth, dark green patina. Ex-coll. V. Simkhovitch.

The youth stands cross-legged wearing a chlamys pulled tight around his body, his shoulders left bare. Its folds are shallow, but plastically rendered for decorative effect. The pose is far more complicated than a similar piece in Boston (96.709, ill. E. Hill, *Magazine of Art*, 33 [1940], fig. 15), and produces several satisfying views in spite of anatomical inconsistencies; the disproportionate size of r. shoulder in relation to hip gives the figure a twisting, abstracted quality. The side view gives an impression of a sagging frame, but this is offset by the lively face with large shallow eyes and a slightly crooked smile. The owner suggests, probably rightly, that it belongs to the school of Vulci, whereas the piece in Boston is attributed to a provincial Greek school. The combination of complex stance with a late Archaic-transitional face and hair style suggests a date in the mid 5th century B.C. or just before. The piece is mounted on a small plinth and probably served as a finial for a candelabrum (cf. No. 219). It has been variously identified as Herakles, Paris, or a shepherd boy. (AR)

Unpublished.
Lent by the Collection of George Ortiz.

175. Athena Promachos

5th cent. B. C.; H: 0.165, W: 0.065; solid cast, olive and dark green patina. Ex-coll. Conte Mancini di Lucignano.

This type of striding Athena is closely related to Etruscan warriors (cf. No. 163) and to Greek models (cf. No. 36). She wears the Etruscan chiton, without belt or overfold, an aegis, and an Attic helmet. A spear is missing from her pierced r. hand and a shield from her l. H. G. Niemeyer enumerates twelve related Athenas, of which nos. 4 and 10 (Babelon-Blanchet, no. 150 and Reinach, II, 287:4) seem nearest. (SD)

Unpublished. On the type cf. K. A. Neugebauer, *AA* (1922), cols. 95–98; D. K. Hill, *JWalt*, 7–8 (1944–1945), 109 ff.; H. G. Niemeyer, *Promachos* (Waldsassen, 1960), esp. 89–90; J. Balty, *RBPhil*, 39 (1961), 42 ff.

Lent by the Eric de Kolb Collection.

176. Discobolus

Etruscan or Greek, c. 450–430 B. C.; H: 0.109, W: 0.062; bronze half ring filled with ancient solder beneath feet.

The athlete stands in an attitude of prayer, perhaps for success in the contest. His hair is treated in neatly punched circles. The metal between his feet indicates that he may originally have been affixed to a candelabrum (cf. No. 219) or cista lid (cf. No. 209). The head is slightly large for the body, but the grace and anatomical understanding are perhaps worthy of a Greek hand. (SD)

Selection 1966 (Berkeley, 1966), 28–29, fig. 26; *Santa Barbara, 1967*, 41–42, no. 49. Somewhat later but similar is Dutuit, no. 87, pl. 82.

Lent by the R. H. Lowie Museum of Anthropology, University of California, Berkeley (8–100); acquired 1901.

177. Athlete

C. 430 B.C.; H: 0.14; joined to flat rectangular base, round hole for lost object in each hand.

L. leg and arms bent, he leans forward as if for a start. The hands gripped jumping weights *(halteres)* for broad jump. Major muscles are summarily but clearly indicated; the hair forms a short wave at its nape and a peculiar triangle over the forehead. Posture and proportions depend on mid 5th century B.C. models, but such stocky athletes were made (in North Etruria?) into the 4th century B.C. (GMAH)

WAG *Bulletin*, 10:6 (1958), 2. For Greek and Etruscan models, Lamb, pl. 51c; Richter, *Br*, no. 81; P. Arias, *StEtr*, 22 (1952), 69–77 (Ajax from Populonia, athlete from Este). For related pieces, Giglioli, 220:6 –8; Käppeli, no. B19; Mansuelli, 136, pl. 40 (from Monte Capro).

Lent by the R. H. Lowie Museum of Anthropology, University of California, Berkeley (8–3389); acquired 1904.

178. Discobolus

450–375 B.C.; H. with ring raised: 0.156; cast in one piece with connecting loop.

Hooks were probably added around the lower moulding of the base, and the object, suspended from its ring, held ladles or similar utensils, perhaps for symposia. The athlete's stance and stocky proportions suggest Polykleitan influence. He feels the weight of the discus, preparatory to the throw. The features appear Vulcian. (SD)

*Metropolitan, 1959–1960, 40, no. 154, pl. 54; *Pomerance, 106, no. 120, ill.; *Worcester, 1967, no. 58. For similar utensil supports cf. Neugebauer, *Führer*, 94, pl. 31; Von Vacano, 448, pl. 85a. Related but later discus-throwers are Käppeli, no. B19 and S. Haynes, *Apollo* (Feb. 1964), 140, fig. 10.

Lent by The Pomerance Collection; acquired 1962.

179. Horseman

C. 430 B. C.; H: 0.267; solid cast.
Allegedly found at Comacchio (Spina).

Probably modelled upon a Greek
example of the Parthenon era, this
rider illustrates the stiffening of the
original when translated by an
Etruscan. Yet, the body is modelled
with considerable anatomical understanding. He wears the civilian *toga
sine tunica*, a shorter and less
voluminous version of the Roman
toga (cf. No. 243), with curved edge.
A similar head in marble adorns a
sarcophagus from Cerveteri (Giglioli,
241:1); for an ancestor of the facial
type, see No. 164. (SD)

*Detroit, 1947, no. 4, ill. covers;
F. Robinson—E. P. Richardson, *Bulletin
of the Detroit Institute of Arts*, 31
(1951–1952), 67, ill.; E. H. Richardson,
MAAR, 21 (1953), 115–116, 123, fig. 33
(on development of toga); Hanfmann,
14, pl. 23; *"Ancient Italian and
Etruscan Art," Detroit Institute of
Arts, Jan. 15–Feb. 23, 1958; *Walters,
1958.

Lent by The Detroit Institute of Arts
(46.260).

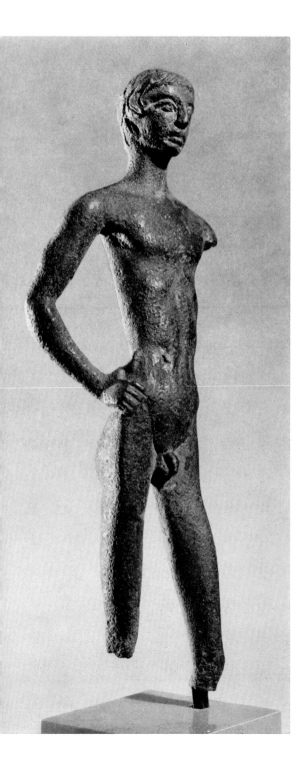

180. Standing Youth

Italic-Etruscan, late 5th–4th cent. B. C.; H: 0.165; lower legs and l. arm missing.

Hand on hip, l. leg bent, he looks challengingly at the world. Locks of hair sweep to the corners of the eyes. As E. H. Richardson has pointed out, the "elongated Geometric" starts about 500 B. C. and flourishes in Umbria, but in this unusual piece the assertive stance, slender canon and wild locks may indicate an additional debt to Scopasian and Lysippan trends in Greek sculpture, and a date of c. 350–300 B. C. (GMAH)

*Odyssey of an Art Collector, Isaac Delgado Museum, New Orleans (Nov. 11, 1966–Jan. 8, 1967), no. 39, ill. Cf. E. H. Richardson, MAAR, 27 (1962), 197, pl. 27 f.; for stance, Lamb, 172, pl. 63c ("Lysippan" Poseidon from Dodona); for breathing mouth and wild locks, R. Lullies, Greek Sculpture (New York, 1960), pls. 214 f. (column drum from Temple of Artemis at Ephesus).

Lent by Mr. and Mrs. Frederick Stafford.

181. Perseus

400–350 B. C.; H: 0.137; feet missing.

Perseus, naked but for his winged cap, is shown holding up the head of the Gorgon, Medusa, which he has just severed with the sickle-shaped knife (*harpe*) he holds in his lowered right hand. The head of Medusa is represented in the manner of an Archaic gorgoneion, with tongue extended. The feet of Perseus, figured in earlier publications, were found to be modern additions when the bronze was cleaned in 1961. One of the best known of Etruscan bronzes, the figure has often been compared to the monumental version of the subject by Benvenuto Cellini. (HH)

Hoffmann 14–15, 38, fig. 43, with earlier bibl. A similar Perseus in Florence is reputed to have been cleaned by Cellini and to have inspired his work (W. Bramfels, *Perseus und Medusa des Benvenuto Cellini*, Kunstbrief 52).

Lent by the Museum für Kunst und Gewerbe, Hamburg (1929.22).

182. Satyr

4th–3rd cent. B. C.; H: 0.109; yellow-brown patina, broken edges dark gray; lower r. leg, toes of l. foot, fingers, tips of ears broken.

The satyr raises his l. foot high, perhaps in a dance step. The brutish face, with eyebrows scrolled into a deep frown and protruding animal ears, suggests the lateral handle figures on the Ficoroni cista lid (Giglioli, 286:1); L. Pomerance also compares the handle group from the "Napoleon" cista (*Encyclopédie photographique de l'art*, III [Paris, 1938], 103). (SD)

*Pomerance, 110, no. 127, ill.
Lent by The Pomerance Collection.

183. Herakles

4th cent B. C.; H: 0.191; light gray-green patina; l. foot missing.

The striding Herakles, brandishing a club in his r. hand, his lionskin draped over his l. arm, is a common Etruscan type; this example is of unusually high quality. He wears the lion's head as a helmet, its forepaws knotted about his neck. In his l. hand he holds a bow. Bayet sees the type as an Italiote product which evolved during the 5th century B. C. and was primarily votive. (SD)

Handbook of the Collections in the William Rockhill Nelson Gallery of Art and the Mary Atkins Museum of Fine Arts (Kansas City, 1959), ill. 30. Cf. J. Bayet, *Herclé* (Paris, 1926), ch. 2.

Lent by the Nelson Gallery-Atkins Museum (Nelson Fund) (49–76).

184. Lasa or Nereid (?)

Late 4th cent. B. C.; H: 0.204, W: 0.080; figure solid cast, object on head hollow cast, green patina, some red-brown areas on r. thigh and back. Ex-coll. F. M. Watkins.

Lightly draped, wearing earrings, arm bracelets, and soft slippers, the nymph holds an alabastron in her l. hand, while a sea-monster entwines itself about her legs. On analogy with a similar statuette in Florence (Giglioli, 310:4; R. Herbig, *Götter und Dämonen der Etrusker* [Mainz,1965], pl. 43) she may have held an aryballos in her r. hand, though thumb and forefinger seem to meet; H. Hoffmann suggests a dip-stick. As in the Florence piece, a five tiered outward-tapering stand may have crowned her head, perhaps for a censer, and she may have stood on a spool-shaped base. Lasa might attend Turan (Aphrodite), the ointment jar alluding to arts of beauty, the monster to Aphrodite's aquatic birthplace (H. Jucker), or she might annoint the dead (Hoffmann); Langlotz thinks her a Nereid. Three semi-draped maidens are related in modelling, muscular proportions, and treatment of hair and eyes: Dutuit, I, 53, no. 85, pl. 80; Giglioli, 367:2; (less close) Walters, 103, no. 638, ill. in S. Haynes, *Etruscan Bronze Utensils* (London, 1965), pl. 13 (cista handle). (SD)

*Worcester, 1967, no. 81. For the monster (a *ketos* or *pistrix*) which has canine-like head and beard, spiky long dorsal fin and pectoral swimming fins, K. Shepard, *The Fish-tailed Monster in Greek and Etruscan Art* (New York, 1940).

Lent by the Fogg Art Museum, Harvard University (1966.109).

185. Lady with a Dove

4th–3rd cent. B. C.; H: 0.220; hollow cast, lustrous dark green patina; feet modern.

She wears a chiton, buttoned at shoulder and top of sleeves, and a himation with border of small punched circles. In her l. hand she holds a dove, or, more probably, a figurine of a dove with incised feathers; the object from her r. hand is missing. Although her stance, with hips thrown to the r., recalls a statuette in the Museo Gregoriano (Giglioli, 260:2), the drapery is more sensitively rendered, and the head suggests the Ficoroni cista handle (Giglioli, 286:1) and the fleeing girl in Florence (Giglioli, 376:2). (HH)

Unpublished.
Lent by a Swiss private collection.

186. Aphrodite (?)

4th cent. B. C.; H: 0.505, H. of head: 0.044; olive green patina. From the sanctuary of Diana, Nemi. Ex-coll. Tyszkiewicz.

The flat figure is sheathed in a chiton, indicated only by the slight flare at her ankles. Below the herm-like shoulders her arms are designated by a groove along each side of her body; the hands taper but the fingers are not modelled. The smooth elongation is broken only by pointed breasts and sharp knees (?); on the large feet are laced upturned boots. Modelling of head and hair owe something to Classical Greek forms, with which the heavily outlined almond-shaped eyes and down-turned mouth contrast sharply. The head is crowned by a diadem decorated with cross-hatching. (JAS)

Froehner, *Vente Tyszkiewicz*, 53, no. 147; A. Heron de Villefosse, *BAntFr*, 9 (1898), 421, no. 56; de Ridder, I, 51, no. 321; *Art et civilisation des étrusques*, Louvre (Oct.–Dec. 1955), 79, no. 345, fig. 47. Cf. de Ridder, I, 51, No. 322, pl. 28; for later group of more cursory workmanship, Giglioli, 222:7,9; for Sanctuary of Diana, Ucelli, 331 ff., with bibl.

Lent by the Musée du Louvre (Br. 321). Shown only in Cambridge.

Drawing by Marjorie B. Cohn

187. Youth

3rd–2nd cent. B. C.; H: 0.316; hollow cast, lustrous blue-green patina; casting tenons under feet left in place, ancient patches on drapery of l. shoulder, l. calf, back of r. leg, back (fallen out).

Two inscriptions are incised on the drapery, below the l. wrist, r. to l., *lel* (J. Heurgon: *lar* (?); first name, perhaps Avle?) *matunas* (family name, attested at Caere, cf. M. Palottino, *Testimonia linguae etruscae* [Florence, 1953], 51) *turce* (gift), and on the back, r. to l., *era*, l. to r., *lur:mutlac* (*mutlacl*, genitive of possession, or *mutlace*, verb). The general meaning (J. Heurgon): *hoc signum illi deo dedit Laris Matunas.*

The "leonine" coiffure is associated with Alexander the Great, and there is a general resemblance to Alexander portraits, although the features, especially the lips, are perhaps too full. The hands are extended in a "blessing" gesture. A piece in Munich (Inv. 3000) may be by the same sculptor. Also similar is Walters, 113, no. 683. Based on the same type is Froehner, *Tyszkiewicz*, pl. 32. (HH)

Unpublished. I am grateful to J. Heurgon, H. Bloesch, H. Jucker, L. Mildenberg, and G. M. A. Hanfmann for epigraphical information.   Lent by a Swiss private collection.

188. Seated Lion

550–500 B.C.; H: 0.085, L: 0.102; shiny dark green patina with brown spots; missing lower hind legs, tail. Ex-coll. G. Ortiz.

The open mouth with lips drawn back on upper and lower jaws reveals teeth and short fangs on either side of the tongue. The lion has a wide forehead with tufted ears laid back. The body narrows to ovoid flanks which have spur-like projecting joints. A classic example of the seated Etruscan lion, it could have adorned a large vessel, piece of furniture, or wheeled brazier. Although from an Etruscan workshop (Vulci?), it is probably based on Ionian prototypes (cf. No. 60). (DGM)

Unpublished. Cf. L. Brown, 90 ff.; Münzen und Medaillen Auktion 22 (May 13, 1961), 37–38, no. 69, pl. 20.

Lent by the Eric de Kolb Collection.

189. Decorative Shield with Lion's Head (Lacunarium)

C. 500 B. C.; diam.: 0.302, H. of head: 0.10; shield hammered, repoussé head made separately, green patina, corrosion on (viewer's) lower r.; eyes have dark glass pupils surrounded by vitreous white paste.

The central lion's head is surrounded by a row of tongues. Such shields, made by a workshop in Tarquinia, are always found in graves. Too small and fragile for military use, they perhaps served as decoration for funerary couches. More than thirty examples are listed by L. Brown, who dates them 530–490 B.C. H. Jucker argues for a late 4th century B.C. date. (GMAH)

*Man in the Ancient World, Queens College, N. Y. (Feb. 10–March 7, 1958), no. 144; *Worcester, 1967, no. 25. Cf. L. Brown, 101, pl. 41d, with bibl.; H. Jucker, Kunst und Leben der Etrusker (Cologne, 1956), 115.

Lent by Mr. and Mrs. Joseph Ternbach.

190. Decorative Shield with Ram's Head

C. 500 B. C.; diam.: 0.28; hammered, ram's head in repoussé made separately, eyes inlaid with vitreous white paste; some restoration on shield.

From the same series as No. 189.

*Pomerance, 105, no. 119, ill., with comparanda.   Lent by The Pomerance Collection; acquired 1954.

191. Incense Stand

Late 6th cent. B.C.; H: 0.400, H. of youth:
0.102; mottled red-green patina; broken in two
and mended, slight restoration of r. shin. Allegedly from Vulci.

A nude youth stands atop a triangular base
with hourglass profile, which rests in turn
upon a tripod base ending in feline paws
standing on balls. From an annular moulding on his head rises a support interrupted
by three discs and a deep bowl, and terminating in a three-pronged calyx. A phiale
is fastened to its center by a dowel.
Numerous stands of this form are known,
varying in detail. Among the closest is one
in Rome (Giglioli, 213:4). GMAH feels the
figure type to be Chiusine. (HH)

Unpublished. Cf. de Ridder, II, no. 3147, pl.
111. On similar stands, R. Zandrino, StEtr, 22
(1952), 329 ff.; K. A. Neugebauer, Berliner
Museen, 45 (1924), 28–35; —, JDI, 58 (1943),
266 ff. (Vulcian); —, RM, 51 (1936), 181 ff.
(Chiusine school). Cf. also *Worcester, 1967,
no. 27.

Lent by a Swiss private collection.

192. Vessel Foot – Herakles Battling Hydra

Late 6th cent. B.C.; H: 0.09, W: 0.075; dark green patina.

A lion's paw supports an Ionic capital with abacus. Above this are a coiled hydra with seven heads and, symmetrically disposed, two figures in profile who beat the hydra with clubs. The beardless nude at (viewer's) l. is Herakles; the figure at r. clad in a short chiton has been called Iolaus, but Bayet and others, studying two nearly identical examples (Reinach II, 234:8 and 235:1; Babelon-Blanchet, 241–242, no. 581), see it as a woman, perhaps Athena aiding Herakles or simply an Etruscan misunderstanding of Ionian prototypes. Bayet suggests Vulcian origin. (SD)

Unpublished. *University Museum, 1964, no. 18. Cf. J. Bayet, *Herclé* (Paris, 1926), 24, n. 5. M. Guarducci *(StEtr,* 10 [1936], 19–21) notes a third example (Walters no. 563) and suggests that the hydra has been inserted into a composition of Herakles battling Hera. For bibliography on Vulcian school see No. 195.

Lent by Dr. and Mrs. Robert Waelder; acquired 1959.

193. Buckle – Herakles and Omphale

525–500 B.C.; H: 0.068, W: 0.054; combination solid-hollow cast, underside of figures concave, green-brown patina with red areas, some incrustation; broken off at r. Ex-coll. Lucien Bonaparte, Prince of Canino; Sturge.

Herakles, draped in a lion skin, its head over his shoulders and one paw hanging down between his legs, holds his club upright before him. On the (viewer's) l. stands a woman in elaborately folded drapery, Phrygian headdress, and upturned shoes, probably Omphale, queen of Lydia. She appears to grip the club as well. Upper and lower edges of the buckle are ornamented with bead-and-reel moulding. As G. M. A. Hanfmann suggests, the figure type appears Vulcian (cf. female figures on No. 195). (SD)

E. H. Richardson, *MAAR,* 21 (1953), 87, fig. 4. On the development of the Herakles type in Etruria, J. Bayet, *Herclé* (Paris, 1926), esp. 36 ff.

Lent by the Royal Ontario Museum, University of Toronto (918.3.113); acquired 1918.

194. Animal Group from Tripod

Vulcian, c. 500 B. C.; H: 0.102, L: 0.076; solid cast, green patina.

The group was made to adorn one of the curved members of a tripod such as No. 195. Parts of the arch, decorated with a single row of tongues, and of the palmette and lyre beneath it remain. The group of panther or lion biting a fallen deer on the flank recurs with only slight variations on several tripods of the Vulcian series (cf. tripods from Spina and Dürkheim). Although carefully conceived, this piece was apparently not finished after casting; this and the broken surfaces indicate that it may have been a faulty casting and never used. (SD)

Unpublished. For discussion of development of such groups see bibl. of No. 195, esp. P. J. Riis, *ActaA*, 10 (1939), 28 and K. A. Neugebauer, *JdI*, 58 (1943), 221 ff. Those of compact composition, such as this piece, are assigned to a single workshop.

Lent by the Virginia Museum of Fine Arts, Richmond, Va. (63–17).

195. Tripod

Vulcian, c. 530–510 B. C.; H: 0.613, W. at base: 0.38, diam. of bowl: 0.200; rough green-black surface, mottled green and red around bowl. Ex-coll. Feoli (?), Kerkerian (sale, Canossa, 1924, no. 47).

The arched supports are topped by paired horse protomes; a lyre and palmette motif lies under each arch. The straight supports end in a floral motif atop which is a running figure. Two are women, in long robes, pointed shoes, and saucer earrings, one wearing a tall pointed hat, the other having a lion skin cape with the lion mask over the back of her head. The male figure wears a ruffled loincloth and holds a weapon handle. The figures are probably mythological, but their identity is uncertain. The piece is an early example in a cohesive tripod series now attributed, on the basis of findspots and style, to Vulci, presumably under strong Ionian influence. Female figures in the British Museum and Fitzwilliam Museum, from tripods, are close. K. A. Neugebauer attributes horse protomes on a slightly later tripod (Walters no. 588) to the same hand.

Manufacture of tripods was short-lived (Riis: 540–470 B. C.; Fischetti: 550–500 B. C.). P. J. Riis suggests the demise resulted from conversion into braziers; as such they were neither sufficiently sturdy nor functional. (SD)

Considerable confusion exists in the literature between this tripod *(MonInst* 2, pl. 49B, with earlier bibl.) and another *(MonInst* 6–7, pl. 69:3, once in Museo Kircheriano) differing in having a nude male figure, "Io" in calf-skin hood, scalloped edges of feet, ring with reclining nymph, satyr, and bird near base. One was in the Feoli Coll. L. Savignoni, *MonAnt*, 7 (1897), cols. 277–376, with earlier bibl., esp. 292 (takes them as identi-

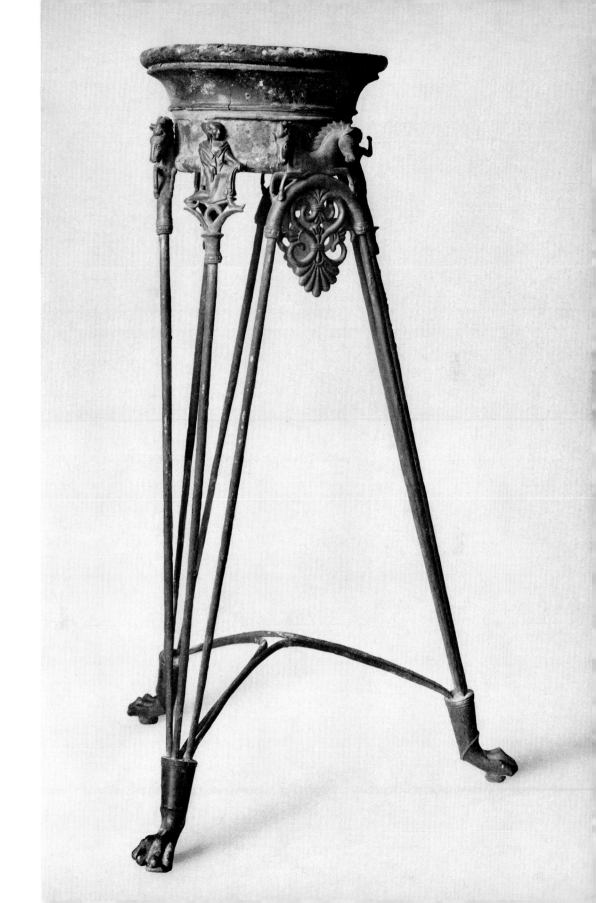

cal); K. A. Neugebauer, *AA* (1923–1924), cols. 302 ff., esp. 304–305(calls the other tripod the Feoli one); CAMSL *Bulletin*, 13:2 (1928), ill. 21; P. J. Riis, *ActaA*, 10 (1939), 1–30, esp. 22, no. 4 (says St. Louis tripod is ex-Feoli, gives bibl. for both as if were one object); G. Fischetti, *StEtr*, 17–18 (1943–1945), 9–27, esp. 10–11, 25, fig. 16 (calls it the St. Louis tripod but describes and illustrates [drawing] the other); K. A. Neugebauer, *JdI*, 58 (1943), 206–278, esp. 216, figs. 7–8 (St. Louis tripod photographed, called ex-Feoli); *Worcester, 1967, no. 19.

Lent by the City Art Museum of Saint Louis (37:26); acquired 1926.

196. Hippocamp from Tripod

550–500 B.C.; total H: 0.295, L. of hippocamp: 0.075; green patina.

The wingless sea horse decorated the arc of the reinforcing support between the legs of a rod tripod (see No. 195). Details of mane and muzzle are finely incised. The intent of the incision near the r. foreleg is not clear; perhaps it represents a pectoral fin. The undulating marine body and tail, incised with scales, are separated from the horse-protome forepart (see No. 69) by a double incised line. Two triple fins are on the back; the tail, again set off by a double line, divides in two with a double arch incision over the center opening and finely incised lines overall. The forepart bears a close resemblance to a protome on a brazier from Vulci (Walters no. 437) with which P. J. Riis *(ActaA, 10 [1939], 3 ff., fig. 2)* associates two hippocamps from Perugia (Giglioli, 86:8, 10); he believes them to be imports from Vulci and dates them c. 570–550 B.C. On stylistic grounds G. M. A. Hanfmann dates the Currier piece c. 550–500 B.C. (JAS)

Unpublished. Cf. Babelon-Blanchet, 341, no. 794.

Lent by the Estates of Audrey B. and Stephen R. Currier.

197. Stamnos Handle with Hippocamps

Early 5th cent. B.C.; H: 0.10, L: 0.162; handle and attachments cast in one piece, blue-green patina.

The handle attachments are addorsed hippocamps, their manes, fins, and tail fins hatched in parallel strokes. Each wears two incised collars, one decorated with punched circles, the other with three sets of two interlocking circles suspended from a single line. H. Hoffmann attributes the handle to Vulci. For an Etruscan hippocamp handle from Dürkheim, see P. Jacobsthal, *Early Celtic Art*, II (Oxford, 1944), pl. 253a. The hippocamp, common on Archaic Etruscan tomb paintings, is probably symbolic of the journey to the other world after death. (SD)

*Schimmel, no. 47, ill.; *Worcester, 1967, no. 52. On the hippocamp as handle ornament, P. Jacobsthal, *Ornamente griechischer Vasen* (Berlin, 1927), 116, n. 200, pl. 70 ff.; U. Jantzen, *AM*, 63–64 (1938–1939), 151, n. 1. For meaning and development of the hippocamp, K. Shepard, *The Fish-tailed Monster in Greek and Etruscan Art* (New York, 1940), *passim*.

Lent by The Schimmel Collection.

198. Amphora

Mid 5th cent. B. C.; H: 0.38 (including lid); hammered, with solid-cast attachments, lustrous olive-green patina; missing two small pieces from rim, one from lid.

The shape is close to Attic 5th century B. C. amphorae, although ceramic examples usually are much narrower in the lower part of the body, slope less at the shoulder, and have more obvious articulation. The elaboration of the handle fittings originally stemmed from the need to provide a firm basis for the rivets. Two rivets are evident at the top of each handle through the horses' necks. The handle has three vertical bands of bead-and-reel ornament separated by narrow incised bands, of which the two inner are cut obliquely. At the base of the handle are two crouching felines which spring obliquely from a palmette whose upper leaves merge with their hind paws and tails. The lightly spreading foot is decorated with tongues.

This amphora is close in shape and decoration to one found in a tumulus near Conliège (Jura) in France, although the latter has a high bell-shaped lid, a taller more elaborate foot, and somewhat different handle decoration. (J. Dechelette, *Manuel d'archéologie préhistorique celtique et gallo-romaine*, II³ [Paris, 1914], 1048, fig. 432). (AR)

P. Jacobsthal, *Die Bronzeschnabelkannen* (Berlin, 1929), 57, pl. 31c, d; E. von Mercklin, *Führer durch das Hamburgische Museum für Kunst und Gewerbe, II. Griechische und römische Altertümer* (Hamburg, 1930), no. 694, pl. 40; Hoffmann, 14, 38, figs. 44–45.

Lent by the Museum für Kunst und Gewerbe, Hamburg (1919.158).

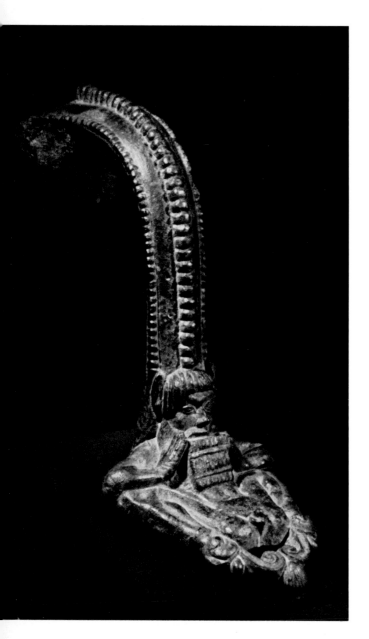

199. Amphora Handle with Satyr Playing Syrinx

South Italian or Etruscan, c. 500–450 B.C.; H: 0.13; green patina.

A syrinx-playing satyr, his elbows resting on knees splayed to the sides, sits at the base of the handle, where it would join the amphora's shoulder. His hoofed feet rest atop a double volute with cockle shell at the juncture. A large medial row of beading and two smaller lateral ones run the length of the handle. Almost identical are handles of amphorae in the Vatican (Lamb, pl. 59b) and Berlin (Neugebauer, *Führer*, pl. 27, one with pipes, the other holding a kantharos), and a handle in Boston (99. 464, *Worcester, 1967, no. 62). (SD)

Archaeology, 2:4 (Winter 1958), ill. 292; *Hesperia Art*, Bulletin 5, no. 59, ill.; *University Museum, 1964, no. 19. Cf. K. A. Neugebauer, *RM*, 38–39 (1923–1924), 341–440, esp. 365–367, 394 summarizes opinions regarding workshops.

Lent by Dr. and Mrs. Robert Waelder; acquired 1958.

200. A and B   Two Handles from a Column Krater

Etruscan or Campanian, probably early 5th cent. B.C.; H: 0.102, 0.104 respectively; light olive-green patina.

These handles are apparently from a column krater, although no parallels for plastic handles on that type of vessel are known (von Bothmer). The silens' inner arms hug their sides, balanced by long tails on their outer flanks; their gesture is the characteristic *aposkopein*. Their hoofed feet rest on inverted volute palmettes, which form the handle base and lower point of attachment. D. von Bothmer suggests that the handles are Campanian, possibly from Capua, where Greek tradition was dominant from the Archaic period. Although more organic than Etruscan work, the schematized anatomical delineation of Campanian bronzes contrasts noticeably with mainland work. Traces of solder on tops of the platforms lead von Bothmer to think they supported another decorative element. (JAS)

*Metropolitan, 1959–1960, no. 152; *Schimmel, no. 48; *Worcester, 1967, no. 37. On Campanian bronzes, P. J. Riis, *An Introduction to Etruscan Art* (Copenhagen, 1953), ch. 3, esp. 42–43.

Lent by The Schimmel Collection.

201. Stamnos Handle with Silenus Masks

Late 5th – 4th cent. B.C.; H. of attachments without handle: 0.12; green patina.

Lanceolate leaves bordered in an "ivy-wreath" motif form the attachments for the fluted handle. Silenus heads fill the lower corners, their beards fitted neatly into the points. Above each lies a symmetrical pair of volutes with half-palmette. Stamnoi with such handles are common and were used as cinerary urns, but the workmanship of this piece is above average. The other handle from the same vessel is in the MFA (64.280). (SD)

˙University Museum, 1964, no. 21; C. C. Vermeule, *CJ*, 61:7 (April 1966), 300. For list of such handles, J. D. Beazley, *Etruscan Vase Painting* (Oxford, 1947), 248–250. On the diffusion of Etruscan stamnoi to Celtic sites, P. Jacobsthal, *Early Celtic Art* (Oxford, 1944), 21–22, no. B6 ff., pl. 220.

Lent by Dr. and Mrs. Robert Waelder.

202. Girdle with Zoomorphic Clasps

Celtic, 400–350 B.C.; restored L: 0.812, W: 0.105, L. of clasps: 0.102; belt hammered, clasps cast solid; restored order of pieces determined by corrosion products (principally malachite, azurite, iron).

The bronze girdle was sewn to a leather backing through the small holes (ancient) along the edges (for examples with leather preserved see Richter, *Br.*, 422 f.). Three pairs of holes with raised edges held the clasps; burrs indicate that they were drilled front to back. At the other end two clasps were attached by iron rivets (now rusted away). P. Jacobsthal dates a similar girdle from Canosa 4th century B.C.; the decorative style probably indicates the first part of the century. He describes a clasp almost identical to these, formerly in the Diergardt Collection, as a stiff palmette with eyes such as those on peacock feathers. The shape of the clasps on the Goodman belt is generally orthopteran; striations on the back are like the folded front wings of grasshoppers or locusts, the long, slender prothorax belonging to the mantids, common insects in Europe. The heads are equine, ears folded back, small eyes on the sides, long slender muzzles. The tongues protrude to form hooks. A spiral, common in Celtic art, lies in front of each wing; a double line encloses a spiral collar. The Celtic artist often combined diverse animal-floral elements into a balanced decorative and functional device. (JAS)

Unpublished. Cf. P. Jacobsthal, *Early Celtic Art* (Oxford, 1944), 146 f., pls. 258d:1a, 260e. A belt with similar clasps is in the McDaniel Collection, Harvard University; a single clasp is in the Pomerance Collection. I am indebted to D. Howard for entomological information, to A. Beale for technical analysis.

Lent by Prof. and Mrs. Nelson Goodman.

203. Oval Toilet Box (Cista)

(see also pl. IV, p. 150)

Praenestine, c. 420–400 B.C.; lid L: 0.404, W: 0.206, handle L: 0.138, L. of figure: 0.10, H. of box: 0.158; box hammered, handle cast, light green patina, red-brown corrosion; several areas of body lost, small breaks at bottom. Lid hinged on both sides, originally closed by pins through three tubes, suspended by chain from hook.

Cistae were used by Etruscan ladies to hold mirrors, combs, hairpins, rouge pots, and similar articles of grooming. The chains served for carrying. Elaborate engraved examples such as this were made in Praeneste, and have been found associated with burials.

Lid: a girl acrobat with short straight hair and summary face stands on cast bud-shaped plates which form centers of the engraved seventeen-petal palmettes occupying the central oval. Outside runs a frieze of circumscribed seven-petal palmettes between guilloche borders.

Body: proceeding l. to r., Side A (undamaged): (1) Goddess with leaf crown and (2) youth with laurel crown drive four-horse chariot to r. She holds one rein in l., raises r. hand (in astonishment or greeting?); youth holds goad in r.; part of quiver appears behind him. (3) Behind chariot, woman in cloak and *sakkos* (head gear) holds branch or tree and looks to l. (4) Before the chariot, running youth in hunter's cloak and boots, olive wreath, holding two spears, looks back (to l.). (5) On end, running woman in long chiton, cloak, hair tied with double diadem, holding torch in r., also looks back (to l.). (6) Girl, clad in chiton, wearing diadem with vertical leaves, holds *thyrsos* (?) (branch ending in bud, with twig) in r.

Side B (damaged): (7) Foreshortened bearded silen races full speed to r., feet off the ground, equine tail streaming back. He wears laurel wreath; a panther skin hangs from his outstretched r. arm. A drinking

horn has fallen from his r. hand. Parts of this figure and the next are lost. (8) Youth and (9) goddess or heroine with short vertical leaf crown who drives four-horse chariot and embraces the youth with her r. arm. She holds one set of reins in her l., he another and a goad in his r. (10) Behind chariot, a woman in long dress and *sakkos,* walking to r. and looking back, raises her hand in astonishment or greeting. (11) Woman running to r., *sakkos* and leaf diadem on her head, gathers folds of her cloak with her r., holds tree in l., and looks back. (12) On end, woman in belted chiton and leaf diadem, running full speed, extends her arms toward (13) a majestic, bearded laurel-crowned man, seated on a rock and holding a long staff, who looks in her direction. (14) On Side A, another woman with extended hands (the bereaved mother?) runs behind the chariot. Her hair is tied in a bun by a double diadem; a cloak with rich hem is thrown over her shoulders.

The excellent linear design is close in style to Greek vase paintings of the early "rich" style (school of the Meidias Painter). The draftsman was a Greek acquainted with the monumental paintings of the period (Parrhasios, Zeuxis). In Greek art one would take the subject to be the rape of the daughters of Leucippus by the Dioscuri. The majestic seated man would be Leucippus, but the silen and women with torches and *thyrsoi* (branches) suggest a Bacchic environment. If the legend is Etruscan, the women in the chariots might be goddesses such as Artemis (with quiver) and Turan. The finely developed overlapping (as in the goddess, youth and the horses), foreshortening (view from back, silen) and landscape elements were among the achievements of Greek monumental painting c. 400 B.C.

The shape of the toilet box, however, is known only from Etruscan and Latin (Praenestine) examples. (GMAH)

*Worcester, 1967, no. 82.

Lent by Mr. and Mrs. Joseph Ternbach.

204. Praenestine Cista

340–300 B. C.; total H: 0.44, H. of body: 0.295, max. diam.: 0.252; body and cover scraped, dark red surface, handle green; chain and holders may not belong, cover slightly re-engraved. Ex-coll. Massarenti.

Cylindrical cistae such as this are the most common type, produced in Praeneste, largely in the 4th and 3rd centuries B.C., though some have been dated as late as 100 B.C. (L. B. Warren, *AJA*, 68 [1964], 35–42). Feet and handles follow several stock types. They were fashioned separately and attached without regard for consistency with the theme of the incised decoration, often even overlapping it. Here the handle is a satyr and maenad; the claw feet are topped by crouching lions, a standard motif (cf. L. Brown, 162). Incised on the cover are two winged figures (Lasae) with ribbons and ivy border. The body is divided into upper foliate zone, lower zone with palmette chain, and central frieze depicting the Rape of Helen, with quadriga, and an abbreviated Judgement of Paris (?). D. K. Hill relates the drawing style to an example in Copenhagen (Giglioli, 292:2). (SD)

Catalogue du Musée de Peinture, Sculpture et Archéologie au Palais Accoramboni, II (Rome, 1897), 27, no. 144; D. K. Hill, *AJA*, 57 (1953), 107 f.; —, *Latomus*, 58 (1962), 809–816, ill., and bibl.; *"Ancient Italian and Etruscan Art," Detroit Institute of Arts, Jan. 15-Feb. 23, 1958; *Treasures in America*, VMFA, (1961), 40, ill. On cistae in general, Richter, *Br.*, 290–291, with bibl.; *Santa Barbara, 1967, 76 bibl.

Lent by The Walters Art Gallery, Baltimore (54.132); purchased 1902.

205. Cista Handle with Wrestlers

4th–3rd cent. B.C.; H. of figures: 0.08, L. of handle: 0.138; dark green patina with some incrustation. Ex-coll. S. Pozzi, Spencer-Churchill.

The combatants are a nude boy and a girl dressed in short chiton with a sleeveless skirt pulled over it ("Peleus and Atalanta"). She grasps his head with her r. hand; both l. hands are locked behind her neck. His r. hand pulls her by the hair. Their inner feet have flat rectangular pegs which pierce the base plate and provide for attachment to the cista lid. The base plate is oval with a rounded protrusion at either end. Quite similar in composition is Walters Art Gallery 54.1387, also from a cista. (SD)

S. Pozzi Collection, sale G. Petit (25–27 June, 1919), 30, no. 417, ill.; Spencer-Churchill Collection, sale, Christie's (June 21–23, 1965), 127, no. 501, pl. 67.
Lent by the Estates of Audrey B. and Stephen R. Currier.

206. Praenestine Cista

Late 4th cent. B.C. or later; total H: 0.191, diam. of lid: 0.178, max. diam. with feet: 0.205; green-black patina; handle missing from lid, chain perhaps not original. Ex-coll: Warneck.

The crouching lions atop claw feet resemble those of No. 204. A single zone of engraved decoration presents enigmatic subject matter, apparently three independent scenes. (1) Nude youth holds glass to lips of Silenus (drinking contest between Herakles or Midas and Silenus?). To the r., two spectators, the elder in Phrygian cap, the younger in *pilos* and royal dress. (2) Old woman weeping stands at l. of table, altar, or box. Behind (over?) it, sleeping child behind rocks (in cloud?); seated woman in foreground (Auge and Telephos before being put into chest, old nurse weeping?). (3) Bearded man with sword in r. hand kicks and strikes at kneeling woman tied to (?) tree (Ajax and Cassandra?, Amazonomachy?). From the tree seems to extend a hand. On the lid, Herakles battles woman (?); ivy border. (SD)

Warneck Collection, sale, Hôtel Drouot (13–16 June, 1905), no. 57.
Lent by the City Art Museum of Saint Louis (16:25); purchased 1925.

207. Acrobat Handle from Cista

4th–3rd cent. B. C.; H: 0.05, L: 0.095; solid cast, green patina.

The nude male acrobat's lithe body, curled into a backbend, forms the handle for a cista lid. His large eyes and mouth are well cut. The pins beneath hands and feet were cast with the body for attachment to a wooden or bronze lid. Acrobats are often featured in vase paintings as well as on cistae (cf. Bieber, *Theater*, figs. 212, 535, 579b). (SD)

Unpublished. Cf. No. 203 and Giglioli, 283:2, 294:4, 295.   Lent by the Eric de Kolb Collection.

208. Praenestine Cista

3rd cent. B. C.; total H: 0.381, H. of body: 0.255, diam. of body: 0.200. Probably excavated at Praeneste, 1869. Ex-coll. F. Martinetti, G. Stroganoff, W. R. Hearst.

Handle: nude male wrestling with female in loincloth ("Peleus and Atalanta"). Feet: claw feet with kneeling winged genius whose mourning pose and inverted torch suggest connection with death. Lid: on rocky ground lion and lioness attack deer; hunter spears flank of lioness. Body, center zone, counterclockwise: (A) Dioscuri lead horses to r. (inscribed in Latin CASTOR and — erroneously — ORIO [N]), woman walking to r. following nude youth who looks back at her (Helen and Paris?), winged goddess (Lasa or Nemesis?); (B) dog, Silenus (SILA . . .) carrying wineskin and dead fawn, standing woman (Juno), seated nude Jupiter ([DIES] PATER), huntress (Diana?) with stag. I. Ryberg suggests the artist copied from three different sources. Side A shows several misunderstandings, including identity of Pollux; Side B represents Diana's asking Jupiter to transform Orion into a constellation, the Silenus suggesting sylvan setting, and Juno included as customary companion of Jupiter. The Paris, Helen, Lasa group is perhaps from a third prototype. The upper and lower zones show animals, but change in character (lions, panthers, griffins; heraldic sea monsters; fowl) corresponding to the three central scenes. (SD)

I. S. Ryberg, *AJA*, 47 (1943), 217–226, figs. 1–6, with earlier bibl. For similar handle, J. Sambon, no. 338, pl. 17. Lent by the Vassar College Classical Museum; purchased 1941.

209. Cista Handle with Two Nude Girls

3rd cent. B. C.; H: 0.089, W: 0.114.

Although a group of two figures with interlaced arms is a common motif for cista handles (Nos. 204, 208, 210; Giglioli, 293:2), the conjunction of two female nudes is unusual. Their base has pointed ends. (SD)

*Fogg, 1955, supplement to catalogue, no. A13.
Lent by Dr. and Mrs. Robert Waelder.

210. Praenestine Cista

3rd cent. B. C. (?); H: 0.295, diam. of cista: 0.159, cover group: 0.085 by 0.075; green patina; lid and bottom of cista relined, feet and handle group attached with modern bolts.

This fine small cista encloses a high frieze of enigmatic subject matter, perhaps Dionysiac, between an upper and lower ivy frieze. In one panel, nude Hermes with caduceus and winged cap turns away from a woman who undresses, laying her r. hand on the head of a kneeling servant removing her shoes. To her r. stand a nude maenad and two nude women who flank a pedestalled basin being filled from a lion-head spout. As in Nos. 204 and 206, the feet are lion's paws surmounted by elongated Ionic capitals bearing crouching lions. The lid group, a nude satyr and girl, perhaps represents wrestlers. (DGM)

Bulletin of the Museum of Art, RISD, 7:4 (1919), 39 ff., ill., 28:1 (1940), 17, 19, figs. 15; *Treasures in the Museum of Art, RISD* (Providence, 1956), ill.; *Worcester, 1967, no. 86.
Lent by the Museum of Art, Rhode Island School of Design (06.014).

211. Stamnos Cover with Satyr and Maenad

Late 4th–3rd cent. B. C.; total H: 0.108, H. of figures: 0.098 (satyr), 0.095 (maenad), diam.: 0.178. Allegedly excavated by A. Castellani near Perugia, late 19th century.

A dancing satyr and maenad, their arms outstretched to form the handle, grace this lid from a large stamnos. The satyr has pointed ears and an equine tail. His consort wears three bracelets, a necklace, and an animal skin which falls diagonally from r. shoulder to below the l. knee. A simple egg-and-dart moulding edges the rim of the lid. The group is not unlike Walters 638 (S. Haynes, *Etruscan Bronze Utensils* [London, 1965], pl. 13), from a Praenestine cista. (SD)

Unpublished. For garment of maenad cf. No. 184.

Lent by The Los Angeles County Museum of Art, The William Randolph Hearst Collection (50.37.20b); acquired 1950.

212. Horse

Etruscan or Campanian, 4th cent. B.C.; H: 0.085, L: 0.10; hollow cast, medium green patina, some cuprite; part of belly missing; bronze pegs for attachment cast with hind legs, modern holes and solder for modern fastening on underside of forehoofs. Ex-coll. Conte Mancini di Lucignano.

The workmanship is Etruscan or Campanian; the forerunners are cauldron horses like *Schimmel, no. 44. This stocky type with fiercely bared teeth is later. The figure is summarily treated but for the sharp, precise tooling of the teeth; the mouth resembles those of the Tarquinian terracotta horses (Hanfmann, pl. 27). (GMAH)

Unpublished.
Lent by the Eric de Kolb Collection.

213. Attachment with Heads of Man and Horse

Celto-Etruscan (?), 4th cent. B.C. (?); H: 0.111, W. including ring: 0.090; light green patina; traces of iron nails, piece at joining of heads and inlays of eyes missing.

A large ring passes through the back of the human head, which is atop a horse's (?) head. Two smaller dentillated rings are attached at the forehead above the short-stroked hair. A cable-patterned torque circumscribes the joining of the heads. A striking piece, it is hard to localize: the "zoomorphic juncture" is not standard Etruscan, nor is the angular style; links to Celtic art are tenuous; nearer in style (eyes, rope pattern) is a "Graeco-Thracian" head on a silver greave from Rumania, 4th century B.C. (GMAH)

Unpublished. For possible use, D. G. Mitten, Fogg Art Museum *Acquisitions* (1965), 140, fig. 2; on Celtic pieces, P. Jacobsthal, *Early Celtic Art* (Oxford, 1944), pls. 25:30, 46:57; on Graeco-Thracian head, E. Condurachi, *Le Rayonnement des civilisations grecque et romaine sur les cultures périphériques*, 8e congrès international d'archéologie classique, Paris, 1963 (Paris, 1965), 324, pl. 65:3.

Lent by Thomas T. Solley, Bloomington, Ind.

Drawing by
Marjorie B. Cohn

214. Mirror with Sun God

5th cent. B. C.; H. including tang: 0.197, diam.: 0.133; solid cast, surface pitted. Found at Orvieto.

The polished back formed the reflecting surface, and the tang was inserted into a handle of wood, bone or ivory. The figure is surrounded by waves ("running dog" pattern) around the rim; from volutes at the handle join grows an upright plant with thick median stem. "The design is hastily, even clumsily sketched but has rude poetry; the sun, a youth, rises from the sea, with a ball of fire, a fiery coal one would say, in each hand. Blake would have liked this . . ." (J. D. Beazley). Mansuelli assigns this mirror and several others to the "Master of the Jugglers." Beazley and Mansuelli judged the piece from a drawing; according to the lender some scholars have expressed doubt as to its authenticity. The sun god, Usil in Etruscan, was important in Italy. (GMAH)

Gerhard, V, pl. 158; P. Ducati, *Storia dell' Arte Etrusca*, I (Florence, 1927), 330; G. Mansuelli, *StEtr*, 17 (1943), 497 ff.; —, *StEtr*, 19 (1946–1947), 14 f., 49, no. 4; J. D. Beazley, *JHS*, 69 (1949), 2, fig. 1. See also H. Rose, *HThR*, 30 (1937), 165.   Lent by The Minneapolis Institute of Arts (L 57.198).

215. Mirror with Winged Lasa

4th cent. B. C.; H: 0.22, diam.: 0.14.

A nude deity, her wings spread to conform to the tondo, dominates the back of this hand mirror. The Lasa wears sandals, necklace, bracelet, and earrings. In her r. hand she holds a dip-stick with which to remove and apply ointment from the alabstron in her l. Single winged figures, both male and female, often adorn Etruscan mirrors, but this example is better composed and more skillfully drawn than most. (SD)

Unpublished. Cf. Gerhard, I, pl. 34:2,4; III, pl. 244, 245:2; V, pl. 29:1,2.
Lent by Dr. and Mrs. Robert Waelder; acquired 1959.

216. Mirror with Marriage Scene

C. 300 B. C.; H: 0.234, diam.: 0.191; reflecting surface has blue-green patina, mostly smooth, decorated surface blackish, probably scraped; handle broken off. Found at Castel Giorgio near Orvieto on property of Count B. Bucciosante. Ex-coll. A. Castellani (sale, Rome, Palais Castellani, 17 March–10 April, 1884, 36, no. 188).

From (viewer's) l. to r., identified by Etruscan inscriptions, are: Herakles (H[E]RCLE), seated, his chlamys draped over his r. thigh and his club between his legs, wearing a headband with crescent in the center; FUFLUNI (misspelling of Fufluns, or Dionysos), holding an oinochoe in his r. hand and a saucer in his l., and nude except for drapery over l. shoulder and arm, necklace, and diadem with radiating points; VESUNA in a similar cor-onet, long chiton and fawn skin, and holding a thyrsus in her r. hand, which reaches behind the shoulders of Fufluns; SVUTAF (V?), a winged male nude whom Beazley identifies with Pothos (Desire) rather than Eros. At the extreme r. and l. are vines; flowers and tendrils fill the empty spaces. Unusual are the effeminate coiffures, jewelry, and modelling of the males, and the inclusion of Vesuna, an Italic goddess not found else-where in Etruscan art. A. Klügmann – G. Körte suggest as prototype a marriage of Dionysos and Ariadne, with Herakles added to fill space and Vesuna capriciously substituted for Adriadne. Mansuelli attributes the piece to the "Master of the Elongated Figures." At the top of the handle tang is a winged male nude. (SD)

Gerhard, V, 44–47, pl. 35, with earlier bibl.; G. Mansuelli, StEtr, 19 (1946–1947), 55, no. 3; J. D. Beazley, JHS, 69 (1949), 14–15, fig. 18, pl. 10b; Fiesel in W. H. Roscher, Ausführliches Lexikon der griechischen und römischen Mytho-logie, 6 (Leipzig, 1924–1937), cols. 273–274 (s. v. Vesuna); *"Ancient Italian and Etruscan Art," Detroit Institute of Arts, Jan. 15–Feb. 23, 1958.

Lent by the Walters Art Gallery, Baltimore (54.85); purchased 1926.

217. Hand Mirror

Late 4th–early 3rd cent. B. C.; diam.: 0.17; piece of disc missing; ivory handle ancient but does not belong. Ex-coll. A. Castellani (sale, Rome, Palais Castellani, 17 March–10 April, 1884, no. 186).

The design is bordered by a running wave pattern; a seven-petal lyre palmette with lateral blossoms lies above the tang. Three figures are identified by inscriptions as Tinia (Jupiter), Lasa, and Maris (Mars). Tinia, bearded, standing with chlamys over one shoulder, holds lightning and scepter. Maris is seated on his chlamys, r. hand on spear, l. gripping his sword. Lasa, wingless, wearing soft shoes and a diadem, places her r. hand on Tinia's shoulder; she appears to assume the role of Venus as daughter of Jupiter and beloved of Mars (for her pose see R. Herbig, *StEtr*, 24 [1955–1956], 194). The hair, rendered in short concentric crescents, is characteristic of Etruscan art of the late 4th century B.C. (cf. J. D. Beazley, *Etruscan Vase Painting* [Oxford, 1947]). The piece is attributed by Mansuelli to the "Master of the Usil Mirror." (HH)

Gerhard, V, pl. I; G. Mansuelli, *StEtr*, 19 (1946–1947), 52; H. Hoffmann, *AA* (1960), 111, no. 33, fig. 52; ——, *HambJb*, 6 (1961), 241; Hoffmann, 15, 39, fig. 48.

Lent by the Museum für Kunst und Gewerbe, Hamburg (1955.69).

218. Mirror with Judgement of Paris

3rd cent. B. C. or later; H: 0.235, diam.: 0.121; solid cast, green patina. Found near Corneto (Tarquinia). Ex-coll. Pasinati (dealer), Rome, 1878.

Inscribed on rim: ELAXSNTRE (Alexandros or Paris), TURAN (Venus), UNI (Juno), [ME]NRVA (Minerva). Paris, seated at (viewer's) l., wears a Phrygian cap and high-laced boots. Juno is richly decked in two bracelets, necklace, and a diagonal band with beaded fringe (?). Minerva appears fully clad and armed. The group is encircled by an abstract garland of leaves, typical of "Class Z" mirrors, as Beazley termed them. R. Herbig (*StEtr*, 24 [1955–1956], 183 ff.) proposes a 1st century B. C. date for this class of mirrors, which he terms *"die Kranzspiegelgruppe."* The handle ends in a stylized ram's head. (SD)

Gerhard, V, 126–127, pl. 98:2; L. Lord, *AJA*, 41 (1937), 602–606, figs. 5, 7; Allen Memorial Art Museum *Bulletin*, 11:2 (1954), pl. 7, 16:2 (1959), 119, 16:3 (1959), ill. 168; *Walters, 1958; *"Treasures from the Allen Memorial Art Museum," Minneapolis Institute of Arts, July 21–Sept. 11, 1966. On Etruscan names, E. Fiesel, *Namen des griechischen Mythos im Etruskischen* (Göttingen, 1928). Mirrors in New York and Rome may be by the same hand (J. D. Beazley, *AJA*, 69 [1949], pl. 11a; Gerhard, V, pl. 84:2, attributed by Mansuelli to the "Master of the Judgement of Paris III").

Lent by the Allen Memorial Art Museum, Oberlin College, Oberlin, Ohio (42.122).

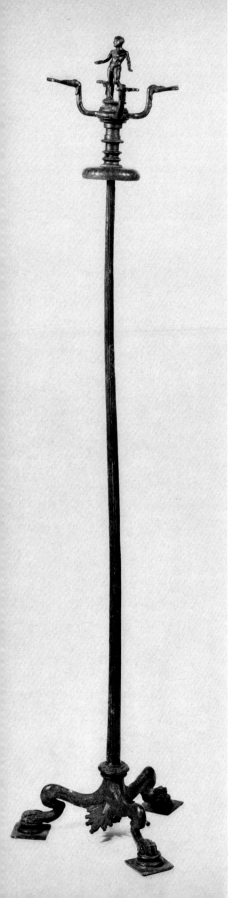

219. Candelabrum with Discobolus

4th cent. B.C.; H: 1.213, H. of figure: 0.098; figure black, other parts mottled green and dark red. Ex-coll. J. Lionberger Davis.

Candles were supported from the four projecting spikes near the top of this typically Etruscan lighting device. Its tripod base consists of three leonine legs, resting on spools which in turn rest on rectangular plinths. Rich scrolls are inscribed along the upper parts of the legs, and palmettes lie between them. The fluted shaft is topped by an inverted bowl with incised tongues. Above it a moulded pedestal supports the four spikes, which end in ducks' heads. The figure stands atop its own spool-shaped base. Its relaxed, Praxitelean stance dates the piece into the 4th century B.C. (SD)

Unpublished. For various Etruscan candelabra, de Ridder, II, nos. 3148–3162, pl. 112.

Lent by the City Art Museum of Saint Louis (187:54); acquired 1954.

220. Thymiaterion

4th cent. B. C.; H: 0.395, max. W. of base: 0.158; solid cast, light gray-green patina, brown incrustation.

The tripod base of this thymiaterion (incense stand) takes the form of three human legs wearing soft shoes, with a short skirt reaching to mid-thigh. Between the legs are ogival leaves with incised center rib and hatching at the edges. Above this lies a disc with traced petal motif (?). A rooster and feline climb the column, which has a traced spiral, except for plain bands opposite the two animals. At the top is a round bowl with square platform below its lip; on the corners of the platform are four doves facing counterclockwise. (SD)

Unpublished. For variations on this type, Giglioli, 311; de Ridder, II, no. 3175, pl. 113; E. Fiumi, *StEtr*, 25 (1957), 485, fig. 10.

Lent by The Johns Hopkins University (401); purchased in Italy.

221. Thymiaterion

3rd cent. B.C.; total H: 0.466, W. at base: 0.155, max. W. at top: 0.120, H. of figures: 0.11, max. L. of pendants to head of top bird: 0.093.

This elaborate incense stand represents the Hellenistic "baroque" phase of Etruscan art. The tripod base consists of spools surmounted by lions' paws emerging from horned eagles' heads. Between the legs are rosettes with eight pointed petals. A moulded pedestal ends in a floral calyx. The male figure (Dionysos or Fufluns?), wearing a leafy garland and standing in the "Meleager pose," puts his r. arm around his companion (maenad or Lasa?), grasping her lowered r. arm just above the elbow. She reaches behind her head with l. hand, to grasp the end of her robe. Both wear heavy necklaces and boots. Above them rises a stem of acanthus supporting a bowl with birds sitting on its four projecting corners (one missing). Suspended on chains from tangs beneath them are other birds in flight (two missing). (SD)

*Santa Barbara, 1967, 46, no. 64, color ill. Cf. piece from Todi in Florence, Lamb, pl. 83a; from Perugia, F. Messerschmidt, *AA* (1933), col. 334, fig. 3.

Lent by the R. H. Lowie Museum of Anthropology, University of California, Berkeley (8–3406); acquired 1904.

222. Basin

Etruscan or Near Eastern Hellenistic (?), 3rd cent. B.C. or later; H: 0.155, diam.: 0.295; bowl hammered, feet and heads cast; green-gray patina. Allegedly from the Near East.

The three feet are in the shape of claws topped by griffins with outspread wings and horn-like ears. At the rim are three Dionysiac heads with long hair, hair bands, and a large rosette on either side. For similar feet from Todi see Milani, pl. 23. The heads occur on a large situla of Roman Republican date, where the rosettes serve as points of attachment for handles (E. Pernice, *Die hellenistische Kunst in Pompeji*, IV [Berlin, 1925], 22, pl. 4). The situla has feet of the same type as this basin though of more developed form. (SD)

Unpublished.
Lent by Olivet College, Olivet, Mich. (38); acquired 1960.

223. Patera

4th–3rd cent B. C.; total H: 0.355, diam. of bowl: 0.199; surface, especially pan, quite yellow — possibly gilded. Ex-coll. Forman.

A female figure, nude except for necklace and soft shoes, forms the handle, supporting on her head and upraised hands the pan, which has a design of concentric circles in center. Inscribed retrograde on rim of pan, near the top, ꟼꟼꟼꟼꟼ *(suthina),* "votive". A ring for suspension is at the end of the handle. Similar pateras have been found at several Etruscan sites (cf. Giglioli, 313; Milani, pl. 23; Richter, *Br.,* no. 598), the figure's stance, with one knee bent and the opposite hip extended, occuring in many examples. Her features suggest a Vulcian origin. (SD)

Forman Collection, sale, Sotheby (June 19, 1899), no. 134. On the Vulcian school of this date, Riis, 91 ff. Lent by The Walters Art Gallery, Baltimore (54.162).

224. Spouted Jug with Trefoil Mouth

4th–3rd cent. B. C.; H: 0.14, W: 0.124, diam.: 0.074; green patina; deep chisel strokes on top and across rim. Allegedly found at Todi.

A nymph leaning on her elbow forms the handle of this pitcher with scalloped profile. Her "hipshot" stance is common among sculptures of this period (cf. No. 211; Giglioli, 311:2, 313:2). With her l. hand she daintily lifts the floral garland running diagonally across her breast. The body of the vessel is ornamented with two bands of guilloche and one of "running dog." The base has an egg-and-dart moulding. Inscribed retrograde in dotted letters vertically beneath l. breast of nymph: *udai*; horizontally just below handle, interrupted by a patch: *suth[i]na*. The two should be read together: "votive of *udai*." (GMAH)

Unpublished. For two similar pitchers, from Todi, Milani, pl. 23; Giglioli, 314:1.
Lent by the Eric de Kolb Collection.

225. Balsamarium with Satyr and Maenad

3rd cent. B.C.; H. including lid: 0.127; hollow cast. Allegedly from North Italy.

This container, for incense or cosmetics, takes the form of two heads back to back and has a lid in the form of an inverted flower. Rings on either side and probably on top held chains for suspension, of which five links are preserved on the l. side and several above the maenad's head. Both heads have ivy garlands, and the maenad also wears a flat band across her forehead, a necklace, and earrings of 3rd century B.C. style. S. Haynes groups related vases, the closest being Walters 758 (her group VI, no. 4, pl. 56:2). (SD)

Unpublished. Cf. S. Haynes—H. Menzel, *Jahrbuch des Römisch-Germanischen Zentralmuseums Mainz*, 6 (1959), 110–127 (group VI:2–8, pls. 56–57).

Lent by Mrs. Charles Goldmann; acquired 1963.

226. Balsamarium in Form of Woman's Head

Late 3rd–mid 2nd cent. B. C.; H: 0.110; hollow cast, base apparently attached with lead seam.

She wears a diadem on her elaborate "melon" coiffure, earrings, and a necklace with pendants. The missing lid was apparently not attached. The precise use of these vases is not known, but they were probably associated with a lady's toilet. Turan (Aphrodite) or one of her attendants (Lasae) may be represented. Cf. No. 114. (SD)

*Pomerance, no. 129. Cf. S. Haynes—H. Menzel, *Jahrbuch des Römisch-Germanischen Zentralmuseums Mainz*, 6 (1959), 110–127 (group III, pls. 44–49).

Lent by The Pomerance Collection; acquired 1960.

227. Helmet

3rd cent. B.C.; total H: 0.305, cheek piece H: 0.133, W. at top of cheek piece: 0.102, knob H: 0.019; green patina. Said to have been excavated by A. Castellani near Perugia, late 19th century, found with a cista and bronze jar.

The helmet represents a variation of the Italic "jockey-type." Its cheek pieces, made separately and hinged so they could be turned up or down, have a scalloped outline and are embossed with three clusters of concentric circles. The simple hemispherical form is topped by a small knob decorated with a rosette. The slight peak which covered the neck and the brim are ornamented with two narrow rows of herringbone trim. Virtually identical are helmets in the Museo Gregoriano (Giglioli, 305:5) and MMA (Richter, *Br.*, 417, no. 1550, ill. 415). (SD)

Unpublished. For list of related examples, E. von Mercklin, *RM*, 38–39 (1923–1924), 129 ff. On helmets, Richter, *Br.*, 410 ff., with bibl.; *Greek and Roman Life,* British Museum (London, 1908), 76 ff.
Lent by The Los Angeles County Museum of Art, The William Randolph Hearst Collection (50.37.19).

Roman Bronzes

ROMAN BRONZES

The selection of 88 Roman bronzes in this exhibition conveys a representative picture of the variety of their forms, the extent of their distribution, and the difficulties of arranging them in a chronological system that likewise takes into account the centers of production. In contrast to Greek and Etruscan bronzes, which were usually confined in their distribution to smaller areas, the easily transportable Roman bronzes, a widely coveted commodity of Roman culture, were carried to the far boundaries of the Roman empire by the armies and by Roman commerce, which spanned the entire ancient world. To peoples on the frontiers of the empire they likewise became highly prized objects.

The golden milestone in the Roman forum was the symbolic hub of the empire. From here emanated the magnificent network of roads which was laid out by Roman legionaries to conquer foreign lands, thus making it possible for tradesmen and merchants to open new markets and areas of trade. The discovery of important treasures in Germany or Afghanistan demonstrates the difficulty of answering the basic question of where the production centers were located.

The conquest of the empires surrounding the Mediterranean Sea and the taking over of Alexander the Great's heritage caused immense riches to flow into Rome which inevitably manifested themselves in luxurious living. Indeed, the occupation of the Greek colonies in Southern Italy and even more so, the plundering of Greece itself, brought such a multitude of works of art to Rome that Roman taste and artistic sensibility were decisively influenced. Because everyone could not share in the stolen spoils, the practice of copying developed rapidly. It is this practice of copying which is responsible for the fact that even in the late era sculptors of ideal subjects basically followed the models adopted earlier. The portrayal of the gods who correspond to Greek gods belongs in this category (Nos. 255, 268, 266, 247, 246, 251).

The *Interpretatio Romana*, however, lent the traits of Roman gods to the indigenous gods of conquered lands. Only characteristic attributes of the local divinities were retained, e.g. the *modius* of Serapis (Nos. 271–273), who supplanted the Egyptian Osiris during the Hellenistic age and, together with Isis and Harpocrates, was highly revered even in Italy. The moon goddess (No. 251) also shows elements of Anatolian piety in the crescent moon; she may also bear a pine cone, symbolic of fertility. Celtic gods were often portrayed. Most prominent was the Celtic hammer god, *Dispater* as Caesar called him. He carries a vessel in one hand and a long-handled hammer in the other. Epona was almost as highly revered; she is usually portrayed sitting between two horses or mules, with fruit in her lap. A stag god and bear goddess were also among the divinities from Celtic nations who enjoyed extensive worship.

Roman legionaries were responsible for the wide dissemination of cults which expressed most strongly their attitude toward life and the ideals they strove to attain, such as the cults of Jupiter Dolichenus and Mithras. Their bronze statuettes were carried with the legions, especially

Plate V, No. 251
Selene

Jupiter Dolichenus, who is portrayed standing on a bull, symbol of invincible strength.

While these gods either originated in the Greek pantheon or arose by endowing indigenous gods with Hellenic forms, the Lar (No. 254) is a genuinely Roman creation. Portrayed as a youth with long, curly hair, a short tunic bound at the waist, and sandals or high shoes, he carried a rhyton in his raised hand and usually a patera in his lowered hand. Lares occur individually or in pairs, at rest or dancing; they are the gods of the crossroads and of family shrines, where they flank the *genius* of the lord of the house. Lares were set up in houses where daily reverence could be paid to them, and where they in return protected the family and its property. The collection of Lares from Nagydem, Hungary, illustrates that this type of devotion was practiced not only in the mother country, Italy, but also in the provinces. These statuettes were dedicated in great numbers in sanctuaries scattered throughout the countryside, in fulfillment of special vows, in gratitude for help received, or in supplication for protection and care. The priest of the temple preserved them in special depots as inviolable possessions. If, however, the shrine were in dire need, he could sell or dispose of them.

Not only small statuettes were bequeathed as sacred offerings. Life-sized statues, too, stood as cult images in the sanctuary of the temple and often formed the focal point of a religion. The Mars of Coligny, now in the museum in Lyon, was a cult image of a sanctuary of Mars which was destroyed during an invasion by Germanic tribes. The bronze statue was smashed into countless pieces. Priests picked up the individual pieces, took them with them as they fled, and buried them when they themselves were endangered. The remnants were uncovered by chance in 1897 by a farmer. Pliny mentions in his *Natural History* a great statue of Mercury for the Avernians in Gaul, on which Zenodorus worked for ten years, an indication of the great importance which such cult images might have.

The inhabitants of Pompeii who survived the catastrophes of 62 and especially 79 A. D. painstakingly unearthed their possessions where the lava and ash deposits were not too deep. But in those places where the layers were two meters thick or more, entire streets with all their houses were untouched until their excavation; thus, we have a picture of life in an ancient city which suddenly stopped, as if frozen. Splendid city dwellings of the prosperous citizenry were filled with decorative statues and statuettes; even the simplest implements, such as coal or fire pots, water-warming vessels, fountain spouts, lamps and lamp stands, or legs of chairs and tables, were ornamented and formed as figures. This more or less rich heritage of bronzes is similarly found in villas of Morocco, cellars of destroyed English houses, fortresses along the German and Danubian *Limes* (fortified zone), and in settlements through the entire Roman Empire.

These discoveries are witnesses of sudden destructions of houses, villages, and cities, the catastrophes which rocked the late antique world.

Buried treasures provide evidence for the same events. Valuable bronzes and statuettes were intentionally consigned to the protecting earth to preserve them from seizure by the plundering foe. Graves do not usually contain statuettes as grave goods, although implements are occasionally included.

Nothing can better characterize the second current of ancient piety than the triangular votive plaque from Pergamon (No. 312). Widespread doubt as to the efficacy of the official gods set in early, and people turned more and more to magic rites, which popular religion offered in rich variety to the masses. It was less a matter of divining the future than of obtaining protection against evil, inimical forces which threatened life and health, good fortune and well-being. Amulets were thought to repel magic; they were worn or attached above house entryways. Among these are countless phallic representations, intended to ward off evil. The efforts to transmit to one god the powers of other divinities also belong to this current, as in the pantheistic monuments (No. 274) or the votive hand of the god Sabazios (No. 313), which both blesses and averts evil.

The portrait and historical relief are among the original creations of Roman art. They, too, were echoed in bronze sculptures. In the imitation of the face (which closely followed nature) and in the accurate revelation of the character of the person being portrayed, Roman portraits reached a high level during the early Republic and rose to impressive heights under the empire. The male portraits from the late Republic and from the end of the second century A.D. (Nos. 228–229), and the portrait of Julia Domna (No. 234) speak for themselves.

The historical relief, which was not only a representation of history but which also had politico-religious significance, is not represented among the bronze sculptures. In its place, however, are themes which represent concepts of the Roman state, such as a citizen in a toga making a sacrifice (No. 243) and other persons performing cultic rites, servants of state, and state officials. Finally, the *tropaeum* (No. 277), the victory memorial erected on the battlefield, appears as a symbol in the minor arts, especially on coins. Busts and statuettes of cuirass-clad emperors and soldiers (Nos. 278–279) also belong in this category. Occasionally the theme of victory, the subjugation of other peoples, is personified in the minor arts by prisoners, as on the vessel handle from the Louvre (No. 307).

Genre figures formed another extensive group of subjects for the bronze sculptor (Nos. 240, 275). Numerous portrayals of grotesques of every kind, a theme which probably originated in Alexandria in the third century B.C., were still extraordinarily popular in Roman times (No. 310).

The amphitheater with its games and gladiators belonged to Roman life as did the daily bread. Legionaries erected arenas even at the boundaries of the empire. Thus it is only natural that this theme would be taken up in art, especially in mosaics. But the minor arts, down to reliefs on lamps, pick up this theme, and in bronzes individual gladiators from the most varied contests are portrayed (No. 265); sometimes they appear individually, sometimes in groups (cf. the silver-plated gladiator group from Autun).

Animals such as the lion and bull (Nos. 283–284) (often the Apis bull, tied in with the Egyptian religion) are represented in the round or in appliqué (No. 286); they abound in the Roman provinces. Almost the entire fauna, down to the smallest animals, are represented in bronze.

Greek art, especially Hellenistic art, had decorated bronze implements such as vases, chests, furniture, lamps, candelabra, and incense stands with figurative elements. Roman art met the desire for ornamentation in a comprehensive way, decorating nearly all implements with figures, sometimes inlaid with silver or niello (Nos. 288, 295).

Bronze table services were done in imitation of opulent silver tableware; they can be supplemented to form a service for three, reflecting the ancient custom of three persons reclining at table. Casseroles, tumblers, sieves, serving plates, ladles, plates and vessels are among those table settings whose development and historical position have been broadly determined through datable discoveries.

Handles and other appliqués to vessels are nearly always figural, and may be inlaid in silver, especially in the early period (Nos. 288, 306). The vessel reproducing the bust of a Syrian or Egyptian (No. 310) belongs to a special type. That head-vases were popular in the ancient world is well-documented; this object appeals as well to the interest in exotic types. Negroes were also popular as head and bust vessels. Also employing the bust and head form were weights for steelyards, moved along a balanced arm to determine the weight of an object fastened on a hook (No. 315). Reliefs on burial monuments show scenes of weighing in offices. This type of weighing apparently took precedence among the Romans over the two-arm scale with pans.

The small "panther" on an oval base (No. 285), as well as the decorative attachments with maenad busts (No. 289 A and B) are doubtless parts of the adornment of a vehicle. Tomb reliefs and coins convey to us a general picture of ancient vehicles, as do discoveries of actual vehicles. A variety of types occurs, depending on use. There are two- and four-wheeled models, passenger and freight vehicles, those used for postal service, war chariots, racing chariots, and triumphal chariots, simple vehicles with only one seat for passengers, and very luxuriously appointed vehicles. Arm and back rests of seats were ornamented with figural bronzes, sometimes mounted on or nailed to wooden parts. A large number of such vehicles were found in the so-called "vehicle burials" of Bulgaria and Hungary. They also have been found on the Rhine and in France, but not in Italy. These vehicle burials represent a custom peculiar to the people who practiced them; they tend to fuse with the notion of a journey into the other world, often combined with elements of Dionysian piety, to which figures of panthers, satyrs, Bacchus, maenads, Amor and Hercules give eloquent testimony.

Furniture such as chests and beds also often had rich bronze ornamentation, either as appliqués (No. 301) or plastic attachments, such as couch finials (Nos. 302–303) which take the form of heads of Molossian hounds, horses, mules, and geese. Table legs almost without exception terminate in animal protomes. Lamps, too, used figural motifs, either to ornament handles (No. 297) or to define the shape of the lamp itself (No. 298).

This brief outline should make it apparent that wherever bronze implements were used in Roman life they were decorated with figural ornament which, at least in the early period, was often apotropaic in nature. This is the way we must interpret fountain spouts terminating in wolf and lion heads and the lion and Medusa masks which ornamented furniture and chests. Even the lock on a clothes closet had a mask to ward off evil.

*　　　*　　　*

It is a peculiarity of the method of producing bronze statuettes that the mold had to be destroyed (see technical introduction), so that each finished object was highly individual. This process, however, makes it extremely difficult to combine groups and thus determine the workshop in which they were made. Furthermore, we may assume that craftsmen travelled to meet special demands.

Numerous small statuettes of Mars and Mercury (Nos. 247–250, 267–269) can help us envisage this activity, its products, and the extent of production. These statuettes came, for example, from temple precincts in the Mosel region, and were doubtless votive offerings (in addition to the less expensive terracottas). They can be traced to a few basic types which mostly occur in well-defined regional areas. Thus, for example, the material from the Trier region is almost identical with that from the Luxembourg region with respect to small votive statuettes. Shrines such as those at Möhn, Dhronecken, and Gusenberg, from the territory of the Treveri, must be regarded as centers of devotion which attracted craftsmen as well as devotees.

One further example should be mentioned, a silver treasure rather than a deposit of bronzes: Berthouville. This site, at which a temple group and theater were excavated, lay on the crossroads of important Roman highways and on a frontier adjacent to three Gallic tribes. It was a great marketplace where large crowds gathered at certain times of year to buy goods, visit the famous shrine of Mercury decorated with large silver statues, and seek diversion in the nearby theater. In the vicinity there was only one villa, and no city or town. One may surmise that during the great fairs, which lasted several days, merchants and traders produced and sold their wares, including statuettes, in the area. On the other hand it can be assumed with certainty that important cities such as Rome, Trier, Lyon, and Cologne had permanent workshops which not only accepted commissions for small statuettes to be produced quickly, but also executed monumental sculptures. The remains of such large statues (which are widely dispersed and not adequately known) demonstrate that such activity took place in permanent, and more efficient, workshops.

The paucity of material also prevents a solution to the question of connections between workshops. Generally only outstanding individual works have been brought to our attention, usually out of context. The first attempt to provide a survey came from the pen of Salomon Reinach, who published the originals and copies of Gallic bronzes in the museum of St. Germain-en-Laye. Publications of the large holdings of the Louvre, the Bibliothèque Nationale in Paris, the British Museum, and the Metropolitan Museum of Art either preceded or followed Reinach's publication, but lacked a systematic inventory of objects according to entire regions and areas. This has only recently been begun. France has made a start with the work of G. Faider-Feytmans, P. Lebel, and H. Rolland. The bronzes discovered in Austria have been published by R. Fleischer; A. N. Zadoks-Jitta, W. J. T. Peters, and W. A. von Es are well along in their work on Roman bronzes from the Netherlands. The first two volumes of the projected complete publication of Roman bronzes from Germany have appeared, from the museums at Speyer (Palatinate) and Trier (Mosel region). Two catalogues of the exhibition, "Arte e civiltà romana nell'Italia settentrionale dalla repubblica alla tetrarchia," in Bologna in 1964 afford a good survey for northern Italy. But only complete publication of all Roman bronzes (which lies in the distant future) will clarify many questions, and even then not all.

The chronological periodization and identification of this abundant material encounters equally great difficulties. The general development and sequence of art in the city of Rome doubtless offers many important clues for the evaluation of bronze sculptures elsewhere, but the answer to the chronological question is more difficult when an established type recurs constantly, a process which can go on for centuries. Here only clearly defined finds with datable attendant materials can help. Finds of treasures are important for this purpose. We strive to ascertain precisely the time of burial of such bronze treasures as those from Neuvy-en-Sullias or Chalon-sur-Saône in France, from Detzem or Straubing in Germany, Avenches in Switzerland, Monteu da Po (Industria) or Montorio Veronese in Italy, Mauer an der Url in Austria, or Tamási in Hungary, to name a few. But even the unequivocal answer to this question raises further questions. The date of actual production of the bronzes is not determined by the time of their burial, nor does it follow that they form a "closed group," i. e. that all the buried pieces were made at the same time. If pieces within a find originated in different periods, then they were also produced in different workshops. Finally, the assessment of quality raises the problem of defining local or regional characteristics which might be traced back to ethnic peculiarities.

It is an important observation that the density of finds of bronzes in the provinces surpasses that of the mother country. This might be because the Italian materials have only been made known to a limited degree, but may also indicate that workshops were massed in the provinces, where the demand was greater, since new cities and settlements were being established there and the number of estates, some of them very important, was greater than in Italy. Furthermore, production was cheaper there than in Italy; for example, the production of *terra sigillata* pottery also gradually shifted to the provinces.

Viewed by itself, the bronze statuette is not only the transmitter of a meaning, that is, the bearer of a certain function, be it as a votive offering in a temple or decorative element in a house; it is also a work of art. The plainest and even the most carelessly worked piece is still a link in a long chain which originated in and took as its model a statuary prototype. Thus, our efforts must be directed toward finding these models and understanding the links of transmission whose modifications and reshaping determined the image which we now encounter in the statues and statuettes which have come down to us. The first results of such investigations are now at hand; others must be undertaken, with the additional goals of determining the chronology and defining the workshops which produced these statuettes.

Heinz Menzel

228. Portrait Bust of a Man

Late Republican, 40–30 B.C.; H: 0.38; repatination recently removed, revealing scattered traces of cuprite and original green corrosion; eye inlays missing. For insertion in a herm (?). Allegedly excavated shortly before 1928.

The indecision of this troubled individual during a period of great uncertainty is paralleled by the stylistic tension between Republican desire for accurate description and the increased interest in classicism and classical formulations. The hair, a cap of finely elaborated locks, is reminiscent of Hellenistic rulers (Richter, *Portraits*, 263, 271, figs. 1808–1809, 1878). (JAS)

*M. Milkovich, *Roman Portraits*, Worcester Art Museum (April 6–May 14, 1961), no. 5, with earlier bibl.; Hanfmann, *Roman*, no. 69; C. C. Vermeule, *ProcPhilSoc.*, 108:2 (1964), 103, n. 19. Cf. Richter, *Br., 142 ff., no. 325.*

Lent by The Cleveland Museum of Art, John Huntington Collection (46.28).

229. Portrait of a Man

1st cent. A.D., H: 0.22; very dark green patina; break along l. of neck, part of r. ear missing.

A narrow face, the skin pulled tight over the cheekbones, characterizes this Roman portrait. The low forehead has two thin wrinkles. The short, wavy hair starts from the crown of the head and falls in single strands all over the head; it is cut straight over the forehead. The eyes were presumably inlaid with silver. The date of this head is controversial. De Ridder puts it in the time of Sulla. R. West connects it with the mature Augustan bronze head in the MMA, pointing especially to the stern, harsh expression, the emphasis on bone structure in both heads, and the stylization of the hair. But the treatment of the hair and even more, the classicistic attitude of the head in New York makes the difference apparent; an Augustan dating can hardly be maintained. B. Schweitzer mentions the head among Republican portraits and puts it at the end of the first third of the 1st century B.C., drawing attention to the unique hairdo with fine overlapping hair tips. He remarks, however, that early Flavian portraits often emulate the style of the time of Sulla. Nonetheless, the extraordinarily realistic tightness and tension suggest a date at the end of the 1st century A.D. in the reign of Trajan. Compare the bronze head from Zuglio Carnico in the Museo Cividale, R. Horn, *AA* (1938), 631, fig. 7 and G. Daltrop, *Die stadtrömischen, männlichen Privatbildnisse trajanischer und hadrianischer Zeit* (Münster, 1958), 51, fig. 27, although the different handling of the hair should not be overlooked. (HM)

De Ridder, I (1913), 10, no. 21, pl. 5; R. West, *Römische Portraitplastik*, I (Munich, 1933), 144, fig. 156, pl. 37; B. Schweitzer, *Die Bildniskunst der römischen Republik* (Leipzig, 1948), 67.

Lent by the Musée du Louvre (Inv. no. Longp. 638). Shown only in Cambridge.

230. Bust of a Man (Caligula?)

1st cent. A. D.; H: 0.143, diam. of base: 0.048; solid mass of bronze connects globe from beneath to tip of bust, surface dark brown; broken areas on globe, eyes originally inlaid.

The receding lower lip, long nose and flat head are characteristic of portraits of Caligula as identified by coins. This bronze most closely resembles one in Zürich dated by Jucker c. 41 A.D. The amount of the bust portrayed and the resemblance to Caligula substantiate a 1st century A.D. date. (JAS)

Unpublished. For the Zürich bronze, H. Jucker, I, 48–49, 137, no. B1, II, pl. 12; for a bronze similarly placed on an orb from Essex, E. Strong, *JRS*, 6 (1916), 27 ff. Cf. V. Poulsen, *Meddelelser fra Ny Carlsberg Glyptotek*, 14 (1947), 29–47; G. M. A. Richter, *Roman Portraits* (New York, 1948), nos. 36–40.

Lent by the Department of Ancient Art, The Brooklyn Museum (21.497.12); acquired 1921.

231. Bust of a Lady

Late Hadrianic, 130–140 A.D.; H: 0.205; hollow cast (part of core remains), surface blackish brown with cuprous and green areas.

Hair style and restrained treatment of the features are comparable to known portraits of the court ladies of Hadrian's reign who followed the fashions of the Empress Sabina. This lady closely resembles a marble bust from Ostia dated 130–140 A.D. (R. Calza, *Scavi di Ostia* V, *I Ritratti* I [1964], 80, no. 128, pl. 76). The Elliott bust rests on an acanthus leaf, a foliate "cup" understood by Jucker as a syncretistic symbol of resurrection rooted in the religions of Egypt and the Near East. (JAS)

Unpublished. Cf. H. Jucker, I, 72, 216; II, pl. 24:St.9. For portraits of Sabina, M. Wegner, *Das römische Herrscherbild* II, *Hadrian* (Berlin, 1956), 126 ff.; on hair style, —, *AA* (1938), 275 ff.

Lent by the collection of John B. Elliott; acquired 1959.

232. Bust of a Lady (Empress Livia?)

20–30 A. D.; H: 0.11; circular plinth with modern support, eyes originally inlaid.

The small bust rests on a double leaf. The hair is arranged in waves, with five circular curls below each temple; two large tresses are rolled back from the sides and tied in a bun subdivided into seven parts on her neck. Her profile closely resembles some disputed portraits of the Empress Livia, wife of Augustus (58 B. C. – 29 A. D.). Although her face seems longer, comparison with Salus coins of 22 A. D. is persuasive. Such a small bronze bust of Augustus was kept in a shrine (lararium) in the Emperor Hadrian's bedroom (Suetonius, Augustus, 7). (GMAH)

Unpublished. For small bronze busts, H. Jucker, 48 ff., no. B1 (Caligula), no. B2 (a doubtful "Livia"), no. B3 (woman from excavations in Alesia). For Livia comparisons: Salus coin, W. H. Gross, Iulia Augusta (Göttingen, 1962), pl. 2:2–3; Livia from Villa dei Misteri, nose preserved, Hanfmann, Roman, fig. 70; Marlborough cameo, C. C. Vermeule, Greek and Roman Portraits (Boston, 1959), fig. 41. Gaze and front view resemble heads of Livia and Earth (with Livia's features?) on Ara Pacis and other acknowledged Livia portraits, see Gross, op. cit., pls. 12 f., 16, 22 f., 25, 29 f. Gross' scepticism of Salus coins and Misteri head is rejected by H. von Heintze, AJA, 68 (1964), 320, and G. M. A. Hanfmann, GGA, 218 (1966), 29.

Lent by Hon. and Mrs. Edwin L. Weisl, Jr.

233. Bust of a Lady

C. 165–185 A. D.; H: 0.546; cast in two pieces, light and dark green patina on head, patination largely removed on bust; eyes perhaps originally inlaid. Allegedly found in southwestern Anatolia.

The face is that of a young, mature woman, with an expressionless, slightly melancholy look, typical of Antonine female portraiture. The modelling of the head and the treatment of the elaborate coiffure demonstrate a sensitivity unexcelled in Roman portraiture. Despite similarities to the coinage likenesses of Faustina the Younger and, more especially, her daughter Lucilla, the portrait does not represent either empress. The resemblance is close enough to be familial, but identification with any members of the far-flung branches of the Antonine family is tenuous in the extreme. (R. S. Teitz)

R. S. Teitz, "A Bronze Bust of an Antonine Lady" (paper delivered at College Art Association Meeting, Jan. 27, 1967). For portraits of Faustina Minore and Lucilla, M. Wegner, *Die Herrscherbildnisse in antoninischer Zeit* (Berlin, 1939), 48–55, 74–78, pls. 34–38, 47, 63, 65a–k.

Lent by the Worcester Art Museum, Worcester, Mass. (1966.67).

234. Julia Domna

193–217 A.D.; H: 0.305; hollow cast of thin bronze, various casting faults, gray-green surface; unfinished, top of head partially worked, three holes in hair for diadem.

Learning from the horoscopes that the daughter of the high priest of the sun god at Emesa, Syria, was destined to become an empress, Septimius Severus made her his wife. After the death of Pertinax in 193 A.D. he triumphed among the claimants and ascended the throne with Julia Domna as his consort. Unusual in material and expressiveness, the bronze has the immediacy of a portrait although probably intended as a cult image. A bronze head of the Empress in the Fogg Museum, from Syria (*Annual Report* [1955–1956], 42–43), bears corresponding casting faults near the eyes. The Dusenbery portrait is dated early 3rd century A.D. by D. von Bothmer, before 200 A.D. by M. Milkovich on the basis of hair style and coin types; the earlier date is apparently accepted by C.C. Vermeule. The rather youthful serenity of the broad, heavy facial forms is consistent with her earlier years as empress, during which she played a powerful diplomatic role. After Severus' death in 211 A.D., she mediated between her two quarrelling sons who jointly assumed the government, only to have Geta, the younger, murdered in her arms at the instigation of Caracalla, the older. She held great power during Caracalla's reign until his death, soon after which she died (217 A.D.). (JAS)

*M. Milkovich, *Roman Portraits*, Worcester Art Museum (April 6 – May 14, 1961), 60, no. 26, ill.; *Metropolitan, 1959–1960, 43, no. 162, pl. 39; C. C. Vermeule, *ProcPhilSoc.*, 108:2 (1964), 99. Forthcoming publication (with Fogg head) by U. Hiesinger. For a tiny, similarly expressive head from Athens, H. Thompson, *Hesperia*, 27:2 (1958), 155, with comparanda and bibl. concerning her deification at Athens; for deified representations in Africa and Rome, I. Ryberg, *MAAR*, 22 (1955), 136 ff.

Lent by Mr. and Mrs. John Dusenbery.

234 A. Portrait of a Man (Caracalla?)

Early 3rd cent. A.D.; H: 0.216; hollow cast, greenish black patina, some incrustation; fragmentary, back and top of head, part of r. side (including ear and bearded portion of cheek) missing, somewhat distorted through crushing; several casting flaws, patched in antiquity (some patches now missing). Allegedly from Asia Minor.

The countenance is determined by a low forehead, full beard with lower lip unbearded, and short thick nose. Despite damage, the head imparts a voluminous impression. The emphatically modelled cheek bones strengthen the effect of full, well-rounded cheeks. The beard is arranged in tiers of comb-like strands that become wider and longer on the cheeks; curls are arranged above the forehead. A short mustache covers the upper lip entirely, but does not extend beyond the corners of the mouth. The identification of this portrait is not without problems. At first glance, especially when viewed from the front, it might be considered a portrait of the emperor Caracalla. Yet the tranquil expression of the profile is difficult to reconcile with the image of Caracalla as known through a series of portraits such as those in Berlin (R. Delbrück, Antike Porträts [Bonn, 1912], pl. 50; C. Blümel, Staatliche Museen zu Berlin, Katalog der Sammlung antiker Skulpturen. Römische Bildnisse [Berlin, 1933], pls. 59, 60, R 96) and Naples (A. Hekler, Die Bildniskunst der Griechen und Römer [Stuttgart, 1912], pl. 290). These imperial portraits emphasize the suspicious, almost sinister aspect of the subject's personality through knit brows and a mustache drawn down over the corners of the mouth. Coin portraits also show the emperor with tightly closed mouth and emphatically sculpted brows. Their general impression, however, is somewhat gentler than that of the marble portraits (see H. Mattingly and E. Sydenham, Roman Imperial Coinage, V:I [London, 1936], pl. 12, nos. 14–15, 17, 19, or H. Mattingly, Coins of the Roman Empire in the British Museum, V [London], pl. 76, nos. 5, 7, 8). Of the latter, several examples in the Museo Nazionale Romano show somewhat more pacific features than do the Berlin and Naples heads (B. M. Felleti Maj. Museo Nazionale Romano, I Ritratti [Rome, 1953], nos. 266–268; no. 265 cannot be considered in this context because of its poor preservation). Finally the Caracalla portrait in Kansas City, and especially the one in the University Museum, Philadelphia, might be compared (C. C. Vermeule, ProcPhilSoc 108 [1964], 133, figs. 40–41). The former comes from the surroundings of Istanbul; the relative calm of its physiognomy is a characteristic of Roman imperial sculpture from the Greek East. Eastern — as opposed to the harsher and more realistic Western — tendencies are also clearly in evidence in the Caracalla portrait from Pergamon, in which realistic details are suppressed in favor of a generalized overall likeness (J. Inan and E. Rosenbaum, Roman and Early Byzantine Portrait Sculpture in Asia Minor [London, 1966], pl. 38:1–2). Although it is not possible to identify this head as Caracalla with absolute certainty, its eastern provenance links it with the more idealized portraits of the emperor from Asia Minor. We must also take into consideration the fact that gilding, now lost, would certainly have altered the overall impression of the piece. If not a portrait of Caracalla himself, the head represents a person whose likeness is remarkably akin to that of the famous emperor. (HM)

Lent by the Schimmel Collection.

235. Portrait of a Bearded Man

Severan, early 3rd cent. A. D.; H: 0.31; hollow cast, dark greenish black patina; r. side of head above ear pushed in. Allegedly found in the Tiber (Ponte Sisto, Rome). Ex-coll. E. P. Warren.

This compelling portrait, full of psychological insight and brooding intensity, may be that of a senator, perhaps during the troubled years of Caracalla's reign (211–217 A.D.). Although strongly reminiscent of Antonine conventions in the hair style, the impressionistic clipped beard, compressed lips, and deeply hollowed pupils, glancing upward, betray the onset of the politically and spiritually unsettled 3rd century A.D. (DGM)

E. Robinson, MFA *Annual Report* (1896), 27; *AA* (1897), 73 (Antoninus Pius?); *BMFA*, 1 (1903), 15; G. Dehn, *RM*, 26 (1911), 253 f., fig. 10a–b; Reinach, V², 317:7; L. D. Caskey, *Catalogue of Greek and Roman Sculpture in the Museum of Fine Arts* (Cambridge, 1925), 233 ff., no. 132, ill.; K. Kluge – K. Lehmann-Hartleben, *Die antiken Großbronzen*, II (Berlin, 1927), 44 f., fig. 2; E. Strong, *Art in Ancient Rome*, II (New York, 1928), 193; C. C. Vermeule, *Greek and Roman Portraits* (Boston, 1959), no. 61, ill.; Vermeule, 221, 237, 250, no. 228.

Lent by the Museum of Fine Arts, Boston (96.703); C. P. Perkins Collection.

236. Portait Bust of a Man

260–268 A. D.; H: 0.193; not tooled after casting, details at back of head crude, green and blue patina. From the house of Laberius Gallus, Bolsena, Ex-coll. Massarenti.

The bust was wrongly attached to a bronze tablet in honor of Ancaria Luperca, and was previously published as representing her husband, Laberius Gallus (d. before 224 A.D.). D. K. Hill now believes it to be later on the basis of style and toga type, depicting a subsequent owner of the house who kept the earlier tablet. The intellectual aspect is characteristic of the time of Gallienus. The plasticity, evident in the hair, contrasts with the linearism of mid 3rd century A.D. portraits, which is retained in the beard. (JAS)

Hill, 51–52, no. 106, pl. 21, with earlier bibl. See L. Wilson, *The Roman Toga* (Baltimore, 1924), 89 ff. For stylistic development during the period, C. C. Vermeule, *DOPapers*, 15 (1961), esp. 6.

Lent by The Walters Art Gallery, Baltimore (54.1148); purchased 1902.

237. Side of a Draped Male Statue (Polygatus)

C. 2nd cent. A. D.; H: 1.52; hollow cast, green patina. Found at Casanuovo, near Reggio. Ex-coll. E. P. Warren.

C. C. Vermeule notes that this battered but impressive fragment belongs to a life-sized clothed statue of the *polygatus* type, clad in a more complex costume that the *togatus*. The subject may have been a provincial official, scholar, poet, or emperor, and is typical of the innumerable honorific statues of bronze erected by decrees of local city governments all over the empire, most of which were melted down in the Middle Ages. (DGM)

E. Robinson, MFA *Annual Report* (1901), 36; —, *AA* (1902), col. 131; *AJA*, 6 (1902), 377; C. C. Vermeule, *Berytus*, 15 (1964), 96.

Lent by the Museum of Fine Arts, Boston (01.7524).

238. Hercules

1st cent. B. C.–1st cent. A. D.; H: 0.191; hollow cast, green patina, traces of brown, red, orange, surface somewhat abraded, especially back of head; hole drilled in pelt opposite l. buttock.

One of many small copies of the great work of Lysippos which may have stood in the Athenian Agora, it closely corresponds in stance and accentuation of muscles to the Hercules Farnese in Naples. Modelled completely in the round, the weary hero rests on his club, over which is draped the lion skin. The r. hand may have grasped apples as does the Farnese statue. The heavy, curly hair is wreathed and tied with a fillet. (JAS)

Unpublished. On Farnese type, F. Johnson, *Lysippos* (Durham, N. C., 1927), 197. List of examples, Picard, IV², 574 ff.; cf. Bieber, *Hellenistic*, 37; F. Imhoof-Blumer– P. Gardner, *Numismatic Commentary on Pausanias* (Chicago, 1964), 171; E. Sjøqvist, *Lysippos* (Cincinnati, Louis Taft Semple lectures, 1966).

Lent by the collection of Dr. and Mrs. Irving F. Burton; acquired 1960.

239. Dancing Satyr

1st cent. A. D.; H: 0.215, W. including arm: 0.115; solid cast, dark brown-green patina, deposits of cuprous oxide over most of surface; l. arm missing from shoulder, r. arm recast into shoulder in antiquity, feet joined by bar.

The satyr wears a headdress of vine leaves secured at the back by a fillet. Bearing close resemblance to Hellenistic satyrs, his flattened nose, pupils indicated by hollow circles, and frenzied expression are similar to a marble head in the Louvre (Bieber, *Hellenistic,* fig. 574). (JAS)

Casson, 15, no. 126; Herbert, 120, no. 428. For Hellenistic satyr from Pergamon, Neugebauer, *Kat.,* II, 66 ff., no. 61, pl. 29. Cf. F. K. Dörner, *Inschriften und Denkmäler aus Bithynien* (Berlin, 1941), 49, no. 10 (marble statuette very similar in modelling and lines of pelt), no. 11 (bronze satyr, subsequently published with arm re-attached in *Istanbul Arkeoloji Müzeleri Yayinlarinden,* 16:3 [1949], 86; 16:6 [1953], fig. 6, thought to be from a chariot). Similar figure of comparable size on a lamp stand, C. Simonett, *AA* (1939), 503–505, fig. 20.

Lent by the Warren Collection, Bowdoin College Museum of Art (1930.215).

240. Dancing Girl

1st cent. A. D.; H: 0.22, surface red to brownish black with green areas; cleaned. Ex-coll. J. Lionberger Davis.

The vine-wreathed head identifies her as a maenad, dancing in a Dionysiac rite. Such figures appeared in groups in the Hellenistic period (Charbonneaux, pl. 30). Though detail is somewhat lacking, the swelling bodily curves and swirling drapery epitomize the ecstatic dance. (JAS)

Unpublished. Cf. Hill, 104, no. 235, pl. 44. For earlier painted representations and development of the dance, L. Lawler, *MAAR*, 6 (1927), 69 ff.

Lent by the City Art Museum of Saint Louis (203:54); acquired 1954.

241. Seated Philosopher

Roman copy of Greek 4th cent. B.C. original; H: 0.067; solid cast, granular patina.

The philosopher, his himation draped over his l. shoulder, supports his head with his l. fist and holds a scroll on his lap with his r. On the back rest of the chair are three incised rosettes, the center one with eight petals, the lateral ones with sixteen. The disproportionately short legs and shallow seat of the chair show the Roman copyist's misunderstanding of the Greek *klismos*. The philosopher may be Anaximander (cf. Richter, *Portraits*, I, figs. 290–300); the figure also somewhat resembles portraits of Plato (cf. *Ibid.*, II, 164–170, figs. 903–972), although the beard is shorter, the head more square. (HH)

Unpublished. For *klismoi*, Richter, *Furniture*, 33–37, 101–102; 37, n. 29 for the rosette decoration.

Lent by a Swiss private collection.

242. Helmeted Head

C. 200 A.D.; H: 0.048; solid cast; broken off at collar, crest of helmet broken off, edge of visor damaged, chin and mouth abraded, considerable chasing on beard and face. Allegedly from Pergamon.

This piece may have been a bust rather than a complete figure, as the even, circular grooves at the collar suggest. A raised area in front of the crown of the helmet once supported a crest attached at the front. His hair appears under the neck guard at the back. There is a similar, full size, helmet in Hamburg without crest, tentatively called Hellenistic from comparisons with Pergamene weapon reliefs (R. Pagenstecher, *AA* [1917], 91, fig. 12). A later, closer example is on a Medea sarcophagus, Museo delle Terme, Rome, dated in the Antonine age (J. M. C. Toynbee, *The Hadrianic School* [Cambridge, 1934], 173, pl. 42:3). The eyebrows, mouth, and hair are sharply chiseled. The style is reminiscent of Hellenistic Pergamene; the type, of heads of distinguished generals. The face and beard may be associated with the heavy forms at the end of the Antonine age. (AR)

Unpublished.

Lent by the Museum of Art and Archaeology, University of Missouri (61.50).

243. Togatus Sacrificing

Early 1st cent. A. D.; H: 0.13; dark green-brown patina; missing l. foot, object in r. hand, silver inlay from eyes and stripe in r. sleeve (*clavus*); ancient crack and repair at back, chips missing from forehead and r. hand.

Such typified figures in tunic with toga over the head can be identified only by attributes, here an incense box (*acerra*). The r. hand probably held a lump of incense. The features of many examples are generally similar, recalling the Augustan prototype, but the heavy hair low on the forehead might indicate a Claudian date. Probably from a domestic *lararium* where inclusion of the *Genius Augusti* in the private worship of the Lares had led to regular worship of the individual *paterfamilias*. (JAS)

N. Leipen, ROM *Bulletin* (Dec. 1956), 27. For closest parallels, Babelon-Blanchet, nos. 868, 869; Walters, no. 1584; Hill, no. 138; Bieber, *Cassel*, no. 225. For Etruscan origin of the type and toga, E. Richardson, *MAAR*, 21 (1953), 110 ff. On religious significance, Lamb, 218; I. Ryberg, *MAAR*, 22 (1955), esp. 53 ff. For painted Lararium figures, G. K. Boyce, *MAAR*, 14 (1937), pl. 30:2.

Lent by the Royal Ontario Museum, University of Toronto (956.7); purchased 1956.

244. Roundel with Head of Oceanus

1st cent. A.D.; diam.: 0.108; green-brown surface, silver and copper inlays; top of roundel broken.

Two tortoise heads (or crab claws) rise like horns from Oceanus' wavy hair; two more occur both at the temples and ends of the mustache. Rectangular silver inlays are let into the center of the forehead, nose, and cheeks. Downward pointing lancet leaves form the beard; the background is covered with a scale-like pattern, or perhaps rounded leaves. The object is a fine rendering of a Hellenistic-Pergamene prototype of the 2nd century B.C. (GMAH)

R.S. Teitz, Worcester Art Museum *Bulletin* (Nov. 1966), fig. 2 (as a comparison with Worcester Eros, No. 301); forthcoming publication by R. S. Teitz. Cf. mask in Morocco, *Paris, 1963, 154–155, no. 708, pl. 51.

Lent by The Minneapolis Institute of Arts (61.58); acquired 1961.

245. Narcissus

1st cent. A. D.; H: 0.24; dark green patina. Found 1837 between Speyer and Germersheim, east of Mechtersheim, Germany.

A youth with a strong body stands on his l. leg, with the r. leg drawn back, the hip thrown out. This movement is accentuated by the head bent forward to the r. The r. arm points downward, the hand is half opened. His l. rests lightly on his hip. K. A. Neugebauer has given the youth a spear in his r. hand and called him Narcissus, pointing to representations in Pompeian wall paintings and on gems. Compare the youth in Bonn (Neugebauer, figs. 16–19) and Narcissus from Pollantia (A. García y Bellido, *Esculturas romanas* [Madrid, 1949], pl. 101). According to Neugebauer, the statuette comes from a workshop in Gaul. P. W. Lehmann, however (*Statues on Coins of Southern Italy and Sicily in the Classical Period* [New York, 1946], 37 f.), cites a half-stater from Metapontum of the 5th century B.C. representing Apollo, his r. hand on his hip, a bow in his l. hand. The statuettes from Karlsruhe, Bonn, and Madrid reverse the half-stater types and ultimately go back to a model of the mid 4th century B.C. Between the Roman replicas and the original work we must assume an intermediate manneristic statue. (HM)

E. Wagner, *Die großherzoglich Badische Altertümersammlung in Karlsruhe*, II (1878), pl. 8; J. Friedlaender in A. von Sallet, *ZfN*, 9 (1882), 14; K. Schumacher, *Beschreibung der Sammlung antiker Bronzen* (Karlsruhe, 1890), pl. 27; A. Furtwängler, *Meisterwerke der griechischen Plastik* (Leipzig, 1893), 520, fig. 95; Reinach, II, 102:3; F. Hildenbrand, *Der römische Steinsaal des Historischen Museums der Pfalz zu Speyer* (1911), 199, fig. 171; *Germania Romana* (Bamberg, 1922), pl. 74:3; G. Lippold, *Handbuch der Archäologie* V:1 (Munich, 1950), 275, n. 4; K. A. Neugebauer, *87th Winckelmannsprogramm* (Berlin, 1927), detailed description; *Paris, 1963, no. 581; B. Cämmerer, *Römer am Rhein* (Cologne, 1967).

Lent by the Badisches Landesmuseum, Karlsruhe (C 504); acquired 1837.

246. Bacchus

1st cent. A. D.; H: 0.665; lightly flecked green patina, nipples iron, eyes silver; arms broken off at shoulder, part of r. foot missing, in back a large rectangular cut with protruding prong, dented on l. side of back, parts broken off on r. side. Found August 1966 in Avenches (Aventicum), Switzerland, northwest of Insula 5, at the foot of the Roman city wall.

The nude god stands on his r. leg, crossed by the l. leg which is set forward. He wears shoes of fur. The youthful body swings the r. hip slightly outward. The head is bent l. and forward. His hair, which is held by a ribbon over his forehead, is worked in delicate, flat, undulating waves. He wears a leafy wreath with grapes at both sides. The r. arm was perhaps stretched upwards holding a bunch of grapes, or bent over the head touching it lightly. The l. arm may have been bent and have rested on a pillar or tree trunk, as in Praxiteles' work (cf. G. E. Rizzo, *Prassitele* [1932], pl. 19 and 48–49); crossed legs occur in sculptures by Skopas (cf. replica of the Pothos, G. A. Mansuelli, *Galleria degli Uffizi, Le sculture,* I [Rome, 1958], fig. 32). Similar is a marble statue found on Via Cassia in Rome, E. Gatti, *(NSc* [1925], 390, fig. 9), of the nude Bacchus supporting himself on a pillar. Bacchus with crossed feet is seen not infrequently among bronzes (cf. statuette from Velleja di Lugagnano from the Val d'Arda, *Arte e civiltà romana nell'Italia settentrionale della repubblica alla tetrarchia,* Catalogo I [Bologna, 1964], no. 630, pl. 35, 74; Catalogo II [Bologna, 1965], 283, no. 388). He is sometimes grouped with Pan (cf. de Ridder, I, no. 1061, pl. 62). (HM)

Unpublished.
Lent by the Musée Romain Avenches, Switzerland.

247. Mercury

1st cent. A. D.; H: 0.152; green-brown patina, some incrustation; missing silver inlays from eyes and nipples. Ex-coll. Sir W. Francis Cook (Cook bronzes sold at Christie's, July 14–17, 1925).

The workmanship is Roman, the figure Polykleitos' Doryphoros, to which the attributes of Mercury have been added: the l. hand held the caduceus (missing with forefinger); the r., the purse, a Roman attribute of the god. The type, popular for portraits of Hellenistic rulers, was used in Roman times for both emperor and ordinary mortal. (JAS)

A. Michaelis, *Ancient Marbles in Great Britain* (Cambridge, 1882), 628, no. 22; A. Furtwängler, *Masterpieces of Greek Sculpture* (London, 1895), 232–233; *Burlington, 1904, 48, no. 44, pl. 55; C. Smith – C. Hutton, *Catalogue of the Antiquities in the Collection of the Late Wyndam Francis Cook, Esq.* (London, 1908), 105, pl. 27:18. Cf. C. Smith, no. 825, pl. 24; Hill, 19, no. 31, pl. 7. For copy of Doryphoros from Pompeii, Reusch, no. 808; for general discussion of type, Bieber, *Hellenistic,* 85 ff., 167 ff.; for association of Augustus with Hermes, I. Ryberg, *MAAR,* 22 (1955), 38, with bibl.

Lent by the Royal Ontario Museum, University of Toronto (949.25.2).

248. Seated Mercury

1st cent. A. D.; H: 0.265; dark green patina; top of r. index finger, most of l. fifth finger broken off. Found in Feurs, France. Ex-coll. J. Loeb.

The figure is a nude Mercury. His strong muscular body is slightly bent forward. His r. arm rests on his thigh. The l. hand lay on a support. See also Nos. 249 and 250. (HM)

S. Reinach, *RA*, 35 (1899), 58; —, *Catalogue illustré du Musée des Antiquités Nationales au Château de Saint Germain-en-Laye*, II (Paris, 1921), 172, fig. 86; J. Sieveking, *MJb*, 1 (1924), 1 ff.; —, *Bronzen, Terrakotten, Vasen der Sammlung Loeb* (Munich, 1930), 2 ff., pls. 3–4; Bieber, *Hellenistic*, 41, fig. 109; Beschi, 45, with bibl. on type; *Paris, 1963, no. 303. The type resembles the seated Hercules, cf. P. Lehmann, *Statues on Coins* (New York, 1946), 40 ff.

Lent by the Antikensammlungen München, Germany (S.L. 43); gift of J. Loeb, 1932.

249. Seated Mercury

1st cent. A. D.; H: 0.29; glossy green patina; attributes missing. Found in Augst.

The nude Mercury is seated on a rock; he wears the winged hat. The body is strong and well proportioned, the r. arm stretched forward, the l. arm lifted. The rock is ancient. The type is the same as Nos. 248 and 250. (HM)

C. Simonett, *AA* (1939), 484 ff., fig. 7; W. Deonna, *L'art romain en Suisse* (Geneva, 1942), fig. 32; F. Staehelin, *Die Schweiz in römischer Zeit* (Basel, 1948), fig. 110; Beschi, 52; *Paris, 1963, no. 555; R. Laur-Belart, *Führer durch Augusta Raurica* (1966), fig. 80.

Lent by the Römerhaus und Museum Augst, Switzerland (A 1757); acquired 1957.

250. Seated Mercury

2nd cent. A. D.; H: 0.159, W: 0.076; torso hollow cast, lower arms and legs solid, surface emerald green, reddish brown on r. shoulder, whitish coloration on l. thigh, high polish; missing l. hand, l. foot, r. arm below elbow, r. leg below knee.

Identified as Mercury by a chlamys pinned on his l. shoulder, the figure was originally seated on a rock, l. leg advanced, in an attitude of suspended action. A projection above the hair indicates that the head may have been winged. The type recalls a famous bronze in Naples thought by some to be a Roman copy, by others a Hellenistic original of the circle of Lysippos. (JAS)

Unpublished. Position of body and legs close to Hill, 66, no. 35, fig. 66, and Beschi, 48–49. For Naples bronze, Ruesch, no. 841. Position of arms may derive from a second Lysippan example, discussed by Picard, IV², 595 ff., Babelon-Blanchet, no. 345. Cf. also F. Johnson, *Lysippos* (Durham, N.C., 1927) and bibl. for Nos. 248–249. I am grateful to Prof. J. G. Pedley for examining the bronze.

Lent by the collection of Prof. and Mrs. George H. Forsyth, University of Michigan.

251. Selene

(see plate V, p. 226)
1st cent. A. D.; H: 0.11, W: 0.075; black patina, some light green; niello (?) inlays in cloak; torches from both hands broken off, r. foot missing. Ex-coll. Bellori.

Selene is shown floating, dressed in a belted garment. The head is bent forward and topped by a crescent. With both hands she grasps her cloak, which billows like a sail over her head. (HM)

C. Friederichs, *Berlins antike Bildwerke*, II, *Geräte und Broncen im Alten Museum* (Berlin, 1871), 394, no. 1845; Neugebauer, 111 f., pl. 58; —, *Führer*, 58, pl. 68; —, *MZ*, 28 (1933), 85, fig. 2. For the type of Selene, cf. *Ibid.*, 83 ff.

Lent by the Staatliche Museen Berlin, Antikenabteilung (Fr. 1845).

252. Youth

Early 1st cent. A. D.; H: 0.603;
hollow cast, surface mottled brown
with green spots; missing r. foot,
tips of three fingers; both legs repaired at knee, r. arm at armpit;
mouth misshapen, possibly through
attempted repair. Ultra-violet examination has shown extensive
repair. Allegedly from Spain. Ex-
coll. C. Ruxton Love.

The face is round — chubby —
with a heavy chin; the hair,
drawn back from the center, lies
on the neck in slightly wavy locks.
He is reminiscent of late Hellenistic representations of Eros as a
youth, but the pose is more frontal, the forms stolid. The awk-
wardly placed arms and open
hands may have held attributes;
they illustrate the persistence of
a native Italic element called by
R. Brilliant the "appendage aesthetic" (Gesture and Rank in Roman
Art [New Haven, 1963], 26 f.).
(JAS)

Mentioned Art Quarterly, 16 (1953),
146. For Eros type, Bieber, Hellenistic, 98; W. Klein, Praxiteles (Leipzig, 1898), 219 ff., fig. 237. Cf. Thouvenot, 11, no. 11, pl. 2; P. Lebel,
Catalogue des collections archéologiques de Besançon, V, Les bronzes
figurés, Annales Litteraires de
l'Université de Besançon, V, 26
(1959), fig. 1, pl. 26; de Ridder, 55,
no. 345, pl. 30 (Dionysos).

Lent by the Portland Art Museum,
Ore. (52.179).

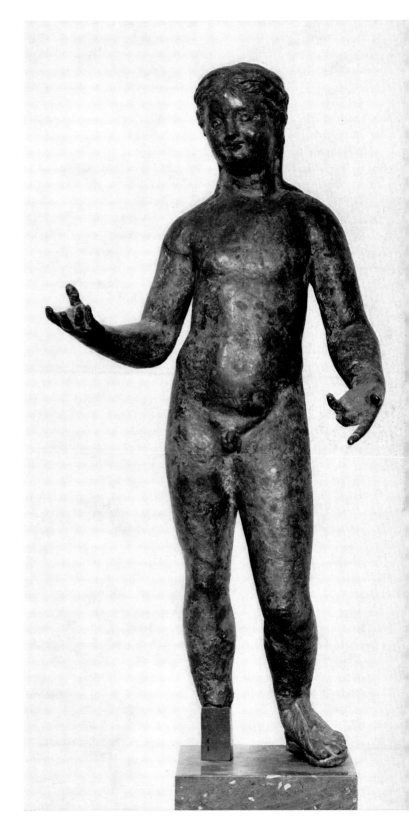

253. Diana

1st cent. A.D.; H: 0.133; glossy dark green patina; r. lower arm, originally worked separately, now missing, r. breast badly damaged, core partly visible in back, eyes originally inlaid. Allegedly from Yugoslavia.

The goddess wears high shoes and a belted chiton with sleeves. A quiver hangs behind her r. shoulder. The extended r. hand originally held a bow. The fingers of her l. hand are closed around an object, perhaps a strap or leash. On front and back run two vertical bands whose silver inlay is partly preserved. (HM)

Unpublished. HH suggests that the bands, which do not conform to the fall of draperies or serve any apparent decorative function, might have been intended as an optic guide for the sculptor employing this piece as a model for a large-scale sculpture. He suggests that the figure was part of a group of Diana hunting with her hound.

Lent by M. and Mme. Niklaus Dürr, Carouge, Switzerland.

254. Dancing Lar

C. 100 A. D. or later; H: 0.167; solid cast, surface corroded and tarnished with some breaks; hands missing at wrists.

Protector of the Roman family *(Lar familiaris)*, he held a cornucopia or rhyton in his raised r. hand, libation bowl in his lowered l. The liveliness of motion argues for a Flavian or Trajanic date. Painted and bronze examples flanking the *genius* of the master of the house (No. 243) were preserved in private family shrines *(lararia)* in Pompeii (G. Boyce, *MAAR*, 14 [1937], esp. pls. 18:1, 31:1). Derived from the Hellenistic dancer type through painting (Theodotus in the 2nd century B. C.), this statuary type was probably created when Augustus introduced the cult of the *Lares Augusti*. (GMAH)

Unpublished. For preserved bases, dedicatory inscriptions, dancing type, H. Klumbach, *Römische Kleinkunst* (Mainz, 1957), pls. 4–5; G. Behrens, *Germania*, I (1917), 95, ill. 96. For discussion, Menzel, *Speyer*, 12; —, *Trier*, 25, no. 53. Cf. sale, Sotheby (June 13, 1966), no. 162, close to Gallo-Roman Lar, no. 166. For cult revival under Augustus, I. Ryberg, *MAAR*, 22 (1953), 53, figs. 28b, 37c.

Lent by Mr. and Mrs. Joseph Ternbach.

255. Jupiter

1st–2nd cent. A. D.; H. with base: 0.595, diam. of base: 0.205; brownish patina, eyes, lips, nipples, ornaments on sandals inlaid with silver and copper; ancient repairs. Allegedly found in a Roman well in Brée, Province Limburg, Belgium.

The god stands on his r. leg on a simple moulded base; his l. leg is set back. The r. arm is lowered and the hand holds a bundle of thunderbolts. The l. arm is bent upwards, a cloak draped over it. The body is strong and well modelled.

This beautifully worked and excellently preserved statuette of Jupiter, as well as the statuette of Zeus from Goethe's collection (cf. L. Curtius, *RM*, 45 [1930], 1 ff., pls. 1–2, supplemented by K. A. Neugebauer, *AA* [1935], 321 ff.), may probably be traced back to a bronze statuette in Florence (Curtius, *op. cit.*, 88, n. 5, pls. 3–5). Neugebauer proved, however, that the original of the bronze Zeus in Weimar was a statuette found at Freienwalde, from which a cast was made for Goethe. The original statuette was possibly made in Gaul, not before the mid 2nd century A.D. Neugebauer considers it an eclectic work, not a copy of a 5th century B. C. original. The same question may be raised about the statuette in Brussels. In certain details the statuette undoubtedly is similar to the one in Florence, but here also eclecticism is evident; while consciously going back to peculiarities of 5th century B.C. sculptures, an essentially Roman work of art results. This can be seen especially in the proportions of the body and its compactness. Thus the Jupiter from Brée is the last link in a chain which perhaps began with the Zeus from Florence. (HM)

Unpublished. Forthcoming publication by H. Menzel in *Antike Plastik*.

Lent by the Musées royaux d'Art et d'Histoire, Brussels (Inv. A 3288); acquired 1936.

Plate VI, No. 255
Jupiter from Brée

256. Venus

1st–2nd cent. A. D.; H: 0.20;
glossy patina; missing r. arm,
l. lower leg, l. ear. Found 1877
in Augsburg, Lueginslandgäß-
chen.

The goddess stands on her l. leg and unties her sandal on her r. foot, reversing the pose of most such compositions (cf. No. 135). A cloak covers her back and winds around her r. thigh. Breast and body are uncovered. The head is turned sideways. Her eyes and garment have silver inlay. (HM)

P. Arndt–W. Amelung, *Photographische Einzelaufnahmen antiker Sculpturen*, IV (Munich, 1899), 24, no. 1060–1061; *Germania Romana* (Bamberg, 1922), pl. 74:8; *Germania Romana*[2] IV (1928), pl. 39:8; M. Berhart in *Das Schwäbische Museum* (Augsburg, 1930), 28 ff.; W. Schleiermacher, *Augusta, 955–1955* (Munich, 1955), fig. 5, pl. 3; W. Hübner, *Jahrbuch des Römisch-Germanischen Zentralmuseums Mainz*, 5 (1958), 179, no. 10; *Paris, 1963, 139, no. 639. For the type, Bieber, *Hellenistic*, 144.

Lent by the Städtische Kunstsammlungen – Römisches Museum, Augsburg (169/1).

257. Vulcan

2nd cent. A. D.; H: 0.37, W: 0.195; r. foot broken off, attributes and front of l. foot missing, leg broken and repaired.

Dressed in a short tunic *(exomis)* and round felt cap *(pilos)*, the bearded god stands on his r. leg; his l. leg is drawn back. Both arms are stretched forward. His open hands originally held a hammer and tongs, attributes of the god of the forge. (HM)

Genava, 29 (1951), 3, pl. 1; W. Deonna, *Musées de Genève* (April, 1951); *Basel, 1957, 127, no. 37; for Vulcan, P. M. Duval, *Gallia,* 10 (1952), 43 ff.

Lent by the Musée d'art et d'histoire, Geneva, Switzerland (19229).

258. Bust of Female Divinity (Ceres?)

Late 2nd or 3rd cent. A. D.; preserved H: 0.095, W: 0.08; shiny dark brown patina; major gap in upper r. arm (casting failure?), numerous small perforations in the metal.

The large, simple proportions and grand air of this figure proclaim her as descended from a Phidian prototype, perhaps by way of a secondary version in the 2nd century B.C. Her gaze follows the implied motion of her arms to the l. Detailing of the sleeve seams, hair, eyes, and wreath is mechanically competent. Her brow, framed by loose locks, gains added mass and impressiveness from the tubular wreath of leaves and berries. (DGM)

Unpublished. Cf. colossal marble bust of woman (cult statue?) from Temple of Poseidon on the Isthmus, O. Broneer, *Hesperia*, 22 (1953), 189–191, pl. 59a–c.

Lent by the Museum of Art, Rhode Island School of Design (59.022).

260. Boy in Armor Reading Scroll

1st cent. A.D.; H: 0.074. Allegedly from Syria.

Unfolding a scroll *(volumen)*, the boy wears an undecorated battle cuirass, cloak thrown over his r. shoulder, and military boots. Ordinary schoolboys did not wear armor; the owner suggests that a prince might be represented. "Born in a camp ... brought up in the dress of a common soldier" (Suetonius), the Emperor Gaius (37–41 A.D.) was, as a child, the darling of the army. In 18–19 A.D., at the age of six or seven, he visited Syrian Antioch with his Imperial parents Germanicus and Agrippina. To appear as a little soldier even in school would be in character for Gaius, nicknamed Caligula ("Little Boots") by the soldiers. The tragic death at the age of thirty-seven of Germanicus, the popular commander at Antioch, allegedly by poisoning (Piso was suspected) would have increased the sympathy for Caligula. He might even have been envisaged as *"imperator"* reading an announcement. The rendering seems very sympathetic. There is something of a child bending forward, reading with effort; yet no attempt is made to ridicule the masquerade as an emperor. The bronze might be a votive offering of one of the officers close to Germanicus. (GMAH)

Unpublished. For armor, *CAH*, vol. of plates, IV, 136b, 140a (showing Caligula's father Germanicus?); C. C. Vermeule, *Berytus*, 13 (1959), 3 ff. See Suetonius, *Lives of the Twelve Caesars*, ch. 4. For schoolboys reciting, Hanfmann, *Roman*, fig. 133; for Caligula, No. 230.

Lent by a private collection.

259. Philosopher

Late Hadrianic-early Antonine, 130–160 A.D.; H: 0.183; hollow cast, surface predominately blue-black; missing r. arm from above elbow, l. forearm and foot. Allegedly from Asia Minor.

The figure wears the *pallium*, the Roman adaptation of the Greek himation, with sleeved chiton, garments of the philosopher. Hellenistic prototypes are suggested (Bieber, *Hellenistic*, figs. 224–225, 226–229), but unlike much Hadrianic neo-classical sculpture, the bronze is a sensitive portrayal of the intellectual and contemplative man. The idealization of features, plasticity of hair, and general resemblance to Hadrian are consistent with the owner's date, c. 140 A.D. The philosopher type has been adapted to imperial portrayal, as is observed by C. Morey regarding its occurrence on later sarcophagi. (JAS)

Unpublished. Cf. seated philosopher from a *lararium* group, Beschi, 11 ff., pls. 1–2. For sculptured types on Asiatic sarcophagi, C. Morey, *Sardis* V:1, *The Sarcophagus of Claudia Antonia Sabina* (Princeton, 1942), 67–68, esp. figs. 12, 106. For the *pallium*, L. Wilson, *The Clothing of the Ancient Romans* (Baltimore, 1938), 78 ff.

Lent by the Collection of George Ortiz.

261. Tipsy Hercules

2nd–3rd cent. A. D.; H: 0.167;
glossy green-brown patina.

Hercules here relaxes from the
tension and fatigue of his labors,
although his posture, as if caught
in a heel-kicking Irish jig and almost floating above the rock on
which he is meant to sit, is unsure.
Cradling his club upright in his
l. arm, he grips a kantharos in his
r., from which he could be pouring a libation or spilling his drink
This merry interpretation of the
garlanded, inebriated hero could
serve equally well for Mercury or
Bacchus. (DGM)

E. Robinson, MFA *Annual Report*
(1901), 36; —, *AA* (1902), col. 131;
AJA, 6 (1902), 377.

Lent by the Museum of Fine Arts,
Boston (01.8375).

262. Bust of Victory on Plaque

2nd cent. A.D.; H. with plaque: 0.277; solid cast, traces of black magnesium deposit from fire, sand; three original, two secondary nail holes; missing top lock of hair, r. wing tip, (viewer's) l. part of plaque.

The bust is attached obliquely to a curving plaque. According to L. Casson (by letter), she was probably the name emblem of a ship ("Victoria"). Representations of Hellenistic and Roman ships show
such plaques *(epotides)* attached to ends of a cross beam (outrigger) in front of the rowers; a late Hellenistic pair, Bacchus and Adriadne, was found in the shipwreck at Mahdia (120 B.C., Fuchs, 15, pls. 10 f.).
Despite her fine Classic profile, Victory's immediate model was late Hellenistic like the "breathing"
Athena bust from Mahdia (Fuchs, 22, pl. 24). Solid flesh, sharply cut eyebrows, and emphatic eyes
characterize Roman workmanship. W. Fuchs and H. Menzel consider such busts parts of votive models, not of real ships. (GMAH)

G. M. A. Hanfmann, *Fogg Newsletter*, 3:5 (June 1966), ill. Cf. Ucelli, fig. 290; M. Floriani-Squarciapino, *Scavi
di Ostia*, 5:3 (Rome, 1955), 191, pls. 32, 42 f.; Menzel, *Trier*, no. 279, pl. 88.

Lent by the Fogg Art Museum, Harvard University (1966.12).

263. Mercury

2nd–3rd cent. A.D.; H: 0.135; green patina through which bronze shows in part; surface cracked, flaked off in places. Found in Wawern, Kr. Prüm, Germany.

The nude god is seated. The body is muscular and athletic. The head, with a dull face, is almost too small for the body. The r. hand on his thigh holds a three-cornered pouch. The l. arm lies across the stomach with index finger stretched out. The piece is very similar to No. 248, which in turn goes back to an original of the early 4th cent. B.C. representing the youthful Herakles at rest (P. Lehmann, *Statues on Coins of Southern Italy and Sicily in the Classical Period* [New York, 1946], 49 ff.). (HM)

Philantrop, 3 (1846); F. Hettner, *Illustrierter Führer durch das Provinzialmuseum in Trier* (1903), 87, ill.; Reinach, IV, 96:8; Menzel, *Trier,* 19 f., no. 38, pl. 18–19.

Lent by the Rheinisches Landesmuseum, Trier (G 36).

264. Lady

C. 200 A.D.; H: 0.154. Allegedly from Syria.

The attractive figurine is a descendant of the late Classical (c. 300 B.C.) "large Herculanum" type. Originally portraying a goddess (Demeter?), it was often adapted for Roman portrait statues. This hairdo was popular under the Syrian Empress Julia Domna (c. 193–217 A.D.). The soft, serious face is also characteristic of the Severan age. (GMAH)

Unpublished. Cf. Bieber, *Hellenistic,* 176, fig. 748. For hairdo, G. M. A. Richter, *Catalogue of Engraved Gems, Greek, Etruscan, and Roman,* MMA (Rome, 1956), nos. 496, 498; for expression, C. Blümel, *Römische Bildnisse* (Berlin, 1933), no. R 87, pl. 53.

Lent by a private collection.

265. Gladiator

1st cent. A. D.; H: 0.078, W: 0.043; solid cast, surface green with cuprite.

Gladiators were grouped in schools and trained in different methods of combat. They were identified by their armor and equipment. The r. arm sleeved in metal or leather rising above the shoulder, girdle held by a double belt, greaves, and visored helmet with crest identify this one as a member of the Samnite school. He was free-standing and probably grouped with an opponent of a different type; his l. foot may have rested on a fallen foe. (JAS)

Unpublished. For group, J. Sambon, 42, no. 365, pl. 46, also 8, no. 53, pl. 5 (lamp with Thracian vs. Samnite gladiator). Cf. Hill, no. 122. On the subject, A. Balil, *La ley gladiatoria de Italica* (Madrid, 1961), esp. 37 ff., 107 f.

Lent by the Eric de Kolb Collection.

266. Jupiter

2nd–3rd cent. A. D.; H: 0.20; dark brown patina; base missing. Found in Vleuten, The Netherlands.

Jupiter stands erect on his r. leg and has the l. leg set to the side. His l. arm is stretched forward, the hand grasping a thunderbolt. His r. arm is raised. A cloak draped over the shoulder falls over the upper arm, goes across the back, and winds over the lower part of his r. arm. (HM)

G. van Hoorn, *Gids door de Verzameling van Nederlandsche en Romeinsche Oudheden in het Centraal Museum te Utrecht* (1928), 19, fig. 12; ——, *Catalogus van een keurcollectie uit de Archaeologische Verzameling van het Provinciaal Utrechts Genootschap van Kunsten en Wetenschappen in het Centraal Museum te Utrecht* (n. d.), 10, fig. 6; ——, *Meded*, 5 (1935), 27 ff., fig. 2; J. H. Jongkees, *Verslag van den conservator over 1964* (Utrecht, 1965), 64, puts the Jupiter of Vleuten among the descendants of Zeus Brontaios of Leochares; *Paris, 1963, 134, no. 614, pl. 44. On Leochares, J. Charbonneaux, *MonPiot*, 53 (1963), 9 ff.

Lent by Provinciaal Oudheidkundig Museum, Utrecht, The Netherlands (3393); acquired 1865.

267. Mars

2nd–3rd cent. A.D.; H: 0.211; geen patina, surface slightly granular; thumb of r. hand, l. hand, r. foot, and l. leg below knee broken off. Found in Neumagen, Germany.

The nude youthful god stands on his l. leg, the r. leg drawn back. His r. arm is lifted, his l. arm stretched forward. He wears a tall Corinthian helmet; the crest is supported by a sphinx. (HM)

E. Gose, *TrZ*, 27 (1964), 260 f., pl. 47; Menzel, *Trier*, 7, no. 12, pls. 6–8. Closely related is a Mars in Reims, de Ridder, I, 127, no. 1045, pl. 61. For the type, to which No. 268 also belongs, cf. K. A. Neugebauer, *BonnJbb*, 147 (1942), 228 ff.

Lent by the Rheinisches Landesmuseum Trier (55.49).

268. Mars

2nd–3rd cent. A. D.; H: 0.166, W: 0.086; no patina, slightly corroded. Found in Tzum, Gem. Franekeradeel, 1911.

The youthful nude god stands on his r. leg; the l. leg is drawn back. His r. arm is lifted high, his l. is bent. On his head is a tall Corinthian helmet. (HM)

Verslag Friesch Genootschap 83 (1910–1911), 19; P. C. J. A. Boeles, *Friesland in den Romeinschen Tijd* (1917), 32 ff.; *Steden-spiegel,* Gemeentemuseum, The Hague (1964), no. 43, pl. 8; A. N. Zadoks-Jitta – W. J. T. Peters – W. A. van Es, *Roman Bronze Statuettes from The Netherlands,* I (1967), no. 18. With No. 267 it belongs to the type of Gallo-Roman Mars discussed by K. A. Neugebauer, *BonnJbb,* 147 (1942), 228 ff.

Lent by the Fries Museum, Leeuwarden, The Netherlands (Inv. No. 123–106).

269. Mars

2nd–3rd cent. A. D.; H: 0.20;
green patina; r. hand and front of
plume broken off, r. front side of
helmet dented. Found 1965 in Blicquy, Hainaut, Belgium.

The youthful nude god stands on
his r. leg; the l. is drawn back.
The r. arm is lifted and the l. arm
is stretched forward. He holds in
his l. hand a sword which leans
against his shoulder. He wears a
tall Corinthian helmet. (HM)

M. Amand, *Latomus*, 26 (1967), 82–91,
ill. For Mars carrying a sword, K. A. Neugebauer, *BonnJbb*, 147 (1942), 230 ff.;
H. Menzel, *Jahrbuch des Emsländi-
schen Heimatvereins*, 7 (1960), 46 ff.
The piece does not exactly belong
with Nos. 267–268, but resembles
closely a Mars from Dronrijp in the
Museum Leeuwarden (A. N. Zadoks-
Jitta – W. J. T. Peters – W. A. van
Es, *Roman Bronze Statuettes from
The Netherlands*, I [1967], no. 22];
cf. also H. Menzel, *Latomus*, 26
(1967), 92–95 ill.

Lent by M. and Mme. Victor Carton,
Blicquy, Belgium.

270. Isis

2nd cent. A.D.; H: 0.114; base and head hollow cast, blue-green patina, surface somewhat worn but detail not obscured; head inserted into base (probably ancient) and affixed from underside.

The figure bears the attributes of Isis: the globe surrounded by ears of corn with the *uraeus* on her head; the fringed shawl held by an "Isis knot" (cf. No. 124). The face and hair strongly resemble statuettes of Isis (Vermeule, fig. 245; de Ridder, no. 790) and a monumental grave relief from Alexandria (K. Parlasca, *RM*, 71 [1964], 195 ff., pl. 57:2). H. Jucker (I, 188 ff.) documents the association of acanthus leaf with the goddess and points out that a disproportionate number of images of Serapis are limited to the bust, many resting in an acanthus "cup." Probably the piece is a domestic cult image of Isis, pendant to one of Serapis such as that found in Ostia (H. Jucker, II, fig. 85). (JAS)

Mentioned *Art Journal*, 25:1 (1965), 66. For the Serapis bust, M. Floriani-Squarciapino, *I culti orientali ad Ostia* (Leiden, 1962), 26 f., pl. 5:8b.
Lent by Mount Holyoke College, South Hadley, Mass. (CG 10.1965).

271. Bust of Serapis

2nd cent. A.D.; H: 0.385; H. of bust: 0.20, of modius: 0.05, of eagle: 0.135; green patina with red speckles; eyes silver inlaid, inlay of pupils missing. Allegedly from Asia Minor.

This bust of Serapis is dressed in a garment which comes close to the neck. On his head is the *modius* (crown shaped like a corn measure) topped by an eagle. Olive branches in relief appear on the *modius*. Corkscrew curls falling on the forehead are strongly undercut like the enframing hair. At the back the hair is wavy but smooth with a wide wreath of corkscrew curls at the neck. The bust belongs to a common type going back to the enthroned Serapis which, despite all doubts, must be assigned to Bryaxis (G. Lippold in *Festschrift Paul Arndt* [Munich, 1925], 115 ff.; J. Charbonneaux, *MonPiot* 52 [1962], 15 ff.; Picard IV², 878 ff., figs. 364 f., pl. 22). The eagle atop the *modius* on this statuette is unusual. It must be interpreted as an association or equation of Serapis with Jupiter, here symbolized by the eagle. (HM)

Unpublished. For similar busts: Serapis in Villa Albani (J. Charbonneaux, *MonPiot*, 52 [1962], 23, fig. 7); Prague, (L. Castiglione, *Bulletin du Musée National Hongrois des Beaux-Arts*, 12 [1958], 19, fig. 6); Vatican (G. Lippold in *Festschrift Paul Arndt* [Munich, 1925], 124, fig. 8); from Hama, Syria, in Copenhagen, (H. Jucker, *Genava*, 8 [1960], 117, fig. 2). Jupiter busts with eagle occur on lamp disks, H. Menzel, *Antike Lampen*, *Römisch-Germanisches Zentralmuseum zu Mainz*, *Katalog 15* (Mainz, 1954), no. 204, fig. 33:1. For the significance of the eagle in the apotheosis, G. Bruns, *104th Winckelmannsprogramm* (Berlin, 1948), 25 ff.
Lent by The Roger Peyrefitte Collection, Paris..

272. Seated Serapis

1st–2nd cent. A.D.; H: 0.115, W: 0.063; hollow cast, possibly lead filled, green patina; missing lower forearms, hands, throne. Ex-coll. E. Schaefer.

The great cult statue in the Serapaeon at Alexandria was created for Ptolemy II by Bryaxis the Younger; many small images in bronze and terracotta follow it in pose and arrangement of drapery with remarkable constancy. The god bears on his head the *modius*, symbolic of his association with Osiris and the underworld. (JAS)

Unpublished. Cf. van Gulik, 38 f., no. 58; Bieber, *Hellenistic*, 83 f.; Picard, IV², 879 ff., 883, list of comparanda; for painted stucco image at Ostia, M. Floriani-Squarciapino, *I Culti orientali ad Ostia* (Leiden, 1962), 21 f., pl. 6.

Lent by The Newark Museum, Eugene Schaefer Collection (50.1954); gift of Mrs. Eugene Schaefer, 1950.

273. Serapis – Zeus Ammon

Late 3rd–early 4th cent. A.D.; H: 0.146, preserved W. at arms: 0.08; solid cast, surface cleaned; missing r. foot, both hands. Found by the University of Michigan excavations in Karanis, Egypt, in a datable level, 1927; cleaned during late 1950's.

The bearded figure, overlaid with sleeved chiton and draped mantle, was used equally for Jupiter and Serapis. There is apparently no Hellenistic prototype for the standing Serapis; it is, rather, the creation of the early Empire (Istituto per gli Studi Storici Veronesi, *Verona* I [1960], 532). Symbolic of the solar pantheism of the late Empire, this important, dated example bears rams' horns, symbol of Ammon, on either side of his head topped by a headdress once sacred to Osiris. (JAS)

Unpublished. Cf. Perdrizet, 48, no. 79, pl. 21; C. Smith, no. 8, pl. 3. For headdress, *Archaeological Calendar* (Jan. 15–28, 1967) (wooden Ptolmaic panel, N. Schimmel Coll.)

Lent by The Kelsey Museum of Archaeology, The University of Michigan (10881).

274. Pantheistic Divinity on a Couch

150–250 A.D.; H: 0.102, W: 0.082, max. L: 0.137; irregular green patina.

Reclining against a thick cushion on a ceremonial couch, the goddess nurses a baby. She wears a crested cap, probably indicating Phrygian origin, chiton and himation. The many attributes surrounding her exemplify the religious syncretism of the late Empire: purse and caduceus, thunderbolt, cymbals, tamborine, pipes, balances, serpent, frog, tortoise, salamander, seven little goblets. A reclining mother and child is a traditional scene on Sabazios hands (No. 313). (JAS)

C. C. Vermeule, *CJ*, 62 (1966), 108–109, fig. 20. See Reinach, II, 423, no. 5; Babelon-Blanchet, 26, no. 57. On the "Great Mother," M. Nilsson, *Geschichte der griechischen Religionen* (Munich, 1961), 640 ff., esp. 641–642.

Lent by the Museum of Fine Arts, Boston (65.100); Harriet Otis Cruft Fund.

275. Seated Actor

2nd cent. A.D.; H: 0.064; hollow cast, dark green patina. Found below ruins of Temple of Neptune at Sorrento, 1951.

Wearing the comic actor's mask and banquet wreath, dressed in tunic and scanty mantle of a slave, the figure crouches apprehensively on an altar. The buskins, once the mark of god or hero, hint at satiric intent. The type, developed for New Comedy, persisted virtually unchanged through the 2nd century A.D. (JAS)

Unpublished. Cf. de Ridder, I, no. 719; Bieber, *Theater*, figs. 410–413, 556–558, 587, and bibl.; *The Theater in Ancient Art*, The Art Museum, Princeton (1951–1952), nos. 35–36, 38; C. Grandjouan, *Agora* VI, 85, appendix by T. B. L. Webster.

Lent by the Milwaukee Art Center (M65.118); gift of Edmund B. Nielsen.

276. Legionary

Late 2nd cent. A. D.; H: 0.11, W: 0.05; solid cast, patina olive to dark green, traces of iron on r. leg, remnants of incrustation on front, top of helmet; l. foot broken off.

The soldier once held a weapon in his r. hand, a shield or lance in his l.; a sword probably swung from his shoulder. He wears a cuirass with *pteryges* but no insignia. The more summary treatment of the back, a triangular hole for a peg, and traces of a break along the buttocks indicate that he was attached to a vase rim. The grim face with drilled points for the eyes recalls soldiers on the column of Marcus Aurelius. (JAS)

Unpublished. Cf. Richter, *Br.*, 141, no. 305. For Marcus column, G. Becatti, *La colonna coclide istorica* (Rome, 1960), esp. pl. 26. For warrior and barbarian attachments, Bienkowski, 45 ff.

Lent by the collection of Mr. and Mrs. Benjamin Hertzberg; acquired 1960.

277. Tropaeum

1st–2nd cent. A. D.; H: 0.221; sparse, light green patina; helmet missing, modern damage to r. shoulder blade.

A Roman cuirass hangs on a tree stump to which a horizontal pole is nailed. Under it are greaves. The cuirass is ornamented with silver inlays. A sign of victory, the single set of enemy's armor on a stake was erected on the battlefield and sometimes in sanctuaries of victory-giving gods. (HM)

C. Friederichs, *Berlins antike Bildwerke* II, *Geräthe und Broncen im Alten Museum* (Berlin, 1871), 249, no. 1193a; Neugebauer, *Führer*, 65 f., pl. 60; Bruns, 66, fig. 46. For the development of the tropaeum, K. Woelcke, *BonnJbb*, 120 (1911), 127 ff.; C. Picard, *Les trophées romains* (1957).

Lent by the Staatliche Museen Berlin, Antikenabteilung (Fr. 1193a).

278. Cuirass Statuette of a Roman Emperor

Late 2nd–early 3rd cent. A. D.; H: 0.274, W: 0.12; hollow cast over blackened sand core (remains inside), filled with lead, limbs (missing) cast separately, area of join cut flat and hollowed for l. leg, solder and rough projection for r. leg; lead remains where arms were soldered (l. arm went back and down, r. was raised); red-brown to dark green patina; repair at neck, rectangular box on r. shoulder with hole for pin at back. Allegedly from England.

The bearded face, long hair, and deeply drilled eyes (perhaps silver inlaid or enlivened by nails) suggest a representation of one of the Antonine emperors, probably Marcus Aurelius. The cuirass with acanthus tendrils, knotted *cingulum*, gorgoneion, and a single row of *pteryges* embellished with lion head in center and undecorated discs, is consistent with an Antonine date (C. C. Vermeule, *Berytus*, 13 [1959], 64, figs. 60–62). D. K. Hill's argument that the Cairo molds (see below) were pattern parts which could be variously combined (*Hesperia*, 27 [1958], 318 ff.) would be eminently applicable to cuirass statuettes; cuirass, head, posture could be varied at will. (JAS)

Unpublished. For Alexandrian cuirass mold, C. C. Edgar, *Catalogue général des antiquités égyptiennes du Musée du Caire*, VIII, *Greek Moulds* (Cairo, 1903), 10, no. 32033, pl. 6.

Lent by the Eric de Kolb Collection.

279. Provincial Cuirass Statuette

Late 2nd–early 3rd cent. A. D.;
H: 0.307, W: 0.164, D: 0.075; hollow
cast, core of soft, blackened, sandy
material preserved, limbs (missing)
cast separately, head apparently
cast with body; surface dark brown
with cuprite, traces of bright green;
break on chest exposes core, figure bent
inward at bottom. Allegedly from
England.

Provincial workmanship is revealed by the almond-shaped eyes
outlined by deep incisions, schematized gouges indicating hair,
and columnar torso. He wears a
broken wreath with star in center.
The cuirass is embellished with
a *cingulum* knotted over the chest
and a crescent-shaped *insigne*
with lion's head. The face resembles that of a bust, possibly
of Commodus, found in Britain.
The work is a generalized image
of an emperor produced by a
Gallic or British craftsman. (JAS)

Unpublished. For the head men-
tioned, J. M. C. Toynbee, *Art in
Roman Britain* (London, 1963),
125 f., no. 5, pl. 5, also nos. 2–4.
DGM suggests it is one of the
usurper emperors who detached
Gaul and Britain from the Roman
Empire, 275–280 A. D.). For Com-
modus in Britain, M. Rostovtseff,
JRS, 13 (1923), 21 ff.

Lent by the Eric de Kolb Collection.

280. Minerva

Late 3rd–early 4th cent. A. D.;
H: 0.292; hollow cast in two parts,
traces of red pigment on palla,
perhaps originally gilded. Ex-coll.
Trivulzio, Milan.

Though of a size appropriate to
the *lararium* of a wealthy house-
hold, she may reflect a larger cult
statue. The l. hand originally held
a spear, the r. possibly an owl or
patera. An aegis with Medusa
head serves as her breastplate.
The helmet is inscribed on the
back, near the lower edge:
MINERVA. A heavy fold of drapery falling over her l. arm and
across the abdomen conceals the
joining of two separate pieces;
the join shows clearly in back.
Her hair fans out behind her
shoulders in stiff cord-like strands,
hatched in a herringbone pattern.
Simplification of modelling (note
the tubular neck), dry rendering
of drapery, and expression indicate a Constantinian date. (SD)

E. P. Richardson–F. Robinson, *Bulletin of the Detroit Institute of Arts*, 31:3–4 (1951–1952), 71–72, ill.
Lent by The Detroit Institute of Arts (51.229).

281. Hero or Mars

3rd cent. A. D.; H: 0.117; green patina, helmet and back corroded.

This burly fighter, nude except for a high-crested helmet with rams' heads, may be Mars or Alexander the Great. He probably brandished a lance in his clenched r. fist; his l. may have held another weapon or a shield. His barrel-shaped torso, rippling with muscles, harks back to the exaggerated brawn of Hellenistic professional athletes, like one in the Terme Museum. C. C. Vermeule's connection of the broadened physique connoting superhuman strength with the bronze statue of Trebonianus Gallus (251–254 A. D.) in the MMA narrows the date of this figure, in which both a reinterpretation and the incipient disintegration of the Classical canon for the nude male figure are evident. (DGM)

C. C. Vermeule, MFA *Annual Report* (1964), 33; MFA *Calendar of Events 1965*, 1; C. C. Vermeule, *CJ*, 61 (1966), 302, 305 ff., fig. 22. For Trebonianus Gallus, Richter, *Br.*, 154–159, no. 350; cf. also Nos. 267–269; Sieveking, 50–51, pl. 20.
Lent by the Museum of Fine Arts, Boston (64.702); William E. Nickerson Fund.

282. Emperor Constantinus Magnus (306–337 A. D.)

C. 306 A. D.; H: 0.186; green patina; r. arm and l. hand broken off; tang between feet. Allegedly from Gaul.

Represented as an officer of the legions, the Emperor wears the Imperial diadem, an undecorated cuirass with *cingulum*, tunic, and boots. A pelt is pinned on the r. shoulder. Large head and large, upturned eyes impart an icon-like quality to the face, but the striding figure is not rigid. The face resembles those on the Christ-Peter sarcophagi more closely than those of the Constantinian reliefs on the Arch of Constantine (Hanfmann, *Roman*, 124, nos. 141, 142). (JAS)

C. C. Vermeule, MFA *Annual Report* (1962), 32; —, *Berytus*, 15 (1964), 109, no. 320A, pl. 22, figs. 12, 12A.

Lent by the Museum of Fine Arts, Boston (62.1204); gift of Prof. and Mrs. Benjamin Rowland, Jr.

283. Bull

1st cent. B. C.–79 A. D.; H. with base: 0.171, L: 0.159. Found March 18, 1899 in shrine of Roman villa at Scafati, near Pompeii, buried by eruption of Vesuvius in 79 A. D. Ex-coll. M. Guilhou (sale, Hôtel Drouot, 16–18 March, 1905, 44, no. 301, pl. 13); Canessa, Paris; J. P. Morgan (sale, Parke-Bernet, March 22–25, 1944, 25, no. 110); P. Tozzi.

This majestic bull stands atop its original pedestal. A trace of an attribute on the back of its head suggests it may represent the Egyptian bull-god Apis. The discovery with it of other syncretistic Egyptianizing objects strengthens this interpretation, indicating that the villa's owner espoused the neo-Egyptian cults then popular in Rome. The pose was a standard one (cf. Reinach, III, 214:6, IV, 487:5). The same dignified monumentality, with similar handling of details such as the tuft of hair at the end of the tail, hooves, and neck region occurs on a larger bull in Cincinnati. (SD)

A. Sogliano, *NSc*, 24 (1899), 395, fig. 6; A. Furtwängler, *BonnJbb*, 107 (1901), 37–65, cf. also —, *BonnJbb*, 108–109 (1902), 239–240 and 114–115 (1906), 199–201 (further discussion of the Apis type); O. Theatès, *Le Musée*, 5 (1908), 26, ill. 25; Reinach, III, 214:9, IV, 485:5; *Detroit, 1947, 12, 48, no. 88, ill.; E. Richardson–F. Robinson, *Bulletin of the Detroit Institute of Arts*, 31:3–4 (1951–1952), 70, ill.; *Bulletin of the Allen Memorial Art Museum*, 11:3 (1954), 151, no. 10 ("Exhibition of Ancient Bronzes," Feb. 24–March 14, 1954).

Lent by The Detroit Institute of Arts (45.120).

284. Lion

1st cent. B. C.–1st cent. A. D.; H: 0.064, L: 0.114, W: 0.038; hollow cast, silver teeth.

The striding lion bares silver teeth. Two small depressed circles lie along the side of the spine over the hindquarter. The vivid naturalism of the piece can only have resulted from observation of a living beast. An identical lion of almost exactly the same dimensions in Madrid, less well preserved and lacking its teeth, appears to be a casting failure which was never chased. (SD)

Mentioned *Art Quarterly*, 24 (1961), 97. For the Madrid piece, Thouvenot, 70, no. 345, pl. 19; cf. Menzel, *Trier*, no. 278a.
Lent by the Seattle Art Museum. Eugene Fuller Memorial Collection (Cs11.37).

285. Leopard

1st cent. B. C.–1st cent. A. D.; H: 0.038; solid cast, green patina; part of tail missing. Allegedly from Tarentum.

The great cats were prized in the arena; the use of leopard, lynx, lion, and others is documented by Jennison, who points out that the term "panther," derived from the Latin *panthera*, most often meaning leopard, does not designate a distinct zoological species. Although the forms are heavy, the artist has accurately observed the animal at bay, uncertain whether to attack or retreat. Three holes in the oval base (one preserving traces of iron) show that it was intended for attachment, possibly to the *antyx* (rim) of a chariot. (JAS)

Unpublished. Cf. C. Smith, 20, no. 50. On leopards, G. Jennison, *Animals for Show and Pleasure in Ancient Rome* (Manchester, 1937), esp. 183 ff.; L. Brown, 170 ff.

Lent by The Art Museum, Princeton University (38–4); acquired 1938.

286. Running Griffin

2nd–3rd cent. A.D.; H: 0.04, W: 0.014, L: 0.06; solid cast, light green patina; missing r. foreleg and wing tip, most of l. wing. Ex-coll. E. Schaefer.

The beauty of execution of the Greek griffin, a potent symbol (cf. Nos. 65, 67), has given way to manufacture of little more than an amulet. The craftsman knew the form expected and even developed the muscles somewhat, but detailing of wings and feathers has been reduced to a series of curved grooves and hasty gouges. (JAS)

The Museum, n. s. 3:2 (1951), 16, ill. For running griffins on chariot sides, E. von Mercklin, *Jdl*, 48 (1933), 84 ff., figs. 66, 74–77.

Lent by the Newark Museum, Eugene Schaefer Collection (50.374); gift of Mrs. Eugene Schaefer, 1950.

287. Lion Protome

1st cent. A.D.; preserved L: 0.22; hollow cast, gray-green patina, traces of gilding in mouth and mane; hole for attachment on underside, hole in r. side of tube, which is raggedly broken; missing l. forepaw. Allegedly found in the ruins of Iconium (Konya), Turkey, in a garden with No. 293.

In proportions, curving form and position of attachment hole it resembles a hippopotamus protome in Athens, used as a chariot attachment. The hippo has a rectangular shaft with loop and two hooks attached on its underside at the corolla. A similar device was probably attached to the lion. The naturalistically rendered animal seems ready to give his all to the race, bursting forth from the corolla with forelegs stretched, mouth open, mane disordered. (JAS)

Unpublished. Cf. E. von Mercklin, *Jdl*, 48 (1933), 125 ff., hippo protome, fig. 46. A later example: P. La Baume, *Römisches Kunstgewerbe* (Braunschweig, 1964), 257, fig. 242.

Lent by the University Museum, University of Pennsylvania (48-2-291).

288. Dolphin Handle

Probably Augustan, H: 0.135; dull green-brown patina, plaque and dolphins cast in one piece, eyes of dolphins and fish inlaid with silver.

Two dolphins dive into a sea inhabited by two scaly fish and an octopus; their tails form the handle of a large vessel. There are no known parallels. The extraordinary beauty of execution and the symbolic attachment of the dolphin to many gods might suggest the handle's application to a ritual vessel. (JAS)

Münzen und Medaillen, Auktion 22, 13 May 1961, no. 86; *Schimmel, no. 36. For the meaning of the dolphin in paganism, E. Goodenough, *Jewish Symbols in the Graeco-Roman Period*, V (New York, 1958), 22 ff.

Lent by The Schimmel Collection.

289. A and B. Chariot Fittings – Two Maenads

C. 200 A.D.; H. of each: 0.185, H. of base: 0.038, W: 0.055, L: 0.06, W. of loop: 0.04; hollow cast, dark green patina.

The two maenads are virtually identical, inclining their heads in opposite directions. Each has her hair pulled into a low bun in back and wears a wreath of pine; small locks fall in front of the ears. The sideward and upward gaze imitates a Hellenistic model. The lips are parted, the eyes are drilled for insertion of pins. The busts grow out of a leafy chalice. Below this is a profiled rectangular box, open at the back and pierced at the sides. Presumably a triangular chariot pole was inserted into the back and fastened by a transverse pin through the side holes. The heavy semicircular loop below may have guided the reins. (GMAH)

Unpublished. For similar "box-base" cf. Menzel, *Speyer*, 45, pl. 51, metal fitting from Geinsheim-Bobingen, found with horse trappings and other chariot parts, with bibl.

Lent by Mr. and Mrs. Joseph Ternbach.

290. Helmeted Male Bust

Probably 3rd cent. A.D.; H: 0.205, W: 0.126; solid cast, plated with thin sheet of silver which remains on l. shoulder, chest, hair, helmet.

The use of this bronze is suggested by a somewhat earlier bust of Minerva from what was probably a state quadriga from Thrace, dated 1st century A.D. (G. Seure, *BCH*, 28 [1904], 210 ff., esp. 237, figs. 31 and 36). Seure suggests it was placed on the chariot rim (*antyx*) just before it curved outward, and served as a handle. The loop at the back of the neck, the simple crest of the helmet, and the shape of the supporting plaque with hole in back and front correspond to the Missouri piece, which probably represents Mars. (JAS)

Missouri Alumnus (March 1963), 7, fig. 15.
Lent by the Museum of Art and Archaeology, University of Missouri, Alumni Achievement Fund Purchase (62.30).

291. Triple Hecate

50–200 A.D.; max. H: 0.176; brown patina; missing two crescents on polos, part of third, two snake heads, two torches, parts of feet. Allegedly from Aegina.

Each wears a belted Doric chiton, polos with three stars and large crescent on top. Two figures held snakes; the third held two torches. According to Pausanias (II, 30, 2) the mysteries of Hecate were established by Orpheos the Thracian on Aegina. He reports a wooden statue by Myron there, but believed that Alcamenes made the first triple image. A 3rd century A.D. plaque (C. Grandjouan, *Agora* VI, 83, no. 1113) showing a triple Hecate with stag and collared dog is apparently based on a famous sculptured group. (JAS)

C. von Stackelberg, *Die Gräber der Hellenen* (Berlin, 1837), 47, pl. 72; Reinach, II¹, 323:9; C. C. Vermeule, *CJ*, 60 (1965), 295, fig. 9. See Walters, nos. 1011, 1012; Bieber, *Cassel*, no. 148; M. Nilsson, *Geschichte der griechischen Religionen* (Munich, 1961), 541 (association with the underworld), 696 (Selene-Hecate); No. 312 (votive plaque).

Lent by the Museum of Fine Arts, Boston (64.6); Edwin E. Jack Fund.

292. Silenus Herm

1st–2nd cent. A.D.; H: 0.135; solid cast, dark brown patina with areas of bright metal on hair, beard, genitals; phallus missing. Incrustation removed from pilaster, 1967. Ex-coll. Edward Perry Warren.

The head and body of a silen surmount a pilaster decorated with a linear, foliate pattern. The body is rendered to the hips in the round. The arms are not represented below the shoulders. The type is Hellenistic, resembling heads found at Mahdia (Fuchs, 21, pl. 22). Similar is a herm from the Dutuit collection (Dutuit, I, 12, no. 11, pl. 13) bearing a cape over its head and thought to be a knife handle. On the Bowdoin herm's head is a flat cap. K. Herbert believed it to be crested, but A. Steinberg has determined that the "crest" is a purely functional peg. An ancient peg protrudes from the back of the pilaster flush with the bottom. (JAS)

Casson, 14, no. 115; Herbert, 120–121, no. 430.

Lent by the Warren Collection, Bowdoin College Museum of Art (1923.38).

293. Herm

1st cent. A.D.; H: 0.234, base 0.032 by 0.02; hollow cast, soft green patina, some incrustation; rectangular opening at base, circular opening (diam.: 0.02) on top of head. Bought in the bazaar, Konya, Turkey, May 23, 1907; allegedly found at Iconium (Konya).

The head is capped and beardless; the body tapers from the shoulder to a flat rectangular pillar. On each side at the bottom is a plastically rendered fern-like leaf. Two pegs protrude from the "shoulders," resembling those by which garlands were hung on herms of Priapus, god of vegetation and fertility. A vine encircles the head, passes over the pegs, and crosses the torso above the phallus. The patina is the same as that on No. 287, with which it is said to have been found. (JAS)

Unpublished.

Lent by the University Museum, University of Pennsylvania (48-2-271).

294. Double Herm

1st cent. A.D.; H: 0.191; hollow cast, green and blue patina; rectangular opening through torso at edge of arms. According to the Dutuit catalogue, Mme. E. Castellani said four such herms were found in 1883 at Torre del Greco, near Pompeii. Ex-coll. W. R. Hearst.

The charming smiling *paniskos* and *paniske* exemplify the best of Hellenistic decorative work as continued by the Romans. The eyes were originally enlivened by metal nails. Both have pointed ears. In the hair of the female vine leaves and berries are intertwined; a ringlet falls on each shoulder. The male wears the pelt of a goat; two slender horns curve back from his forehead. The opening under the arm resembles those on the double herms from the second ship from Nemi (Silen, maenads) which ended in long tapering pillars and have been reconstructed as supports for the ship's balustrade (Ucelli, 175, fig. 189, 220 ff., figs. 241—243). (JAS)

Apparently from the Castellani collection: A. Castellani, vente de Rome (1884), no. 277; Dutuit I, 17—18, no. 20, pl. 23; *Burlington, 1904, 63, no. D106, pl. 67, coll. G. Salting. Three identical objects: *Burlington, 1904, no. B59, pl. 67, coll. W. Rome; Berlin, Antiquarium; W. Froehner, *Collection H. Hoffmann*, sale, Hôtel Drouot, 26—27 May 1886, no. 480, pl. 37. See also Spinazzola, 252, top shelf (five very similar figures); Victoria and Albert Museum, A. 585—1910.

Lent by the Los Angeles County Museum of Art, The William Randolph Hearst Collection (51.18.9).

295. Lamp

C. 20–50 A. D.; H: 0.057, L: 0.203, L. of spout: 0.095, diam. of foot: 0.077; hollow cast, silver and copper inlay, rectangular hole at back for (lost) handle, hole for suspension at join of spout holes.

On the top is an openwork seven-petaled pattern with incised rays, a ring of silver-inlaid ivy leaves, and a copper-inlaid rim with hook (running dog) pattern; on the spout, acanthus step on dissolved palmette. The underside of the spout shows an acanthus tree with spiralling plants and silver-inlaid buds. Side of body: seven alternating palmettes and flowers in arcade formation over acanthus. The bottom is plain with holes for attachment to a metal stand. Ornament depends on Augustan models, but execution is heavier, indicating a Tiberian or Claudian date. (GMAH)

*From the Shipwreck of Time, Staten Island Museum, 1965, no. 9, ill.
Lent by Mr. and Mrs. Joseph Ternbach.

296. Lamp with Sleeping Greyhounds

1st cent. A.D.; L: 0.172; hollow cast, dark olive green patina, small spots of light green corrosion. Edge of spout, end of one volute missing. Allegedly from Alexandria.

In form this handleless lamp (half plastic vase) belongs to a class made in bronze and terracotta chiefly during the Julio-Claudian period. The adaptation of a sleeping greyhound curled around her puppy to the circular lamp discus proclaims the continuing pre-eminence of Alexandria in developing genre themes. (DGM)

C. C. Vermeule, *CJ*, 57 (1962), 150, fig. 6; —, *FA*, 17 (1962), no. 243. For lamps, H. Menzel, *Antike Lampen, Römisch-Germanisches Zentralmuseum zu Mainz, Katalog 15* (Mainz, 1954), 30–40, figs. 31:1–18; 32:1–16; 33:3–16, 18–23; others with greyhounds: H. B. Walters, *Catalogue of Greek and Roman Lamps in the British Museum* (London, 1914), nos. 26, 430 f., fig. 5, pl. 11.

Lent by the Museum of Fine Arts, Boston (60.1451); Harriet Otis Cruft Fund.

297. Lamp with Theatrical Mask

Late 1st cent. B.C.–2nd cent. A.D.; H: 0.127, W: 0.089; hollow cast, natural marine patina, some corrosion around bowl. Allegedly from South Italy.

The handle, surmounted by a theatrical mask, curves downward and flares out into a double-rimmed bowl, tapering toward the wick hole. Probably a chain with ball on it was inserted into the keyhole opening at the wide part of the bowl and led up through the mouth of the mask to be hung from a large lamp stand. The tragic mask frequently appears on lamp handles, probably with apotropaic intent. (JAS)

Unpublished. For lamp stands, F. B. Tarbell, *Chicago Field Museum of Natural History Publication 130*, 7:3 (1909), III, fig. 69; for lamps with masks, Edgar, pl. 12, H. Rolland, *Bronzes antiques de haute provence* (Gallia Supplement 13, Paris, 1965), no. 357.

Lent by the Denver Art Museum Collection (AN-58); acquired 1957.

298. Lamp – Frog Bitten by a Snake

2nd–3rd cent. A. D.; H: 0.05, L: 0.32, L. of frog: 0.13; dark green patina; snake tail broken.

The frog bites a shell; a water snake (ancient *hydra; tropidonotus natrix*) bites his l. hind leg. The shell was a nozzle for the lamp wick; oil was poured into an opening on the frog's back. The group illustrates the loves and hates of animals (Oppian, *Cynegetica*, 38). The water snake was a celebrated destroyer of frogs (*Batrachomyomachy*, 82; Aelian, *De natura animalium*, 9:15; Aesop, *Fabulae*, 76). O. Keller believes frog-shaped lamps in Graeco-Roman Egypt continue an Egyptian belief in the frog as a symbol of resurrection because he was mistakenly thought to die in the winter, revive in the spring. (GMAH)

Unpublished. See M. Fränkel, *JdI*, I (1886), 48; Buschor, III (Berlin, 1935), 15, figs. 212, 216 f.; *Basel, 1960, no. 119; R. V. Nicholls, *Archaeological Reports* (*JHS*, Suppl.) (1966), fig. 10; O. Keller, *Die antike Tierwelt*, II (Leipzig, 1913), 298, 311–317; M. Wellmann, *RE*, 4:1 (1924), 1327–1329.
Lent by Mr. and Mrs. Joseph Ternbach.

300. Seated Bear, Ampulla

200–500 A.D.; H: 0.125, L: 0.115; hollow cast, green and brown patina, some incrustation, esp. on feet; silver (?) inlay missing from harness, surface worn where grasped, visible remains of iron core supports. Allegedly from Asia Minor.

Bears became more popular in the later Empire, possibly because of a shortage of lions and ready supply of bears from Germany. Much more naturalistically rendered than No. 299, this bear is also a container: over the pouring hole on his forehead is a swivel cover; holes in the ears are to release air; a suspension loop is on the hump. G. Jennison (*Animals for Show and Pleasure in Ancient Rome* [Manchester, 1937], pl. facing 167) documents the appearance of bears at games, in provincial menageries, and as domestic pets to the 6th century A.D. They are associated by inscriptions on lamps with Phobas, son of Mars (L. Deubner, *AM*, 27 [1902], 253 ff.). (JAS)

J. T. Green, MFA *Bulletin*, 59 (1961), 111, ill.; C. C. Vermeule, MFA *Annual Report* (1962), 32; —, *FA*, 17 (1962), nos. 239, 244; —, *CJ*, 60 (1965), 298 f. Cf. terracotta double lamp dated 300–350 A.D., C. Grandjouan, *Agora* VI, 127, no. 1092.

Lent by the Museum of Fine Arts, Boston (62.1203); gift of Burton Y. Berry.

299. Dancing Bear

1st cent. A.D. (?); H: 0.098, W: 0.092; interior hollow; corroded, dark green surface.

An example of a charming animal not frequently found in early Roman art, the bear is actually a lamp or censer. The head is hinged at the back; when closed it fits down into the collar. A loop for suspension lies on either side of the neck just below the collar. The animal is conceptual rather than naturalistic; he has squat proportions, exaggerated claws and forepaws, and in lieu of a shaggy coat, an incised shell-pattern covers the body. (JAS)

L. Keimer, *Archiv für Orientforschung*, 17:2 (1956), 342 (18), figs. 22, 23; MFA *Bulletin*, 60:318 (1962), 111. A similar object, G. Dattari, sale, Hôtel Drouot (17–18 June, 1912), no. 463; A. Sambon, no. 76, ill.; J. Brummer, sale, Parke-Bernet (May 11, 1949), no. 164, ill. For inscriptions, J. Bachhofen, *Der Bär in den Religionen des Alterthums* (Basel, 1863).

Lent by the Department of Ancient Art, The Brooklyn Museum (58.97).

301. Roundel with Relief Bust of Winged Eros

1st cent. B. C.–1st cent. A. D.; H: 0.121, W: 0.105; bust hollow, head almost completely modelled in the round; overall greenish patina with small areas of gold and brown, especially on face. Wings broken at edges of roundel, eyes probably once inlaid with silver, some abrasion. Allegedly from Egypt.

The piece probably formed the lower, circular decoration of the *fulcrum* (headboard) of a reclining couch (see No. 147 and drawing). The roundel on late Hellenistic and Roman *fulcra* usually contained a human bust, often with Bacchic connotations which were also applied to Eros (*Les Antiquités du Musée de Mariemont* [Catalogue published by Fondation Universitaire, Brussels, 1952] no. G. 100). (JAS)

R. Teitz, *Worcester Art Museum Bulletin*, (Nov. 1966), fig. 1. See Richter, *Furniture*, 107 f., fig. 583; D. K. Hill, *Hesperia*, 32 (1963), 293 ff. On the problem of reproducing Hellenistic decoration by taking casts: G. M. A. Richter, *AJA*, 62 (1958), 369 ff.

Lent by the Worcester Art Museum (1966.39).

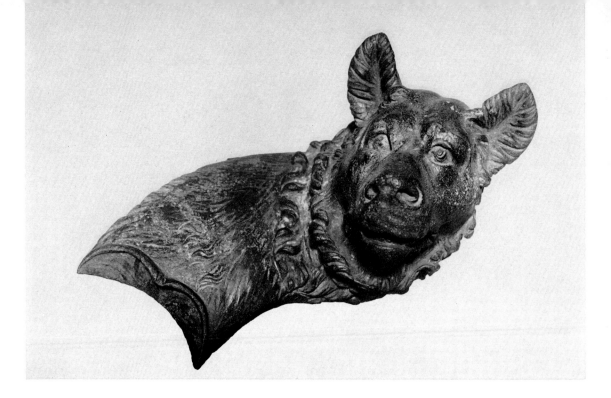

302. Molossian Hound from a Kline

1st–2nd cent. A. D.; H: 0.075, L: 0.15; hollow cast, dark green patina. Found in Sierre, Valais, Switzerland.

This head of a Molossian hound with pricked ears, deep eyes, and slightly opened mouth was an upper finial of a couch headboard *(fulcrum)* (see drawing, No. 147). Protomes of horses and mules, decorated with vine leaves and therefore having a Bacchic connotation, were the most popular of such adornments, but duck and dog heads occur frequently as well (A. Greifenhagen, *RM*, 45 [1930], 143 ff., esp. no. 6). (HM)

Deonna, 299 f., no. 108, pl. 21; Reinach, IV, 520:3; J. Sieveking, *Antike Metallgeräte* (Munich, n. d.), pl. 27; Richter, *Animals*, 33, pl. 55, fig. 173, "copy of Hellenistic original"; W. Deonna, *L'Art romain en Suisse* (Geneva, 1942), fig. 91; *Paris, 1963, no. 181.

Lent by the Musée d'art et d'histoire, Geneva, Switzerland (C 1166).

303. Dog from a Kline

1st–2nd cent. A. D.; H: 0.11, H. at neck: 0.095; dark brown bronze, bright green patina.

This head of a mastiff, mouth open and teeth clearly indicated, once adorned a Roman couch, or *kline* (as No. 302). It apparently had an inlaid collar. The body of the dog is separated from the rim of the *fulcrum* by a rope-like device enclosing two oval areas. The hair of the body is rendered partly plastically, partly in large incisions; that on the face, by very delicate lines. (JAS)

Unpublished. See Richter, *Furniture*, 108, fig. 47 (silver, ends in similar outline), and bibl. for No. 302. For a complete *fulcrum* with dog head, Sotheby sale, 13 June 1966, no. 154, ex-coll. D. H. Burr, Esq.

Lent by the Estates of Audrey B. and Stephen R. Currier.

304. Girl on a Dolphin

Early 2nd cent. A.D.; H: 0.076, W: 0.077; dark green patina, dolphin's eyes inlaid with silver. Ex-coll. S. Casson.

A pipe-like attachment at the back leads through the spout protruding from the dolphin's mouth. The Greeks apparently did not use dolphins as water-spouts, possibly because of the association with un-drinkable salt water. The Romans, however, employed them frequently as fountain spouts. A partially draped female rider rests her l. elbow lightly on the dolphin's head, her r. hand grasping its tail fin, her l. foot joined to the pectoral fin which is lengthened to form a graceful curve. Aphrodite and Nereids are most closely associated with dolphins. (JAS)

Unpublished. See E. Stebbins, *The Dolphin in the Literature and Art of Greece and Rome* (Menasha, Wisc., 1929), esp. 122 ff.

Lent by the Collection of George Ortiz.

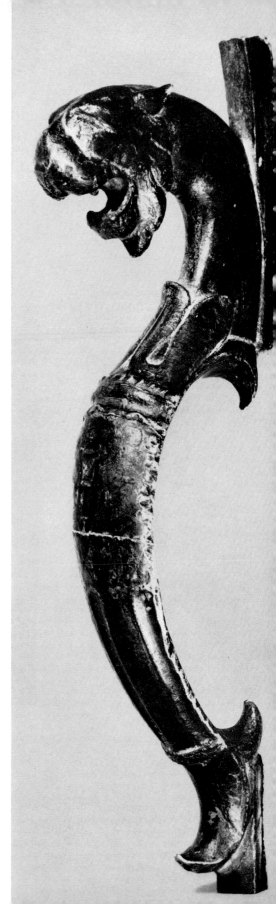

305. Loop Handle from Tripod

3rd cent. A.D., H: 0.286; solid cast, copper inlay; surface worn, metal exposed in places; missing upper r. fang, tip of r. ear.

This piece served as one of three handles on uprights of a Roman collapsible tripod stand, and was held when opening and closing it. The curve of the handle terminates in stylized acanthus leaves at either end. Its lower part is ornamented with elongated tongues, above which is a row of incised rectangles with inscribed X's. The center zone features a kantharos surrounded by curving vines, above which lies plastic fluting. The leopard's neck and head form a graceful reverse curve. His open mouth reveals fangs. Seven other whole or fragmentary tripods are known; a reconstruction has been made at the Walters Art Gallery from fragments of two. D. K. Hill assigns the group to a single workshop. (SD)

Unpublished. Cf. D. K. Hill, *AJA*, 55 (1951), 344–347.

Lent by the Norfolk Museum of Arts and Sciences, Norfolk, Va. (54.4.2), Arthur Morris Sculpture Collection.

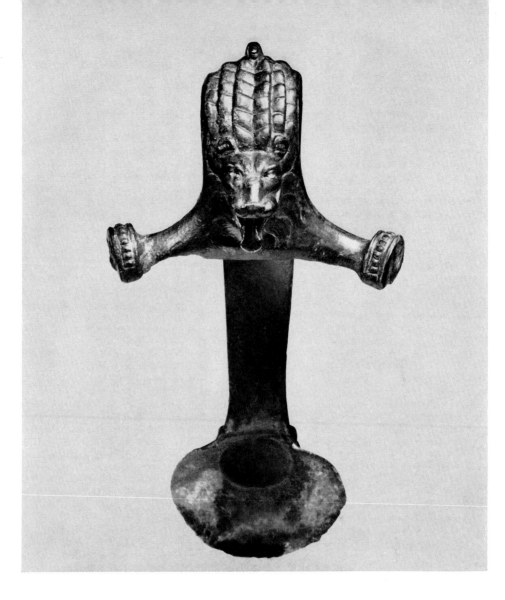

306. Jug Handle with Lion Mask

0–50 A. D.; H: 0.17, W: 0.088; solid cast, brown-green patina, silver inlay.

A lioness with silver-inlaid jaws and eyes spreads onto discs decorated with beads. Her plastic mane adorns the handle shaft to the top of the curve. A vegetable motif runs down the rest of the shaft, ending in a disc with lion's claw, symmetrical plant, and a headless (?) vegetation god. The handle belonged to a squat jug with trefoil mouth. The fine workmanship and vegetable ornament recall Augustus' Altar of Peace and the Hildesheim treasure. (GMAH)

Unpublished. For jug type and lion, Menzel, *Speyer*, 35, pl. 43, with parallels; cf. G. Moretti, *Ara Pacis Augustae* (Rome, 1938); E. Pernice and F. Winter, *Der Hildesheimer Silberfund* (Berlin, 1901); "vegetable god" in Italy 1st cent. B. C. and 1st cent. A. D., G. Azarpay Laws, *AJA*, 65 (1961), 31, pls. 21–22.

Lent by Mr. and Mrs. Joseph Ternbach.

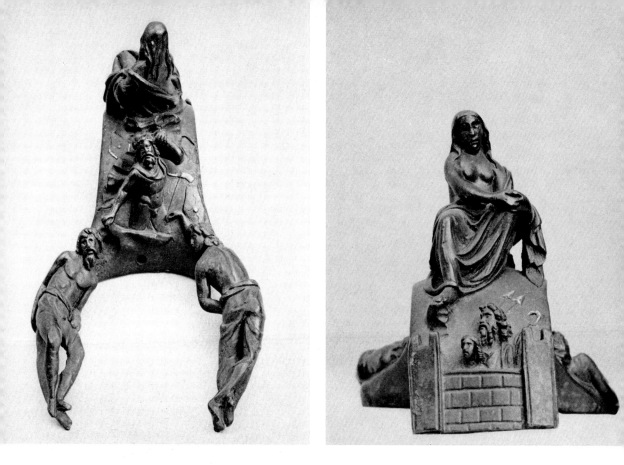

307. Vase Handle

2nd cent. A.D.; L: 0.165, W: 0.037–0.087, H: 0.095; dark patina, spears have silver inlay.

At the bend of the handle is a female figure seated on a rock. Her upper body is nude but her back and lower body are covered by a robe. Below the figure rises a wall with towers, behind which are an older and a younger man. Behind the female figure, on the horizontal part of the handle, is a bearded man. The horseshoe-shaped vase rim is held by two reclining figures. On one side is a bearded man lying on his back and on the other a younger man on his stomach. A parallel for the latter is the bronze statuette of the dead Gaul from Alesia (E. Esperandieu, *Pro Alesia* [1906–1907], 73 ff., pl. 14; A. J. Reinach, *MonPiot*, 18 [1910], 88, fig. 20; Bienkowski, 36, fig. 46); the figure on the vase handle may perhaps be a Celt. The female figure cannot be identified precisely; she must be the personification of a fallen nation. The same is true of the barbarians behind the wall. Some details, as for instance the wall or the barbarian who carries a bundle, remind one of representations on the column of Trajan. If so, the barbarians might be Dacians or Sarmatians, but those on the column of Trajan are dressed differently. Perhaps the vase handle is best understood as a general representation of victory over barbarians, that is, over foreign nations in general. (HM)

A. Blanchet, *RA*, 15 (1890), 341 ff., pl. 9; A. J. Reinach, *op. cit.*, 89 ff., pl. 9; de Ridder, II (1915), 121, no. 2825, pl. 101; Reinach, V, 287:4–5; Bienkowski, 33, fig. 47; Lamb, 235–236, pl. 94; K. Schumacher – H. Klumbach, *Germanendarstellungen, Kataloge des Römisch-Germanischen Zentralmuseums zu Mainz*, 1, 4 (1935), 36 f., pl. 38. Lent by the Musée du Louvre (no. 2825). Shown only in Cambridge.

308. Beaked Pitcher

Probably 1st cent. A.D.; H: 0.325, circum: 0.392. Found at Sandwich, Kent, England.

The vessel has a melon-shaped body, high neck, and trefoil lip with three high points, on two of which perch the forelegs of a winged hippocamp. Its crenelated tail forms the handle, ending with two crossed dolphins. The representation of a fanciful creature is not subordinated to the functionalism of the handle, as is usually the case. (JAS)

Unpublished. Cf. F. Tarbell, *Chicago Field Museum of Natural History Publication 130* (1909), figs. 168–170; Spinazzola, 272 (birds forming similarly unfunctional handle).

Lent by the Vassar College Classical Museum.

309. Askos

1st cent. A.D.; H: 0.095, W. of body: 0.08, H. of foot: c. 0.005; gray-green surface, missing horn of goat on r.

Two finely rendered little goats sit on the rim of the vessel; the handle, embellished with plastic leaves, curves up over them. Near its base the handle divides into three decorative sections, each joined to the body: two bound sheaves flanking a long leaf which rests on the head of a seated amorino, surrounded by a scroll pattern and palmettes. The little figure is winged, his arms are clasped on his breast, his r. leg is folded up under the l., an attitude sometimes associated with Harpokrates *(Society of Hellenic Studies, Archaeological Reports* [1965–1966], 40, fig. 22). (JAS)

Unpublished. Cf. P. La Baume, *Römisches Kunstgewerbe* (Braunschweig, 1964), 153 f., figs. 135–138; Neugebauer, *Führer*, 83, no. 8619, pl. 65; on shape, E. Pernice, *Die hellenistische Kunst in Pompeji*, IV [Berlin, 1925], 13 f., pl. 65.

Lent by The Johns Hopkins University.

310. Vase in Bust Form

2nd–3rd cent. A.D.; H: 0.19; hollow cast, light green and red speckled patina; bottom missing, two large holes on top of head, lower edge broken.

The vase is in the shape of the bust of a beardless, bald man. A lid, cut from the top of the head, moves on a hinge. The handle is a knotty tree branch ending in snakes' heads. The man's ears are large and protruding; his nose and chin are long and pointed. The head suggests a Syrian type, found also in Egypt (cf. Perdrizet, no. 96, pl. 28) and in a grave in Cologne (J. Poppelreuter, *BonnJbb*, 114–115 [1906], 358, fig. 5c). Possibly the piece was meant as a grotesque. More often such vases represent Negroes. (HM)

De Ridder, II, 130, no. 2947, pl. 104; P. Goessler, *Fundberichte aus Schwaben*, n. f. 3 (1926), 96, no. 23; —, *Antike Plastik, W. Amelung zum 60. Geburtstag* (Berlin, 1928), 84; K. Majewski, *Archeologia* (Warsaw), 14 (1964), 122, no. 83; L. Ghali-Kahil, *MonPiot*, 51 (1960), 77, fig. 4. For use as incense vessels, P. Goessler, *op.cit.*, 75 ff.; for dating, F. Coarelli, *Archeologia Classica*, 13 (1961), 168 ff.; R. Fleischer, *Die Römischen Bronzen aus Österreich* (Mainz, 1967), no. 181. For grotesques in Alexandrian art, Bieber, *Hellenistic*, 96 f.; for the Negro in ancient art, G. Beardsley, *The Negro in Greek and Roman Civilization* (Baltimore, 1929).

Lent by the Musée du Louvre (Br. 2947). Shown only in Cambridge.

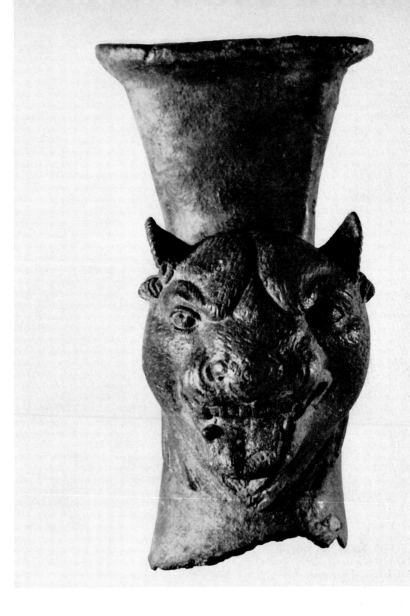

311. Support with Leonine Head

Eastern Roman or Parthian, 2nd cent. A.D.; H: 0.215; solid cast; broken below animal's neck.

A circular tube, open at the top, widens below the neck. The animal wears a "devilish" fierce expression. Mane and eyebrows are deeply cut; light chisel strokes depict the hair. Squarish head and stippled hair seem characteristic of Eastern Roman and Parthian bronzes. Circular hollows for fastening (?) lie on the sides — the object may be a furniture leg, as is a virtually identical piece from Egypt published by De Ridder (II, 189 f., no. 3674, pl. 119). (GMAH)

Unpublished. For use and style: R. Ghirshman, *Persian Art* (New York, 1962), 353, figs. 255, 356; —, *Kunstschätze aus Iran* (Zürich, 1962), no. 882, pl. 58; —, *7000 Years of Iranian Art*, Paris, Oct. 1961–Jan. 1962, no. 472; Richter, D. O., no. 25; W. B. Emery, *Nubian Treasure* (London, 1948), 43D.

Lent by Mrs. Charles Goldman.

312. Votive Plaque

200–250 A. D.; equilateral triangle, L. of each side: 0.265, Th: 0.03; light green patina. Found at Pergamon, near Sultan-Emin Mosque.

A small table lies in the center of the triangular plaque; in the corners in slight relief are the figures of Hecate with the names of Phoibie, Dione, and Nychie. The three figures are dressed in identical chitons and robes but are identified by their attributes: Phoibie holds in her r. hand the key and in her l. hand a torch; Dione holds in her r. hand a whip and in her l. a torch; Nychie has in her r. hand a snake and in her l. hand a short sword. The rest of the surface is covered with magic texts pertaining to the three goddesses. (HM)

A. Conze–C. Schuchhardt, *AM*, 24 (1899), 199 f.; R. Wünsch, *Antikes Zaubergerät aus Pergamon*, *Jdl*, Ergänzungsheft 6 (1905), 10 ff., figs. 1–2, pl. 1; Neugebauer, *Führer*, 80 f.; G. Stuhlfauth, *Das Dreieck* (Stuttgart, 1937), 15 f., pl. 1:4. The magic which was carried out with this plate and other objects found with it such as amulets, ring, nail, etc., is described by Wünsch, *op. cit.*, 47 f.; see also C. Bonner, *Studies in Magical Amulets, chiefly Graeco-Egyptian* (Ann Arbor, 1950), 13 f. On the three-bodied Hecate, T. Kraus, *Hekate* (Heidelberg, 1960); and No. 291.

Lent by the Staatliche Museen Berlin, Antikenabteilung (Inv. no. 8612).

313. Votive Hand

3rd–4th cent. A.D.; H: 0.205; hand with finial hollow cast (base of core remains), god with ram's head solid cast separately and attached, green-black patina; missing head of top figure, head of grasshopper which rested on fifth finger. Interior too rough for fitting on a standard.

The position of the fingers, the *benedictio Latina* of the ancient church, is characteristic of the cult figure on reliefs associated by inscriptions with Sabazios. A Phrygian god whose cult was influential in Thrace, he became identified with Bacchus and Jupiter during the Empire. The figure with a Phrygian cap, also marking the blessing, the hand position, and snake are constant features of Sabazios monuments. In addition, this hand supports an eagle with thunderbolts and snakes in its claws, and a human figure in chlamys on its r. wing. Ganymede comes to mind, but finds no parallel on Sabazios hands; however, Blinkenberg lists five examples with busts of Hermes. Under the Phrygian figure's feet are: ram's head, altar-like table with pine cone, mother bending over child. On the back are chthonic creatures recalling Sabazios' daemonic origin: grasshopper on a serpent, small serpent, scorpion (?), turtle or tortoise, lizard or salamander, frog or toad, rabbit (?); also gate or table, votive cake (?), basket of flowers, two unidentified objects. Such hands have been found over a broad area, more in Europe than in the East. Their meaning is uncertain; Blinkenberg suggests the hand embodies the god's power to help, which is invoked or ensured by the offering. (JAS)

Unpublished. Closest example, W. Roscher, *Ausführliches Lexikon der griechischen und römischen Mythologie* (Leipzig, 1924–1937), X, col. 246, fig. 4; C. Blinkenberg, *Archaeologische Studien*, (Copenhagen, 1904), 66 ff. D. K. Hill in *Essays in Memory of Karl Lehmann*, L. Sandler, ed. (New York, 1964), 132 ff. On cult, M. Nilsson, *Geschichte der griechischen Religionen*, II (Munich, 1961), 658 f. In response to the suggestion of Jupiter Dolichenus, H. Koester points to Syrian origin of that god; the snake could be transferred, but the Phrygian figure could not. I am much indebted to discussion with him and T. Kraabel.

Lent by the City Art Museum of Saint Louis (52:56); acquired 1956.

314. A and B   Openwork Roundels

A. Romano-Celtic, c. mid 2nd cent. A. D.; diam: 0.073, Th: 0.007, scrolls bevelled with flattened tops, back of scrolls concave, three large concave circles at joints.
B. Romano-Celtic, c. mid 2nd cent. A. D.; diam: 0.115, Th: 0.006. Three circular holes on rim.

Prof. C. Hawkes identifies these decorative roundels as work in the so-called "trumpet style" from the Rhine-Danube military districts. Two very similar scrolls from Pannonia in the National Museum, Budapest, decorated the sides of a chariot (CAH, vol. of plates V, 60). Roman technical knowledge combined with native Celtic taste, already influenced by connections with Greece, to produce quantities of this metalwork in the Rhineland, especially Noricum and west Pannonia, which remained relatively stable during the Roman conquest (CAH, XI, 541). A. Riegl traces its development and shows in detail its affiliation with Greek and Imperial relief motifs. It is characterized by variations of a contrapuntal, curvilinear pattern, also found in the prolific enamel work of the same area, which persists into the early Middle Ages. (JAS)

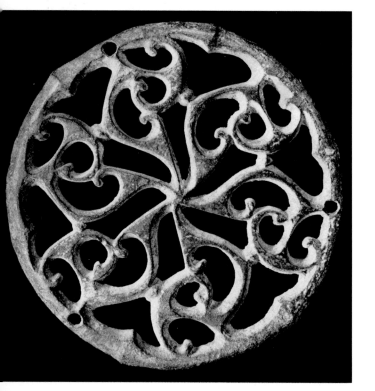

Mentioned, *Art Quarterly*, 22 (1959), 177, ill. 179. Cf. A. Riegl, *Spätrömische Kunstindustrie*[2] (Vienna, 1927), 266 ff., pls. 13–15; F. Drexel–M. Bersu, *Germania Romana, ein Bilderatlas*, V[2] (1930), pls. 9–12; *Kunst und Altertum am Rhein, Führer des Rheinischen Landesmuseums in Bonn* (Düsseldorf, 1963), 77 with bibl., no. 37, for 6th – 7th cent. variant, no. 94; K. Lehmann-Hartleben, *Dura-Europos Ninth Preliminary Report*, I, appendix I (New Haven, 1945), on oriental relationships. I am grateful to Profs. C. Hawkes and H. Hencken for identification and references.

Lent by the Seattle Art Museum, Eugene Fuller Memorial Collection (CeTe 6.1, CeTe 6.2); acquired 1959.

315. Steelyard with Athena Weight

Byzantine, 5th cent. A. D.; L. of yard arm: 0.47; of chain: 0.495; H. of bust and hooks: 0.24; of bust alone: 0.135.

The steelyard consists of a four-sided rod divided into two sections. On the longer are the scale marks; from it is suspended the weight, a bust of Athena. From the shorter section of the rod a chain is suspended on large hooks, to which the object to be weighed was attached. On the top side of this section is a suspension hook from which the entire scale was hung. (JAS)

Unpublished. See M. C. Ross, *Catalogue of the Byzantine and Early Mediaeval Antiquities in the Dumbarton Oaks Collection,* I (Washington D. C., 1962), no. 71 with full bibl.; *Metropolitan, 1959–1960, no. 315, von Bothmer comments that the frontal suspension ring is unusual and cites an earlier example on an Athena weight in the MMA (1959.184).

Lent by the Collection of Lawrence J. Majewski.

316. Europa on a Bull

Coptic, 5th–6th cent. A.D.; H: 0.09, W: 0.08; heavy black patina.

Europa perches cheerfully on her bull, legs crossed in a position typical of Coptic female figures, outstretched arms grasping the bull's tail and horn. In this tubular abstraction the billowing garment and swelling bodily forms of Europa, the naturalistic rendering of the bull in No. 112 are not even remembered. The breakdown of Classical form is complete, but, because the iconographic repertoire originated in Alexandria, the Classical subject persisted as a symbol of the afterlife for Egypt's Christians. (JAS)

Unpublished. For similar bronzes, *Koptische Kunst,* Villa Hügel, Essen, May–Aug. 1963, 271–272, nos. 170–172; general treatment of Coptic art, K. Wessel, *Koptische Kunst* (Recklinghausen, 1963), with bibl.; J. Beckwith, *Coptic Sculpture* (London, 1963).

Lent by Dr. and Mrs. Robert Waelder.

Bibliographical Abbreviations

Agora — The Athenian Agora; results of excavations conducted by the American School of Classical Studies at Athens, vols. 1– (Princeton, 1953–)

Babelon — J. Babelon, *Choix de bronzes et de terres cuites des collections Janzé et Oppermann* (Paris, G. van Oest, 1929)

Babelon-Blanchet — E. Babelon–J.-A. Blanchet, *Catalogue des bronzes antiques de la Bibliothèque Nationale* (Paris, E. Leroux, 1895)

Babelon, *Caylus* — J. Babelon, *Choix de bronzes de la collection Caylus* (Paris, G. van Oest, 1928)

Baker — *Greek, Etruscan, and Roman Antiquities*, Walter Baker Collection, Metropolitan Museum of Art, May 17–September 25, 1950 (New York, The Century Association, 1950), catalogue by D. von Bothmer

Basel, 1957 — Die Schweiz zur Römerzeit, Basel, August 17–October 6, 1957 (Basel, 1957), catalogue by R. Fellmann

*Basel, 1960 — K. Schefold, *Meisterwerke griechischer Kunst*, Kunsthalle Basel, June 18–September 13, 1960 (Basel, B. Schwabe, 1960)

Beschi — L. Beschi, *I bronzetti romani di Montorio veronese*, Istituto veneto di scienze, lettere ed arti, Venezia. Memorie. Classe di scienze morali e lettere, v. 33, fasc. ii (Venezia, 1962)

Bieber, *Cassel* — M. Bieber, *Die antiken Skulpturen und Bronzen des Königl. Museum Fridericianum in Cassel* (Marburg, N. G. Elwert, 1915)

Bieber, *Hellenistic* — M. Bieber, *The Sculpture of the Hellenistic Age* (New York, Columbia University Press, 1961)

Bieber, *Theater* — M. Bieber, *The History of the Greek and Roman Theater* (Princeton, Princeton University Press, 1961)

Bienkowski — P. Bienkowski, *Les Celtes dans les arts mineurs gréco-romains avec des recherches iconographiques sur quelques autres peuples barbares* (Cracow, Imp. de Université des Jagellons à Cracovie, 1928)

Boardman — J. Boardman, *The Cretan Collection in Oxford* (Oxford, Clarendon Press, 1961)

L. Brown — W. L. Brown, *The Etruscan Lion* (Oxford, Clarendon Press, 1960)

Bruns — G. Bruns, *Antike Bronzen* (Berlin, Gebr. Mann, 1947)

Buffalo, 1937 — Master Bronzes selected from Museums and Collections in America, Albright Art Gallery, February, 1937 (Buffalo, 1937)

Burlington, 1904 — Burlington Fine Arts Club, Exhibition of Ancient Greek Art (London, 1904)

Buschor — E. Buschor, *Altsamische Standbilder*, 3 vols. (Berlin, Gebr. Mann, 1934–1935)

Casson — S. Casson, *Descriptive Catalogue of the Warren Classical Collection of Bowdoin College* (Brunswick, Me., 1934)

Charbonneaux — J. Charbonneaux, *Les bronzes grecs* (Paris, Presses Universitaires de France, 1958)

Deonna — W. Deonna, *Catalogue des bronzes figurés antiques*, Musée d'Art et d'Histoire, Geneva, Extrait de l'Indicateur d'antiquités suisses, 1915–1916 (Zürich, Imp. Berichthaus)

*Detroit, 1947 — *An Exhibition of Small Bronzes of the Ancient World*, Detroit Institute of Arts, March 23—April 20, 1947 (Detroit, 1947), introduction by F. W. Robinson

Diehl — E. Diehl, *Die Hydria* (Mainz, von Zabern, 1964)

Dutuit — *Collection Auguste Dutuit, bronzes antiques*, 2 vols. (Paris, 1897—1901), text by W. Froehner

Edgar — C. C. Edgar, *Greek Bronzes, Catalogue général des antiquités égyptiennes du Musée du Caire* (Cairo, Imp. de l'Institut français d'archéologie orientale, 1904)

*Fogg, 1954 — *Ancient Art in American Private Collections*, Fogg Art Museum, December 28, 1954—February 15, 1955 (Cambridge, 1954)

Froehner — W. Froehner, *La collection Tyszkiewicz* (Munich, Verlagsanstalt für Kunst und Wissenschaft, 1894)

Froehner, Gréau — W. Froehner, *Collection Julien Gréau, les bronzes antiques*, vente Hôtel Drouot, 1—9 June, 1885 (Paris, 1885)

Froehner, Vente Tyszkiewicz — W. Froehner, *Collection d'antiquités du Comte Michel Tyszkiewicz*, vente Hôtel des Commissaires-Priseurs, 8—10 June, 1898 (Paris, 1898)

Fuchs — W. Fuchs, *Der Schiffsfund von Mahdia* (Tübingen, E. Wasmuth, 1963)

Furtwängler — A. Furtwängler, *Die Bronzen und die übrigen kleineren Funde von Olympia* (E. Curtius — F. Adler), *Olympia, die Ergebnisse der von dem deutschen Reich veranstalteten Ausgrabungen*, iv (Berlin, A. Asher, 1890)

Gerhard — E. Gerhard, A. Klügmann, G. Körte, *Etruskische Spiegel*, 5 vols. (Berlin, G. Reimer, 1843—1897)

Giglioli — G. Q. Giglioli, *L'arte etrusca*, (Milan, Fratelli Treves, 1935)

HambJb — *Jahrbuch der Hamburger Kunstsammlungen*

Hanfmann — G. M. A. Hanfmann, *Etruskische Plastik* (Stuttgart, H. E. Günther, 1956)

Hanfmann, Roman — G. M. A. Hanfmann, *Roman Art* (Greenwich, Conn., New York Graphic Society, 1964)

Herbert — K. Herbert, *Ancient Art in Bowdoin College* (Cambridge, Harvard University Press, 1964)

Hencken — H. Hencken, *Tarquinia, Villanovans and Early Etruscans*, Bulletin 23, American School of Prehistoric Research, Peabody Museum (Cambridge, 1967)

Hill — D. K. Hill, *Catalogue of Classical Bronze Sculpture in The Walters Art Gallery* (Baltimore, 1949)

Himmelmann-Wildschütz — N. Himmelmann-Wildschütz, *Bemerkungen zur geometrischen Plastik* (Berlin, Gebr. Mann, 1964)

Hoffmann — H. Hoffmann—F. Hewicker, *Kunst des Altertums in Hamburg* (Mainz, von Zabern, 1961)

Jantzen — U. Jantzen, *Griechische Greifenkessel* (Berlin, Gebr. Mann, 1955)

Jantzen, Bronzewerkstätten — U. Jantzen, *Bronzewerkstätten in Großgriechenland und Sizilien*, Jdl, Ergänzungsheft xiii (Berlin, W. de Gruyter, 1937)

Jantzen, Griff — U. Jantzen, *Griechische Griff-Phialen* (Berlin, W. de Gruyter, 1958)

H. Jucker — H. Jucker, *Das Bildnis im Blätterkelch* (Olten, Urs Graf-Verlag, 1961)

H. Jucker, Bronzehenkel — H. Jucker, *Bronzehenkel und Bronzehydria in Pesaro* (Pesaro, Ente Olivieri, 1966)

I. Jucker   I. Jucker, *Der Gestus des Aposko-pein* (Zürich, Juris-Verlag, 1956)

*Käppeli   *Kunstwerke der Antike*, Collection R. Käppeli, Basel, Antikenmuseum (Basel, Schwabe and Co., 1963)

Lamb   W. Lamb, *Greek and Roman Bronzes* (London, Methuen and Co., 1929)

Langlotz   E. Langlotz, *Frühgriechische Bildhauerschulen*, 2 vols. (Nürnberg, E. Frommann & Sohn, 1927)

Latomus   *Latomus; revue d'études latines*

Mansuelli   G. A. Mansuelli, *The Art of Etruria and Early Rome* (New York, Crown Publishers, 1964)

Menzel, *Speyer*   H. Menzel, *Die römischen Bronzen aus Deutschland*, I, *Speyer* (Mainz, Römisch-Germanisches Zentralmuseum, 1960)

Menzel, *Trier*   H. Menzel. *Die römischen Bronzen aus Deutschland*, II, *Trier* (Mainz, von Zabern, 1966)

*Metropolitan 1959–1960   *Ancient Art from New York Private Collections*, Metropolitan Museum of Art, December 17, 1959–February 28, 1960 (New York, 1961), ed. D. von Bothmer

Milani   L. A. Milani, *Il R. Museo Archeologico di Firenze*, 2 vols. (Florence, Enrico Ariani, 1912)

Neugebauer   K. A. Neugebauer, *Antike Bronzestatuetten* (Berlin, Schoetz & Parrhysius, 1912)

Neugebauer, *Führer*   K. A. Neugebauer, *Führer durch das Antiquarium*, I, *Bronzen*, Staatliche Museen zu Berlin (Berlin, W. de Gruyter, 1924)

Neugebauer, *Kat.*   K. A. Neugebauer, *Katalog der statuarischen Bronzen im Antiquarium*, Staatliche Museen zu Berlin, I, *Die minoischen und archaisch griechischen Bronzen* (Berlin, W. de Gruyter, 1931), II, *Die*

griechischen Bronzen der klassischen Zeit und des Hellenismus (Berlin, Akademie-Verlag, 1951)

OlBer   Deutsches Archäologisches Institut, *Bericht über die Ausgrabungen in Olympia* (Berlin, 1936–)

OlFor   Deutsches Archäologisches Institut, *Olympische Forschungen* (Berlin, 1944–)

*Paris, 1963   F. Braemer, *L'Art dans l'Occident romain*, Palais du Louvre, Galerie Mollien, July–October, 1963 (Paris, 1963)

Perdrizet   P. Perdrizet, *Bronzes grecs d'Égypte de la collection Fouquet* (Paris, à la Bibliotheque d'Art et d'Archéologie, 1911)

Picard   C. Picard, *Manuel d'archéologie grecque*, vols 1– (Paris, Éditions Auguste Picard, 1935–)

*Pomerance   *The Pomerance Collection of Ancient Art*, The Brooklyn Museum, June 14–October 2, 1966 (Brooklyn, 1966)

Poulsen   V. H. Poulsen, *Der strenge Stil*, *ActaA*, viii (Copenhagen, E. Munksgaard, 1937)

Reinach   S. Reinach, *Répertoire de la statuaire grecque et romaine*, 5 vols. Paris, E. Leroux, 1908–1924)

Ruesch   A. Ruesch, *Guida illustrata del Museo Nazionale di Napoli* (Naples, 1908)

Richter, *Animals*   G. M. A. Richter, *Animals in Greek Sculpture* (New York, Oxford University Press, 1930)

Richter, *Br.*   G. M. A. Richter, *Greek, Etruscan and Roman Bronzes* (New York, The Metropolitan Museum of Art, 1915)

Richter, *D. O.*   G. M. A. Richter, *Catalogue of the Greek and Roman Antiquities in the Dumbarton Oaks Collection* (Cambridge, Harvard University Press, 1956)

Richter, Etruscans — G. M. A. Richter, *Handbook of the Etruscan Collection* (New York, Metropolitan Museum of Art, 1940)

Richter, Furniture — G. M. A. Richter, *The Furniture of the Greeks, Etruscans, and Romans* (London, Phaidon Press, 1966)

Richter, Greek — G. M. A. Richter, *Handbook of the Greek Collection*, Metropolitan Museum of Art (Cambridge, Harvard University Press, 1953)

Richter, Handbook — G. M. A. Richter, *A Handbook of Greek Art* (New York, Phaidon Press, 1963)

Richter, Kouroi — G. M. A. Richter, *Kouroi, Archaic Greek Youths* (London, Phaidon Press, 1960)

Richter, Portraits — G. M. A. Richter, *The Portraits of the Greeks*, 3 vols. (London, Phaidon Press, 1965)

Richter, Sculpture — G. M. A. Richter, *The Sculpture and Sculptors of the Greeks* (New Haven, Yale University Press, 1950)

de Ridder — A. de Ridder, *Les bronzes antiques*, Musée National du Louvre, Département des antiquités grecques et romaines, 2 vols. (Paris, G. Braun, 1913–1915)

de Ridder, Acropole — A. de Ridder, *Catalogue des bronzes trouvés sur l'Acropole d'Athènes*, Bibliothèque des Écoles françaises d'Athènes et de Rome, 74 (Paris, A. Fontemoing, 1896)

de Ridder, de Clercq — A. de Ridder, *Collection de Clercq*, III, *Les bronzes* (Paris, E. Leroux, 1905)

Riis — P. J. Riis, *Tyrrhenika, An Archaeological Survey of the Etruscan Sculpture in the Archaic and Classical Periods* (Copenhagen, E. Munksgaard, 1941)

A. Sambon — *Collection Arthur Sambon*, vente Galerie Georges Petit, 25–28 May, 1914 (Paris, 1914)

J. Sambon — *Collection Jules Sambon*, vente Galerie Georges Petit, 1, 2, 3 May, 1911 (Paris, 1911)

*Santa Barbara, 1963 — *Greek Art from Private Collections of Southern California*, University of California, November 19–December 17, 1963 (Santa Barbara, 1963), catalogue by M. A. Del Chiaro

*Santa Barbara, 1967 — *Etruscan Art from West Coast Collections*, University of California, February 7–March 15, 1967 (Santa Barbara, 1967), catalogue by M. A. Del Chiaro

*Schimmel — *The Beauty of Ancient Art*, The Norbert Schimmel Collection, Fogg Art Museum, November 15, 1964 – February 14, 1965 (Mainz, von Zabern, 1964), ed. H. Hoffmann

Sieveking — J. Sieveking, *Die Bronzen der Sammlung Loeb* (Munich, 1913)

C. Smith — C. H. Smith, *Bronzes, antique Greek, Roman, etc. . . . Collection of J. Pierpont Morgan* (Paris, Librairie Centrale des Beaux-arts, 1913)

Spinazzola — V. Spinazzola, *Le arti decorative in Pompei e nel Museo Nazionale di Napoli* (Milan, Bestetti e Tumminelli, 1928)

Staïs — V. Staïs, *Guide illustré, marbres et bronzes du Musée National*, I (Athens, Impr. P. D. Sakellarios, 1910)

Stothart — H. Stothart, *A Handbook of the Sculpture in the J. Paul Getty Museum* (Malibu, Calif., 1965)

Thouvenot — R. Thouvenot, *Catalogue des figurines et objets de bronze du Musée Archéologique de Madrid*, I, *Bronzes grecs et romains*, Bibliothèque de l'École des Hautes Études Hispaniques, fasc. xii, 1 (Bordeaux, Feret & fils, 1927)

Ucelli   G. Ucelli, *Le navi di Nemi* (Rome, La Libreria dello Stato, 1950)

*University Museum, 1964   *What We Don't Know*, The University Museum, University of Pennsylvania (August 24–29, 1964)

van Gulik   H. C. van Gulik, *Catalogue of the Bronzes in the Allard Pierson Museum at Amsterdam*, Part 1 (Allard Pierson Stichting, Archaeologisch-historische bijdragen VII) Amsterdam, N.V. Noord-hollandsche uitgevers-mij, 1940)

Vermeule   C. C. Vermeule – G. H. Chase, *Greek, Etruscan, and Roman Art* (Boston, Museum of Fine Arts, 1963)

von Vacano   O.-W. von Vacano, *Die Etrusker: Werden und geistige Welt* (Stuttgart, W. Kohlhammer, 1955)

Walters   H. B. Walters, *Catalogue of the Bronzes, Greek, Roman and Etruscan*, Department of Greek and Roman Antiquities, British Museum (London, The British Museum, 1899)

*Walters, 1958   *The Etruscans: Artists of Early Italy*, Walters Art Gallery, Baltimore, March 16–May 4, 1958, no catalogue

*Worcester, 1967   *Masterpieces of Etruscan Art*, Worcester Art Museum, Mass., April 21–June 4, 1967, catalogue by R. S. Teitz

Züchner   W. Züchner, *Griechische Klappspiegel* (Berlin, W. de Gruyter, 1942)

Museum Abbreviations

CAMSL   City Art Museum of Saint Louis, Mo.

LACMA   Los Angeles County Museum of Art, Calif.

MFA   Museum of Fine Arts, Boston, Mass.

MMA   Metropolitan Museum of Art, New York

RISD   Rhode Island School of Design, Providence

ROM   Royal Ontario Museum, University of Toronto, Canada

VMFA   Virginia Museum of Fine Arts, Richmond

WAG   The Walters Art Gallery, Baltimore, Md.

Photographic Credits

Unless listed below, illustrations are from museum photographs or from photographs kindly furnished by the owners.

Boissonas, Geneva   *119B, 253*

R. Bersier, Fribourg   *246*

E. Irving Blomstrann, New Britain, Conn.,   *49*

Geoffrey Clements, New York   *26, 143—144, 196, 205, 303*

Vincent S. D'Addario, Holyoke, Mass.   *270*

Walter Dräyer, Zurich   *55, 169, 172, 185, 187, 191, 241*

Dumbarton Oaks, Washington D. C.   *127, 232*

P. Richard Eells, Milwaukee   *275*

Fogg Art Museum   *16, 25, 43—44, 66, 75, 90, 94, 103, 126, 129, 141, 146, 150, 167, 194, 202, 220, 239, 292, 309*

Friedrich Hewicker, Kaltenkirchen/Holstein, *181, 198 (detail)*

Peter A. Juley, New York   *231*

Kelsey Museum of Art and Archaeology   *250*

Joseph Klima, Jr., Detroit   *121, 238*

Hartwig Koppermann, Munich   *248*

Stuart Lynn, New Orleans, La.   *15*

Elizabeth Menzies, Princeton, N. J.   *285*

Lida Moser, New York   *222, 311*

O. E. Nelson, New York   *8, 10, 14, 19, 23, 28—32, 34, 37, 40, 45, 51, 54, 62, 68, 70, 72, 77, 79, 117, 122, 140, 151, 153, 159, 166, 170, 175, 178, 188, 189, 197, 200, 203, 207, 224, 226, 234 A, 254, 265, 278, 279, 289 A and B, 295, 298, 306, I, II, IV*

Walter Rosenblum, New York   *190*

Sperryn's Ltd., London   *119A*

Taylor & Dull, Inc., New York   *65*

Roy Trahan, New Orleans   *3, 180*

Dietrich Widmer, Basel   *64, 81, 84, 97, 120, 123—124, 165, 174, 264, 288*

Alfred J. Wyatt, Philadelphia   *53, 201, 209, 316*

Robert Young, Indianapolis, Ind.   *213*

DESIGNED
AND PRINTED BY
PHILIPP VON ZABERN
MAINZ ON RHINE, GERMANY